A WRITING LIFE

A Writing Life

Celebrating Nadine Gordimer

Edited by
ANDRIES WALTER OLIPHANT

Photographs by
DAVID GOLDBLATT

VIKING

VIKING
Published by the Penguin Group
27 Wrights Lane, London W8 5TZ, England
Viking Penguin, a division of Penguin Books USA Inc, 375 Hudson Street,
New York, New York 10014, USA
Penguin Books Australia Ltd, Ringwood, Victoria, Australia
Penguin Books (NZ) Ltd, Cnr Rosedale and Airborne Roads, Albany,
Auckland, New Zealand
Penguin Books (South Africa) (Pty) Ltd, Pallinghurst Road, Parktown,
South Africa 2193

Penguin Books (South Africa) (Pty) Ltd, Registered Offices:
Pallinghurst Road, Parktown, South Africa 2193

First published by Penguin Books (South Africa) (Pty) Ltd 1998

ISBN 0670 88583 5

Typeset in 10.5 on 13 point Sabon
Cover photograph by David Goldblatt: Nadine Gordimer, Johannesburg,
April 1984
Cover design by David Goldblatt and Shahn Irwin
Printed and bound by ABC Press

Contents

POETRY FOR A WRITING LIFE

FICTION FOR A WRITING LIFE

INTERVIEWS ON A WRITING LIFE

PLACES OF A WRITING LIFE

A PLAY FOR A WRITING LIFE

Acknowledgements

Earlier versions of some of the work appearing in this publication have been published before. Thanks are due to the authors for granting permission to reprint it here: André Brink for 'All's Unfair in Love and War', first published in *Leadership* in 1997; Dorothy Driver for 'The Critical Reception of Nadine Gordimer' which first appeared as 'Gordimer at 70' in the *Southern African Review of Books* in 1993; David Goldblatt for photographs first published in *On The Mines* (Struik, 1973) and *Lifetimes: Under Apartheid* (Alfred A Knopf, 1986); Jeremy Gordin for 'Two Poems' due to be published in 1998 by Random House in *Pomegranates For My Son*; Antjie Krog for 'Summer Poems for the Beloveds' which first appeared in the *Mail & Guardian* in 1997/98; Karen Ruth Lazar for 'An Interview with Nadine Gordimer' which first appeared as ' "A Feeling of Realistic Optimism": An Interview with Nadine Gordimer' in *Salmagundi* in 1995; Johnny Masilela for 'Song of the Locust' which first appeared in *New Contrast*; Njabulo Ndebele for 'Home for Intimacy' first published in the *Mail & Guardian* in 1996; Per Wästberg for 'On Nadine Gordimer' first published in Swedish in *I Sydafrika: Resan mot Friheten* published by Wahlström & Widstrand in 1995 and translated for this publication by Harry D Watson.

Further thanks are due to David Goldblatt for assisting with the design of the cover and the layout of his photographs; to Alison Lowry, Pam Thornley and Claire Heckrath of Penguin Books for their enthusiasm, support and work, without which this book would not have seen the light of day; to Stephen Clingman for his collaboration; to Maureen Isaacson for her not-so-timely reminder which sparked off this publication and the events around it.

Special thanks are due to all the contributing writers for their work.

This publication was made possible by a grant from the Arts and Culture Trust of the President.

Foreword

ANDRIES WALTER OLIPHANT

Nadine Gordimer is the colossus of South African literature. Her figure as a writer majestically straddles the literary landscape. Although petite, her formidable image looms so large, it seems to fall over every feature of the South African aesthetic topography. This characterisation is not, as one might think, a mere paradox. Neither is it a metaphor of domination. Both these tropes, anyway, do not belong to Gordimer's affirming vocabulary. In her aesthetics, the concept of domination features only as something to be challenged and opposed. Rather, her prominence is the consequence of her genius.

Among such towering figures as Sol Plaatje, Es'kia Mphahlele, Bessie Head, André Brink, J M Coetzee, Miriam Tlali, Zakes Mda, Alan Paton, Njabulo Ndebele, Wally Serote and the many other outstanding writers to have emerged from our country, she occupies a place of prominence and honour. Her pre-eminence is signalled by the fact that she is the first South African writer to receive the Nobel Prize for Literature. In the world of letters, this is the ultimate vindication of her literary greatness. Who, among her peers, will begrudge her this?

While Gordimer is too discreet, too tactful, too modest and independent to project herself as the quintessential literary interpreter of South Africa, she is nevertheless regarded as such by many. Who is she to be so modest?

No writer is ever accorded such a role without earning it through the truth readers seek and find in her work. Such truth, however, does not arise from any metaphysical powers attributed to the writer as a person. It issues from what readers perceive as the imaginative integrity and the veracity of the world represented in the art, which in return, is offered to the world for scrutiny and appraisal. This is to be found in abundance in everything Gordimer has written. Her work, we know, is the product of artistic and ethical deliberation. It is shaped by a form of creativity which, when we encounter it, emboldens us to enlarge our freedom so that no one is excluded from it.

So, to read Gordimer is to be transported into worlds seemingly familiar but always profoundly unconventional which beckon us to meet the challenges they pose. Within the spaces established by her fiction and her essays she crystallises and brings into regard the life, thoughts, feelings, sensations and otherwise imperceptible impulses concealed below the surfaces of everyday life. Reading her is to experience again, and from different perspectives, what it means to have lived in South Africa during the second half of this century. Her writing is charged with the great and subtle forces of our age. At the same time, her texts resonate with what lies beyond the present and the past. Her work therefore makes readable the outlines of our future. Right from the beginning her writing does not await our liberation but enacts it.

It is for this reason that her contemporary, the writer J M Coetzee, citing the Russian writer, Anna Akhmatova, referred to her as 'a visitor from the future'. With this phrase Coetzee suggests the significance of Gordimer for what South Africa was to become long before it actually came into being. While living and writing for most of her life in what was colonial South Africa, her vision reached beyond this stultifying and oppressive world into the future of a free South Africa. This vision, many South Africans, especially those who spent time in prisons and lived in conditions of oppression or in exile, shared with her. In different ways we all worked to realise this. Hers was, and remains the labour of the artist who believed in personal, social and artistic freedom.

To fully grasp this, one must bear in mind that since 1949, when her first novel, *The Lying Days*, was published, she, like all of us was thrown into the world of Apartheid. This world of extremes confronted everyone with stark choices. Unlike so many who, because of their race, saw and seized the opportunities offered by institutionalised racial supremacy, Gordimer began her long and constant critique of colonial domination. In time, her opposition to Apartheid and her commitment would grow more determined and stronger without ever lapsing into facile propaganda. To write well was and remains her vocation.

She has now published twelve novels and more than two hundred short stories collected in several volumes. This, along with a steady output of essays and journalistic work, marks her as a prolific writer who remained a voice of conscience during the years of silence and repression. Her unshakeable sense of justice, her ethical rigour, her moral exactitude and her commitment to social change informed her mercurial gifts. As a writer she now ranks among the best in twentieth-century literature.

In the late 1980s, when South Africa seemed doomed to descend into self-destruction, she articulated the principle of hope in a future of freedom and justice. Her hope, now vindicated, was fully justified because her vision reached beyond the parochial interests of the racially privileged and complicity with illegitimate power, to acknowledge the rights of all South Africans. No country, whether in times of adversity or peace, could wish for a better writer.

She has charted the journey of South Africa from oppression to freedom and democracy. She has done this so compellingly and with such memorable vividness that her work is closely read by many different readers. Her writings intensely engaged legions of critics. In a country and, for that matter, in a world as diverse as ours, her work has opened itself to the most rigorous, sustained and diverse examination. It has emerged almost invulnerable to critical attack and to the passage of time. This is the mark of the artistic brilliance and ethical force inscribed in it.

Like all great writers she has her admirers and her detractors. This is proper. Serious writing and speech, like democracy, after all, cannot flourish without criticism and appreciation. Those who read her with insight know that if one is to grasp the complexities of the process which moved South Africa beyond the confines of colonialism into the realm of democracy, close attention to her writing is essential. Her broad vision combined with her incredible powers of observation and the consummate skills she brings to bear on the novel, the short story, the literary essay and the journalistic article, has given South Africa and the world a body of writing which sets a very high standard for our culture. We treasure and are proud of it.

Regardless of what the future holds for South Africa, its people, its literature and its culture, Nadine Gordimer's work will remain a touchstone for present and future generations. She accompanied us on our journey from the past. She will be beside us in our long journey into the future. Thus in celebrating her seventy-fifth birthday, we exalt the creativity and freedom embodied in her work. Her sustained commitment to social transformation, her relentless probing of our society, our culture and herself, is her gift to us and to the world.

In a recent article she writes with customary eloquence about our journey to liberation:

> In 1994, the struggle, the final process of decolonisation was achieved after decades when the end receded again and again. In April 1994 South Africans of all colours went to the polls and voted into power their own government, for the first time. There are now no overlords and underlings in the eyes of the law. What this means to our millions is something beyond price or reckoning that we know we shall have to work at and put into practice, just as we worked for liberation. We know we have to perform what Flaubert called 'the most difficult and the least glamorous of all tasks: transition.' This is the reality of freedom. This is the great matter.
>
> I am a small matter; but for myself there is something immediate, extraordinary, of strong personal meaning. The other world is no longer the world. My country is the world, whole, a synthesis. I am no longer a colonial. I may now speak of 'my people'.

Speaking for herself, she enjoins us in a dialogue: We are no longer colonised. Indeed, our country is the world. We are free to remake our world and so remake the world. Here, as always in her essays, Gordimer moves by describing the world so truthfully, that we who read her, cannot evade it. It moves us from the facts of history to the tasks before us. In her fiction, it moves still further: her narratives held in our imaginations move right into the nerve centres of consciousness. In this, her instance, her precepts, her presence, her work and our esteem are assured.

Introduction

ANDRIES WALTER OLIPHANT

This volume, as the title states, is a celebration of the writing and life of Nadine Gordimer. The occasion is her seventy-fifth birthday. She was born on 20 November 1923. Life and writing, intertwined as they are in her case, inform this homage by fellow writers. It pays tribute to Gordimer in two ways: directly, through the essays, tributes, stories, poems and interviews which linger over her work and life, are dedicated to her and, as in the case of David Goldblatt's photographs, relate to projects she participated in; and indirectly, in the fiction and poetry which celebrate her birthday through writing. It is a diverse and inspiring panoply.

Taken together, these texts are a regale of creativity. The material, mostly unpublished before, and in a few cases, not published in book form, is worthy of a writer of Gordimer's stature. My sense is that it issues from the genuine esteem of fellow writers. If this does not belie suggestions of indifference, disregard, envy and hostility, it certainly paints a picture of recognition and affection.

At a lifetime, which now spans three-quarters of a century, Gordimer's writing is as vital and productive as it has been since the publication of her first work more than fifty years ago. This is manifested by her unflagging output since she received the Nobel Prize in 1991. Her oeuvre then included ten novels, more than two hundred short stories, two collections of essays, two photographic collaborations and countless reviews. Since then, three novels, a collection of new short stories and a volume of essays have been published. She remains an active participant in current cultural and social debates pertaining to South Africa and other parts of the world.

The range and quality of her work intimates that it will be charted and recharted long after the worlds it depicts have vanished. This can be seen in how her oeuvre, with the passage of time, has steadily grown in value and stature. Her work, as her friend the Swedish writer Per Wästberg suggests, is an imaginative archive without which our knowledge of ourselves and our literature is incomplete. At the same time, her writings also provide perspectives on the present and the future of literature and culture in post-apartheid South Africa. In the last four decades, her work was poised in the space between the shifting present and what seemed like an ever-receding future. It now is the literary site in which post-apartheid South Africa can be glimpsed long before its materialisation. As a bequest to the future, the depth and scope of her work make it one of the most significant oeuvres in South African literature. Its impact on South African culture still awaits assessments commensurate to its import.

This, of course, is not to suggest that her writings occupy *the* central place in South African literature. Such a suggestion would amount to a claim that all South African literature is organised around Gordimer. While such a pattern could be traced now and the possibility of its future crystallisation is not out of the question, this is certainly not what Gordimer's writing is concerned with. Its energy and thrust are directed towards opening up spaces in which South African literature and culture can flourish on the terms set by writers and artists freed from compulsions to mimic subjects and forms authorised by the colonising discourses of some putative world and its culture of which South African literature is no more than an adjunct. Hers, we know, is an aesthetic of cultural and artistic deliverance.

This is evident from the essays published in this text under the heading, 'Readings of a Writing Life'. Gordimer's abiding concern with the ethics of freedom and responsibility are retraced by Stephen Clingman. His emphasis is on the symbolic transgressions and bodily movements which refuse restrictive political, social and cultural categories. He shows how her work, sometimes with ironic sportiveness, posits new possibilities of interaction and thus opportunities for creating new identities. It highlights the degree to which Gordimer's writing engages with the specifics of particular contexts while at the same time gesturing to imaginary or symbolic spaces and times beyond simple historical reference. This 'double movement,' which Lewis Nkosi refers to, seems to have accompanied her at every turn in her career. Doubleness is, of course, one characteristic of her fiction.

The same multivalence is read by Karen Lazar in Gordimer's unfolding representation of women. This aspect is registered in the writer's fiction, her essays and her personal views. Lazar examines the forms these representations assumed during the prolonged crisis which prevailed in South Africa during Apartheid, a time in which the future was in a state of indetermination. Her reading shows how Gordimer's narratives provide perspectives on states of being trapped in relations of domination and how power is inscribed in race and gender. It also points to the types of subjectivity Gordimer's narratives attribute to women from different backgrounds, cultures and strata in South African society. Her fiction is an acute narrative register of what happens when these states of being come under pressure in situations of change and transition.

As Lazar's essay makes clear, the representation of women remains one of the most contentious aspects of Gordimer's writings. It provokes wide-ranging and often critical engagements by feminists and other gender scholars. Gordimer's personal views on feminism have changed and Lazar identifies signs of this in the fiction. It is, I think, unlikely that her narrative articulations will ever coincide neatly with any single cultural, political, philosophical or even aesthetic perspective. Any homology between her narratives and a typology would force her fiction to surrender the space of freedom it has established for itself over several decades.

With regard to this, Gordimer, in her essay, 'A Writer's Freedom', says that the writer everywhere needs nothing more pressingly than: 'The right to be left alone to write what one pleases.' Because, for her, this is the space from which the world is brought into view, this absolute right to freedom is insisted upon but elsewhere it is qualified. In 'The Essential Gesture', freedom is counterbalanced by the awareness that: 'Responsibility is what awaits outside the Eden of creativity.' While for her, the writer's social responsibility is the literary work, she argues that any claim which places an unqualified value on the writer's work 'without reference to a context of responsibilities' is invoking a condition which is not generally available. It was not available in South Africa when she wrote this, nor was it in over-supply in much of the world during this century. Notwithstanding recent changes in global politics, absolute freedom from the imperatives of context is still very much a scarcity. In another, and certainly less pressing social sense, context, understood as the dimensions of time and space, remains an ineluctable aspect of literary and aesthetic discourse which all forms of writing and art must negotiate when being constituted as artefacts and aesthetic objects. So, it is not abstract freedom or indentured obedience which summon Gordimer's attention but the interplay between these categories which absorbs her imagination.

Ronald Suresh Roberts explores the question of race in Gordimer's writing. He focuses on Gordimer's critique of 'whiteness' as a condition of ethnic consciousness which masks and shields itself in a mythology designed to preserve a world of which it sees itself as master. These three essays, ranging across the interrelated discursive fields of identity, gender, race, power and the ethics of writing, form a small part of the ongoing readings, re-readings, appraisals and critical reception of Gordimer's work to which Dorothy Driver refers. Accordingly, with Gordimer's status as a writer now firmly secured, and the historical period which shaped the major part of her oeuvre now behind us, the nuanced readings of her work proposed by Driver are now beginning to flourish. The widespread appreciation of her work is clear from the warm tributes published in this book. But for some sense of where it all began, we must turn to some of Gordimer's texts in which she reflects on the beginnings of her writing life and its subsequent vicissitudes.

Gordimer began writing with a considerable degree of self-awareness very early in her life. This sense of herself moved her to grasp, not without romantic desire, what such a life might be. In her autobiographical essay, 'A Bolter and the Invincible Summer', citing Albert Camus, she refers to such a life as an indestructible season of light. She glimpsed this endless season of illumination in the personality of the poet, Uys Krige, who, as Guy Butler points out, was one of the first to recognise and encourage Gordimer's talent. Those who knew Krige say a translucent lyricism made him appear like a human being penetrated by light. Gordimer's light, however, is not the flash of lyrical irradiation. It is the intricate and often ironic play of finely honed prose, the indirect light of which falls on the darkness lurking within what we, often against our better judgement, are conditioned to think of as light. She writes:

> My writing life began long before I left school, and I began to leave school (frequently) long before the recognised time came, so there is no real demarcation for me between school and the 'professional' life. The quotes are there because I think of professional life as something one enters by way of an examination, not as an obsessional occupation like writing for which you provide your own, often extraordinary or eccentric, qualifications as you go along.

In this oblique and even evasive self-portraiture, one sees how the writing, delicately composed, playfully draws attention to its own inscription. In this intricate lace of the writing something fierce can be discerned: an 'obsessional occupation', driven by the ambition to 'achieve the impossible'. This was to be undertaken without regard for the exacting standards writers set for themselves in relation to the literary tradition they decide to respond to. In the then colonial South Africa, for Gordimer, this meant that: 'No conditioning' could 'excuse the absence of the simple act of courage that would resist it'.

Here, as elsewhere in her work, we sense a double cryptogram: to excel and 'achieve the impossible' in art, on the one hand, coupled to the 'simple courage' to resist social and cultural conditioning, on the other. She did not derive the second code from a specific ideology. Nor did she rely on the 'silence, cunning and exile' which served insurgent modernists like James Joyce. She won her code from the first term. It issued from her struggle with the difficult challenges and exacting demands posed by writing: 'It was learning to write that sent me falling, falling through the surface of the "South African way of life".' This statement, often cited to distance Gordimer from reductive ideologies, is yet another tissue layered with implications.

Its hyper-focalisation on the act of writing offers a clue. It alludes to her unceasing concern with her craft. In this she seems to both pre-empt and embody Roland Barthes' idea of the 'author' who is fully absorbed in her labour and her work, even when she is inspired, socially engaged or indifferent to the world. For her, as for Barthes' author, this involves paying meticulous attention to the technical and compositional aspects of whatever genre she works in. This is her 'obsessional occupation'. It centres on her craft as the expression of her search for perfection. Like Barthes' author, Gordimer, through, as she put it, her efforts at 'learning to write', came to 'radically absorb the world's *why* in *how to write*'. The emphasis is Barthes'. It is there to stress how, in the process of focusing on the ethics of writing a social ethic is engendered. This radical focus on writing has two consequences: writing becomes an end in itself and a startling transformation is also effected:

> And the miracle, so to speak, is that this narcissistic activity has always provoked an interrogation of the world: by enclosing himself in the how to write, the author ultimately discovers the open question par excellence: why the world? What is the meaning of things? In short, it is precisely when the author's work becomes its own end that it regains its mediating character.

Because Gordimer's writing is always nuanced, subtly ironic and filigreed, reading her moves one well beyond the snares of Barthes' somewhat rigid distinction between what he must call the 'writer' for whom language is a means of communicating evidence, a vehicle for explanations or an instrument for imparting information, ideas or thought; and his notion of the 'author' for whom writing does 'not support a praxis but constitutes one'. Gordimer certainly sets out from this rigorous commitment to the intrinsic demands of writing suggested by Barthes' characterisation of the author. But the writerly and aesthetic problems related to the representation of the world in which she found herself gradually, if not dramatically, foregrounded the nature of that world. This was the world she sought to depict. Confronted by the extremities of the colonial order in South Africa, it was not sufficient for her to settle within either one of the spaces proposed by Barthes in his binary typology.

By engaging both the formal questions of writing and the contextual implications of living and writing in South Africa for the greatest part of this century, she sought to negotiate her way through the issues which impinged on her need to establish a place for herself 'in history' as it was fashioned in South Africa, while simultaneously pursuing her search for a transcendental aesthetics. She approached both these matters guided by her profoundly personal sense of truth. It moved her to situate herself and her work 'in history positively' while simultaneously refusing to give up 'values that are beyond history'. This movement for or towards something is checked by a movement against or from aspects implied by the first gesture. It is clear from this that she set herself an arduous and complex task. It would have mired a lesser writer in self-defeating contradiction. An open commitment to a social project could even in Gordimer's case have resulted in a triumph of politics over art. Gordimer's work, especially what Lewis Nkosi calls her 'later work', has been diagnosed by several critics to have succumbed to politics. Is this so?

For Gordimer the gesture of affirming the struggle for democracy and refusing the prescriptiveness inherent to such struggles, was not a contradiction. It constituted the fraught terrain she elected to traverse. If these were not the terms she set for herself as a writer living and working in South Africa, she certainly squared up to the difficulties they posed. Not surprisingly, she openly declared her commitment to the struggle against apartheid as a commitment to 'the order struggling to be born'. Many balked. Some proposed forms of writing through which the question of *how to write* was replaced by crippling prescriptions *on what to write*. This resulted in writing which closed itself off from the specific moment and the broader context in South Africa, in the conviction that literature and art can function without attentiveness to context. In other instances it produced work which was nothing more than the restating of context.

With Gordimer, the actualisation of her declaration to render herself 'positively answerable to the order struggling to be born', the transcendental values of freedom and justice which inform her private and public ethics were inscribed in her work as possibilities whose meanings are not reducible to the much vaunted conflict between art and politics. As Dorothy Driver points out: 'Gordimer's challenge is this, then: to depict a world where "art" and "politics", like "body" and "mind", "black" and "white" have separated as binary oppositions, and to reconstruct a world where they need no longer do so.' This means that the presumed opposition between these terms is replaced by a writing strategy which seeks to narrate the ways through which they interact, overlap and negotiate their relations in a field cluttered with fixed meanings. The terms devised by Gordimer were fashioned in forms of fiction in which irony and indeterminacy are brought to bear on the world she knew and the world she set out to discover. Its quintessential articulation is encoded in the celebrated ending of *July's People* on which Karen Lazar's essay dwells.

Aware of the trap presented by a shallow formalism, which seeks to suspend any explicitly worldly reference in writing in favour of a preoccupation with style, as well as to the dangers of an instrumental aesthetics, which has nothing but the world of politics as its concern, Gordimer sought a different position and a different meaning. It involved an exploration of the relationship between ethical responsibility and artistic freedom. In her essay, 'The Essential Gesture', she concludes:

> The writer is eternally in search of entelechy in his relation to his society. Everywhere in the world he needs to be left alone and at the same time to have a vital connection with others; needs artistic freedom and knows it cannot exist without its wider context; feels two presences within – creative self-absorption and conscionable awareness – and must resolve whether they are resolved in death-struggle, or are really foetuses in a twinship of fecundity.

Gordimer's use of the Aristotelian concept of entelechy, which suggests a search for the complete expression of what is latent in society, also encodes her striving for the perfection which she made her calling as 'a bolter' in the spell of the promise of an eternal summer. My reading of her work suggests that one of the meanings of her work is not simply a matter of synthesis, or what she herself, citing George Lukács calls 'a fusion' of 'the duality between inwardness and outwardness'. My sense is that Gordimer's writing operates from a position in which exteriority and interiority, or any other oppositions, are not closed, suspended or dissolved in a third term. She works from a position through which the implications of the two apparently opposed positions are explored in writing by a writer who, as Jacques Derrida says of Freud, 'writes with both hands'.

If this results in a 'fusion', 'combination' or 'synthesis' then it occurs without deletion, erasure or repression. It is *writing* and it is *life*. Both terms are distinct and intertwined. There are two meanings to this phrase which serves as the title of this volume. They are: 'a life devoted to writing' and 'writing devoted to life'. Both meanings are readable in Gordimer's work. In homage to this, *A Writing Life*, then, was not compiled to produce singularity or uniformity in either tone, style, view or content. This is apposite because Gordimer's self-characterisation playfully alluded to by her self-portrait as a cat, which Clingman refers to, and which features in several of the stories, suggests the idea of different views and multiple perspectives. Since this is an important aspect of her sense of herself as a writer, this text affirms it.

So, while *A Writing Life* belongs to the genre of the *Festschrift*, literally meaning, 'celebration writing', it is not a volume made up solely of celebratory texts offered by friends, associates and fellow writers. Several texts question aspects of Gordimer's work and most differ from her own aesthetic modes and modalities. This is proper, since Gordimer is a writer, who, even when she affirms, still poses questions, refuses conformity and ceaselessly defers meanings. A similar spirit shaped this collection. However, if the motive, the reason and the occasion of this publication, made up as it is of many texts, are explicit, its meanings, as with Gordimer's writing, lie both within these pages and beyond them in the meanings to be made by the readings and re-readings it will hopefully elicit.

What nevertheless emerges very clearly from this text, is that this homage to a writer of great stature, by writers from South Africa and other parts of the world, is a generous acknowledgement of Gordimer's achievements as a novelist, short story writer, essayist, intellectual and social commentator whose work and life are more significant than the scope of this publication accounts for. But without the generosity of the writers whose works appear in this volume, this text would not have been possible.

A Writing Life, therefore, is both a tribute to Gordimer and a celebration of the creativity and insights of all the writers found between these pages.

I am grateful to everyone who responded to the invitation to celebrate Nadine Gordimer at the age of seventy-five. In echoing Lewis Nkosi's words, we all cannot but be 'grateful for Nadine Gordimer's immense contribution to South African life and literature'.

READINGS OF A WRITING LIFE

Nadine Gordimer: A Writing Life

STEPHEN CLINGMAN

I

On 20 November 1923 Nadine Gordimer was born in Springs, a small mining town to the east of Johannesburg in South Africa. As she has recounted a number of times, her father was an impoverished Jewish immigrant from Latvia, who set himself up as a watchmaker and jeweller and became reasonably successful. Her mother, also Jewish, came from an English background which by contrast could appear comparatively genteel, and she consorted for preference with the Scots Presbyterian women of the town. Mrs Gordimer looked down on the Eastern European habits and intonations of her husband: from the start then within the home there were angles of belonging and separation, in which a potential exile from the town was only overcome by importing it into the household and directing it towards the father. Outside were divisions scarcely imagined in their immensity, where the boundaries of race – in the South African sense – were set up and policed in all the most explicit and nuanced of ways. Here Mr Gordimer, who had crossed from one world to another to find himself alienated within his own home, discovered a sense of place in exercising a socially sanctioned authority in relation to South African blacks. A state of exile was transposed once again: such were the ironies and intricacies of power and identity in South African life.

The young Nadine attended a convent school, and though there was no Jewish life to speak of at home, the lines of self, belonging and division were reinforced and complicated once again. She was

3

adept physically from an early age, a dancer, with a poise and agile balance evident in her eyes as much as her body that has not left her since. Nothing delighted her half so much as the outdoor world, an inviting zone of freedom and physical liberation, where – whether playing truant from school out in the open spaces, or haring down the sides of minedumps on a bicycle – the very dimensions of the body could be extended in a sensuous, roving engagement with a surrounding environment. And yet, at this peak of physical extension, another boundary closed in: Nadine's mother, for reasons which appear to have been intricate psychologically, withdrew her from school, on the grounds of a suspected heart ailment. Physicality was curtailed, and with it a social arena which, though fragmented, was at least coextensive with a sense of self. How much in this way is open to chance: those previous energies, directed outwards, changed their inclination: the young Nadine became a reader, voraciously devouring books of all description. The social forum and audience changed too: instead of an unselfconscious circle of friends there was the company of an older sister and a mother's coterie. Nadine became a mimic, reciting for applause the varied habits of her elders. The delight of those elders was unmitigated by the half-suspicion that, were they not in the audience, they would be the very objects of impersonation. Irony, ventriloquism, projection, a different kind of knowing precociousness entered in, and also the power of the performer in words, with its own irresistible intoxications and incentives.

Barred from the outside world, her poise and vitality was expressed in a different, more stylised and mediated form of self-narration. The young Nadine took to writing, publishing short fables in the children's page of the *Sunday Express*. Her first such story, fusing the familiar topography of fairy tales with an incipient sense of the South African veld, appeared when she was thirteen years old; her first fully fledged short story for adults ('Come Again Tomorrow' – its title intriguingly geared towards survival and the future), was published when she was fifteen. The local cultural and political journals became her venue – *Forum, Trek, Common Sense, Jewish Affairs, South African Opinion* – to be followed in due course by the most eminently international – most prominently the *New Yorker*. Her first volume of short stories, *Face to Face*, was published in South Africa in 1949, and when the American house

4

Simon & Schuster, declared it would publish a story collection if Gordimer would write a novel to keep it company, she duly obliged, and *The Soft Voice of the Serpent* and *The Lying Days* appeared in short succession in 1952 and 1953. Earlier than this – when she was just setting out – something had changed within. In later years Gordimer recalled how the Afrikaans writer and translator, Uys Krige, had invited her to lunch. A friend of hers advised her not to go unless she was prepared to take the consequences, for, as he intimated, once she had entered the writer's world, there would be no going back. Nadine Gordimer went to the lunch, a door opened in front, another closed behind, and there was no going back. She became a writer, with everything that meant, a description that came to mean more than enough for her to define the shape and aspirations of her life.[1]

The rest – at least in its external features – is a matter of record. At latest count there have been twelve novels, nine volumes of short stories, three collections of essays, and two photographic essay collaborations, as well as film projects and countless individual pieces; large parts of Gordimer's corpus have been published in translation across the world. Prizes, awards, and other forms of recognition have come their way: among her many appointments, Gordimer is a Fellow of the Royal Society of Literature, an Honorary Member of the American Academy of Arts and Sciences, a *Commandeur dans de l'Ordre des Arts et Lettres*, and the honorary degrees are legion. Her literary prizes include all the most prestigious, from the Booker, to the Nelly Sachs, to – most famously – the Nobel in 1991. Gordimer has become part of a writers' fraternity across the world: friends, collaborators, co-conversationalists have included everyone from Günter Grass, to Arthur Miller, to Susan Sontag, to Czezlaw Milosz, to Amos Oz, to Salman Rushdie, to Kenzaburo Oe, to Octavio Paz, to Chinua Achebe. And yet her primary connections have always been South African: in the 1950s she took up with Es'kia Mphahlele and other members of that generation in an unostentatious commitment of co-writers; through the Black Consciousness era there were the fiery disputations of challenge, respose and ultimate loyalty expressed in her friendship with Mongane Wally Serote; as a founder member of the Congress of South African Writers Nadine Gordimer has not only championed the rights of all South Africans to the benefits of literacy and expression, but modestly and without fuss helped towards that end, participating, as she had for years before, in writers' workshops for the humble and talented alike. She has been a writer first and foremost, yet one who has always felt, and acted upon, a sense of responsibility as a citizen in the world. Though she has often been ignored at home, and frequently been abandoned as a writer as too challenging for her audience, her significance for South Africa has been momumental.

The only difficulty is: how are we to assess it, to estimate its scale? One may well recite the external features of a writing career, and that in its own way tells a story. But Gordimer's own stories are recognised for working through and beyond surface to the hidden patterns of life within. It is impossible here to undertake any comprehensive account of what I would call a writing life – in the end, as Gordimer has herself suggested, the only kind of meaningful life a writer has. But I want to gesture towards some aspects of it, and if I will be forgiven a degree of licence I will do so impressionistically and by association. Here it is not chronology or development that I want to follow, but aspects that underlie them – what Henry James mysteriously called the 'figure in the carpet', the hidden weave beneath the surface designs of a writer's work.[2] I would not be so bold as to assume that I will find the 'master code' – the matrix that generates every varied pattern – and it is part of the point of James's story that the search for such a code it ultimately futile. But there will be no harm in reaching towards a number of the figures in Gordimer's carpet, playing a kind of word-association game as one theme or motif leads to another. Even if we do not find the essential, underlying matrix – the DNA, as it were, of Gordimer's fiction – none the less we may discern some of its more intriguing forms of expression, and in the process point towards the inner structures of a writer's life and work.

I will do so in a certain spirit of play, as befits a celebration of Nadine Gordimer's seventy-fifth birthday – a spirit that may produce its own specific insights. And I want to begin, strangely, with cats.

II

In 1976 the New York bookseller Burt Britton published a volume of self-portraits produced for him at various times by over 700 writers, artists, film-makers, publishers, and the like. Allen Ginsberg is there, and William Burroughs, David Hockney, Joan Didion, Italo Calvino, Derek Walcott, James Tate, Jay Neugeboren, Norman Mailer, Eudora Welty, Kurt Vonnegut, Toni Morrison, and so many others; Woody Allen looks out impishly, a small face on a large page, with eyeless glasses and a smile you know would eventually drive you crazy. Many of the portraits are offered with a degree of self-knowledge or irony that emerges through their originators' varied skills with pen or pencil. And there, on page 206, right next to Chinua Achebe is Nadine Gordimer, yet it is not a face or the 'self' in any recognisable form that emerges, but two cats; or one cat, from two directions. The first cat faces forward, mostly head, with pretty eyes and sharp ears next to (perhaps) a wine decanter and half-filled glass. The second aspect is pure archetype: the cat in rear-view, drawn with three symmetrical question-mark lines for tail and legs and a dot for what lies between. Underneath the author has written: 'Many points of view? With acknowledgements to my son, Hugo.'[3]

It is easy to make too much of this, of course. Yet attentive readers of Gordimer's fiction will have noticed, over the years, the presence of any number of cats loping through her work. Here is just one introductory example: in *A Sport of Nature*, a porcelain Imari cat represents – especially when Hillela breaks it – the stultifying and ultimately fragile confines of her aunt's household, where natural feline sensuality has been reduced to frozen inanimacy and a mannered expression of financial value. By contrast, when Hillela and her cousin Sasha make love, in contravention of all social and familial rules in her other aunt's house, there is a cat that naturally rolls itself up on the bed between them. (But when Sasha and Hillela are discovered, the cat jumps away, as if the whole scene, and the trauma and chaos which ensue, have absolutely nothing to do with it: this cat is a survivor.) It is intriguing then, that a self-portrait should produce this projection, a mask for the self which it has been asked to reproduce. The cat facing head on, with the wine beside, suggests libertinage, engagement, charm; the

7

cat behind is the enemy of all promise or promises, or, as Maureen Smales is called, just after she has drowned a family of kittens in a bucket of water and is running towards the helicopter at the end of *July's People*, an 'enemy of all that would make claims of responsibility'.[4]

We have the doubleness of cats: but what to make of it, especially in the work of a South African writer where so much is expected? Without placing too heavy a hand on a small icon, I would say that it is rather significant. Let us take the head-on cat first. It is no accident that such a cat appears when Hillela is making love, for Hillela is Nadine Gordimer's most feline of creatures, with a bodily sensuality that knows no conventional social bounds. On the one hand this is of course an amoral if not anti-moral body, going where it pleases, unpredictable and therefore dangerous. Yet, in the context of an apartheid world, this disposition also means that Hillela will simply not conform to any of the arbitrary limits of race – among other kinds – that have been placed around her. Hers is an essential liberation of the body, and a fusion between body and mind: exactly what the sensuality of a cat suggests. It is, in a sense, a liberation beyond categories, a simple desire to be free which originates instinctively and by nature. It is a drive that cannot be suppressed: how significant that has been in South Africa. Yet it is a version too of a kind of Paradise before the fall into knowledge, where body and mind are in perfect harmony, where perfect inclination can be exercised. It is – to say the obvious – an *animal* version of liberation, but that is to patronise neither animals nor humans. Nadine Gordimer has always had a sense of the perfect form of liberation that might underlie us all, where our bodies, and with them our minds, might be free. It does not conform to the conventional modes of Western religion, nor – in this aspect – is it divided and Cartesian. It is an individual vision and it derives from the sensuous world; and one can see why such a cat would never have tolerated apartheid.[5]

But that cat also turns its backside, wanders off just when you think you need it most. It is no respecter of persons, or in that sense even of obvious loyalties. Why has it wandered off? It has found something more interesting, its attention has been engaged elsewhere. Sometimes this can be pushed to crisis: Maureen Smales drowns the kittens (a complex image now), abandons her family and previous ties, and runs towards the helicopter and some unnamed apotheosis. That ending of *July's People* produced the greatest amount of consternation and shock: how can a mother simply abandon her children? Is she running towards salvation or destruction? Isn't her action simply the extreme expression of pure selfishness? This is not the place to rehearse the 'meaning' of that ending: the critics have all, in their various ways, had their try. But it is appropriate to register, once again, its radical ambiguity, in the same way that Hillela is radically ambiguous. If the body's drive is to salvation its categories for finding it will be unpredictable. Maureen's ending, in a form vastly more significant than the simply political, is apocalyptic: she has seen the end of time, the time of her past, its deadness and inner decay, and this is a last attempt to find a different kind of future: that, at any rate, is my reading.[6] But what that moment in the novel confronts is the blank horror of a specific reality: Nadine Gordimer is difficult beyond the level at which her sentences sometimes require a second reading. She is difficult because she makes us think of difficult things, from which often we would rather turn away. And all her novels, we might remind ourselves, end in some degree of ambiguity.

The cat wanders off, quite of its own accord. The self-portrait which Gordimer draws turns away from the 'subject' and away from 'reproduction'. This reminds us that reproduction for Gordimer has always been an issue both persistent and fraught. Mothers in particular, in her work, have attracted a fierce emotional concentration. Sometimes, whether surrogate or actual (as in the case of Hillela and her cousin Sasha) they have been cloyingly close – and no one understands the cold fission possible in families in quite the same way as Gordimer. Frequently, though, they have been distinctly unmaternal, questioning at base the strange reality that they should be the unwilling agents of what may appear to be a fairly distasteful bodily function. One of Gordimer's earlier female characters, in *A World of Strangers*, declares, 'You don't know how horrible it is to reproduce yourself, like that',[7] while Hillela's chief satisfaction as a mother is 'not to have reproduced herself'.[8] The latter example makes the political dimensions of the issue apparent, for Hillela has married a black man, and her offspring in that sense is not simply 'white': she has, literally, not reproduced apartheid, but something richer and more mixed.

We can understand it from that point of view – that this is a symbolic enactment of a political view – and yet I think that would be to underrate the phenomenon completely. Where does the symbolic drive come from in the fiction? Not from a political formula, but from something much deeper and more innate. It is partly *because* Nadine Gordimer distrusts simple 'reproduction' that the repressions of apartheid are particularly horrific for her. One crosses boundaries because of an incipient drive to do so; this is in a sense a *genetic* form of politics, though an inversion of the more usual racial kind. For Gordimer cloning is both unsexy, unhealthy and immoral in human terms. The natural drive is towards 'sport' – that is, difference, play, the unpredictable. In the same way, the future cannot be a clone of the past: it is, in its very nature, unknowable, unpredictable, and those who try to fence it in are fencing the untameable.[9] The political vision of Gordimer's writing has come from this intricate, internal disposition rather than the other way round. As Rosa Burger says in *Burger's Daughter*, 'Parents and children don't understand each other . . . Some sort of natural insurance against repetition.'[10] Gordimer's fiction walks the boundary where the natural, instinctive body meets the constraints of political culture.

If the self, in its fulfilment, must meet difference in the world, it is a fact of Gordimer's writing that difference has already entered into the self. Virtually all of her characters are engaged in a dialogue of the self with the self (even Hillela does so eventually), and of the self with the other *within* the self. Rosa Burger captures it most famously: 'One is never talking to oneself, always one is addressed to someone . . . even dreams are performed before an audience.'[11] Mehring, chief character of *The Conservationist*, approaches a dead body buried shallowly both beneath the surface of his farm and beneath the surface of his mind. In terror, in that third pasture, he gets nearer, thinking the body alive, half in conversation with it, hardly knowing whether it is he or the dead man who is speaking: 'You're there. It seems to you that it is to you that observations are being addressed.'[12] Rosa's address is towards a number of people: her boyfriend Conrad; her 'sublime' father, Lionel Burger; her black 'half-brother' from her youth, Zwelinzima, or Baasie (later that dialogue becomes real, externalised in the middle of the night in a phone call of absolutely chilling recrimination and mutual accusation between the two). It is Gordimer's signature to have given this a particular racial stamp in South Africa, as the example of Mehring makes clear. In the symbolic scheme of things in the novel the body represents the accumulated catalogue of history's crimes against black South Africans. In Mehring's mind its presence becomes, increasingly, a personal reproach, because of his own collusion in that system. The more he tries to suppress the meaning of the body, the more insistently it is alive in his thoughts: this is Freud's 'return of the repressed' given a particular, political impression. The body is present in its absence, and the more Mehring wishes its moral implications to be gone, the more profoundly it will never leave him. Mehring, in addressing himself, is addressing the other within him. Gordimer's implication is that apartheid was never fully 'safe' or policed for its proponents, and not merely in the external senses in which this became self-evidently true. Deep within the self was divided, ungrounded, insurrectionary; the internal dynamics of this reality meant that the 'return of the repressed' had a psychic significance in Gordimer's fiction as precise analogue to the political.

In that regard it seems futile to call Nadine Gordimer simply a 'realist' – which has so often been her critical assignation. It is true that on its surface her fiction admits the texture of realism: a particular kind of description, a relation of subject to context. But the reality it penetrates to find – as in the example of Mehring above – has little to do with the usual diagnostic capacities of the form. If this is realism, that is to say, then it is the X-ray version we see in Gordimer, in which what lies on the surface is never enough or most interesting. Moreover, this has to do not only with the conventional distinction between 'appearance' and a more hidden 'reality' – the suggestion of which is quite congenial to realism – but that internal reality is itself like a surface which Gordimer actually *sees*. She lays it out for us on the X-ray plate of her vision: this is realism redefined. Moreover her work, while using these methods, is not always satisfied with a singleness of form or genre. A story from 1972, entitled 'The Intruder', begins with a flirtation and marriage (the wife just emerging from a state of emotional childhood, the husband previously divorced and more urbane) and ends with a vision of horror: an apartment wrecked inexplicably in the middle of the night, with obscene – almost ritualistic – residues which may be equally the parting signature of a demonically malicious invader, or – even more threateningly – externalised emanations from the unconscious of the husband or even, at some deeper level, both individuals in the marriage. *A World of Strangers*, published in 1958, punctuates a realistic sociology of segregated Johannesburg with a rural interlude where the central character enters the equivalent of a medieval blighted landscape to discover the crime against nature with which his complicity in the world of apartheid is associated. The latter irruption suggests that nature provides its own all-encompassing ecology, and we find this again – quite appropriately – in *The Conservationist*. Here, much more fully than is true of Mehring in his sentimental nostalgia for nature, the black workers on the farm seem at one with their environment: the vision, on one level Romantic, becomes in its larger sense of belonging within a place a version of *pastorale*. Even Gordimer's most political novel, *A Guest of Honour*, is in that respect a pastorale: it is a book of belonging – both in life and death – in Africa.

'No Place Like', a story written at about the same time as *A Guest of Honour*, is also set in some unnamed African location. There a woman of advancing age, caught within the confines of an airport building, suddenly decides to break out of her pre-determined journey. Hiding in the bathroom until after her plane takes off, she reconstructs a vision of escape seen earlier by the passengers: 'through the forbidden doorway: grass, bougainvillaea trained like standard roses, a road glimpsed there!' Again Gordimer's fiction intimates the crossing of boundaries; against all odds, Africa remains a place of hope for her, with a future and a sense of personal liberation. The beginning of the story is also intriguing: as the passengers enter the airport building and are prevented from further egress, the bemused words '*Transit? Transit?*' echo through their minds. It reminds us that at base Gordimer's fiction is intricately bound up with *transition* – of the kind the woman in the airport goes through. Perhaps this is true of all fiction: the short story or novel, taken up with life in time, presents sequences of essential passage for its characters. And yet few writers have presented the notion of transition so intensely as Gordimer: all her novels are taken up with the kinds of *becoming* of her characters, and this is usually enacted against the backdrop of a larger social world both itself in transition and demanding transition from its inhabitants. The preface to *July's People*, drawn from Antonio Gramsci, sets it up in its darkest form, when change is most difficult: 'The old is dying and the new cannot be born; in this interregnum there arises a great diversity of morbid symptoms.' But all of Gordimer's fiction is, in this larger sense, involved in the transition from one world into another, occupying a time and place of interregnum. This is apparent in her later work – *My Son's Story, None to Accompany Me, The House Gun* – in which South Africa itself is undergoing the most troubling and challenging kinds of upheaval and transformation. Yet if Gordimer observes this, she does so again as a writer who delves far deeper than the normal platitudes of everyday experience. For the central point about these novels is that everything about them is in transition and 'mixed': politics, ethics, art, identity, the past, present and future – all are in collision, fission and fusion. From that point of view it is perhaps no accident that in *My Son's Story* – the first of these novels to be set in a time of actual political transformation – the central character is of 'mixed' race, or 'coloured' in South African terms. Sonny – caught between his roles as teacher and politician, a lover of Shakespeare who must reconcile himself to the banality of political language, a father and husband whose sense of identity is in total flux – is in this regard completely between one state and another. And we are all, suggests Gordimer, 'mixed' to some or other extent in such a period, all caught up in the space-between.

The idea of transition means that Gordimer's writing is always in some way in dialogue with an absent future. Mehring addresses himself to a black body whose unburial represents a future which alone can reclaim and redeem the present: its absence speaks through our present as our present addresses itself to that absence. This reminds us of how important the very notion of dialogue is for Gordimer's work, at every level at which it operates. One sees this even as an insistent stylistic feature – not least where characters are in some form of conversation. Readers approaching *The Conservationist* (which might have been called, as I have observed elsewhere, *The Conversationist*) or *Burger's Daughter* for the first time are naturally puzzled by where the narrative is coming from or to whom, within the text, it is addressed. Quotation marks – as in Joyce – have disappeared; both Mehring and Rosa Burger speak to different 'yous' in their minds whom it takes some time and familiarity to identify; partly because of this it is hard to say where one voice ends and another begins. But one thing Gordimer has insisted on is that style in her work fits function to form – and one can see how this is true. That is the whole point about Mehring: the black body whom he addresses in his mind cannot be separated, in some way, from his own identity – or more precisely, from the dialogue within his own identity. Rosa constructs her father, lover, 'half-brother', even as she addresses them and is constructed by others. From this point of view Gordimer's writing is revealed as essentially dialogic, in the form in which Bakhtin detected it in Dostoevsky: 'where consciousness began, there dialogue began for him as well.'[13] And how fitting that it is revealed on the page stylistically in 'dialogue', where one character speaks to another! Through a feature as apparently mutable as style Gordimer has recognised and embodied something crucial in the world around her, with all its complications and fragmentations in South African reality.

In Gordimer's most recent novel, *The House Gun*, this is if anything taken a stage further, because there speech is somehow triangulated in its very formulation. Where father, mother and son are caught up in the tragedy of a murder which makes them question the foundations of their lives, each perception is modulated simultaneously through the eyes and voice not only of the self, but also through the voices and eyes of others as the self might expect them to see or speak. *Who*, Gordimer is forcing us to ask, is the subject? Who, indeed in these circumstances are *we*? Just where are our edges or boundaries? There is a flow of consciousness and time that envelops us all, and when that time is one of radical transition, the edges of self and other both fragment and overlap in the most startling ways. In such a moment of flux we are all, in the very deepest sense, responsible for each other's reality. The understanding, evinced as a matter of being, shades necessarily and insistently towards the ethical. Again, it is not simply 'realism' that reveals this – or if it is, then the meaning of the word has itself been transformed. It is quite extraordinary writing.

III

How to summarise all or even some of this? I have, I fear, only skimmed the surface. One might mention other issues scarcely touched upon so far – for instance, an incipient theme of resurrection in Gordimer's work, but one which is only tangentially metaphysical. The black body rises in *The Conservationist* to reclaim the land, and to be buried with due respect by the black farmworkers. *A Sport of Nature* contains themes of death (of Whaila, Hillela's husband) and of resurrection – both the insistent resurrections from death of organic and human life, as well as political forms of rebirth. From the reverse angle one might talk of irony in Gordimer's work – writing as insistently ironical as any in this century, apparently the opposite of a transcendent vision. But irony can work as a cleansing agent and a test of honesty: if there are visions of resurrection or rebirth to be registered they must be purged of the merely sentimental or nostalgic. In a way that is not often recognised – because her writing can be so astringent – Gordimer's fiction can in fact embody deep feeling. There are few works that contain, for me, the implicit emotion of reclamation that attends the ending of *The Conservationist*, or the delicacy with which Rosa Burger's last poignant solitude is so attentively portrayed, even in its distinct unsentimentality. A story such as 'The Ultimate Safari', which inhabits the first-person voice of a child refugee who has walked in the midst of war from Mozambique to South Africa, is filled to the brim with understated, numbed and overwhelming pain and hope. 'My Father Leaves Home' confronts the past Gordimer had never recognised, or had turned away from in the life of her father, and does so with an unmistakable depth of feeling. Such emotion is all the more real, we might say, for having been concentrated, divested of all extraneities, in this way.

Thinking of Gordimer's relation to her father and mother, her family's own lines of belonging, fragmentation and division, it is intriguing that one feature of her life and writing should then have been an innate drive to test and cross boundaries. This has been enacted in space – the social space of South Africa, riven so badly in every direction, yet somehow still a unity to which all South Africans belong – but it has also been enacted in time, as Gordimer has addressed the inner history of her society and, as I have suggested, approached an absent and perhaps impossible future that would be required to complete it. Thinking back to 1923, when she was born, we might say that it too was a time of transition and postponement: the First World War five years past, the Russian Revolution six years old, South Africa about to enter its time of modernity in which race, industrialisation, and the savage barbarisms of apartheid were all woven into their own kind of figure in the carpet, the threads of which, only seventy years later, would suddenly unravel. The era of her birth still had links to the colonial nineteenth century; the year 1998, approaching the end of the millennium, marks both in South Africa and across the globe a very different universe in every way. In this sense – and looking back through her work at such an astonishing century – one might say that Nadine Gordimer has lived from one world into another; that her writing has attended an extraordinarily long period of birth; that it has, throughout this period of interregnum – and which period in history is not also one of interregnum? – worked through the jagged, shiny, misleading, brutal surfaces of our time to an approximation of depth: of all those underlying stories beneath.

But, whether or not I am able to summarise, I feel the need to make some final connections – especially about the writer and her writing life – and think I shall do so by returning to the idea of dialogue. For dialogue at some level has to mean questioning, and whatever else Gordimer's writing is there can be no doubt that it is questioning writing. Though she is frequently held to be the archetypal political writer, her work implicitly questions the relationship – walks yet another edge – between writing and politics. This is true in the case of Sonny in *My Son's Story*: can political language tell the truth in the way that fiction can? That is part of Sonny's transitional problem. One language speaks to another, finds the presence of the other within it, but also the sense of difference. Yet as in everything else suggested here, at a deeper level writing that questions politics becomes political in its most authentic form: it begins to guarantee real meanings, real debates, real dialogues that can neither be imagined nor censored by the conventional languages of power. That other version of power is part of the mystery of writing, part of its essential significance: we find out here what we never expected to find.

Writing of that kind is, in the exact sense, unpredictable: it has not been said before, it could not have been said before; it took the writer to come along and say it. That is what Nadine Gordimer does: it is something like a physical drive in which body and mind rove where they are drawn to and where they have to go.

The cat wanders off quite of its own accord, because it has found something more interesting. The writer *wonders* off because she has seen something to capture her mind, and she will never stop wondering. The eyes of the cat that face us are unblinking: it will not turn away, it will see what we may not want it to see, it has – sometimes – a frightening as well as charming clarity. As for the cat that is walking away, that really doesn't mind what we think, that has found something so completely more enticing to occupy its attention: though it may look like the enemy of engagement and responsibility, it turns out to be the most engaged and responsible of all.

Endnotes

1. For an early autobiographical version of some of the information given here, see 'A Bolter and the Invincible Summer', in *Nadine Gordimer, The Essential Gesture: Writing, Politics and Places*, ed. Stephen Clingman (London: Cape; New York: Knopf; Johannesburg/Cape Town: Taurus/David Philip; 1988). For other accounts of the importance of Gordimer's early life and family background for her writing, see Andrew Vogel Ettin, *Betrayals of the Body Politic: The Literary Commitments of Nadine Gordimer* (Charlottesville and London: University Press of Virginia, 1993), and John Cooke, *The Novels of Nadine Gordimer: Private Lives/Public Landscapes* (Baton Rouge and London: Louisiana State University Press, 1985). There are of course other commentaries of interest, as well as a number of relevant interviews in *Conversations With Nadine Gordimer*, ed. Nancy Topping Bazin and Marilyn Dallman Seymour (Jackson and London: University Press of Mississippi, 1990).

2. Henry James, *The Figure in the Carpet and Other Stories*, ed. Frank Kermode (Harmondsworth: Penguin, 1986).

3. Burt Britton, *Self-Portrait: Book People Picture Themselves* (New York: Random House, 1976).

4. Nadine Gordimer, *July's People* (London: Cape, 1981), p.160.

5. There is a more extensive discussion of some of the issues raised here in Stephen Clingman, 'Nadine Gordimer and the Boundaries of Fiction',

in *The Later Fiction of Nadine Gordimer*, ed. Bruce King (New York: St Martin's, 1993), as well as in the Preface to the 2nd edn of his *The Novels of Nadine Gordimer: History from the Inside* (Amherst: University of Massachusetts Press, 1992; London: Bloomsbury, 1993); also see Ettin, *Betrayals of the Body Politic*, ch.3.

6.   For a fine essay on the apocalyptic element in *July's People*, see Nicholas Visser, 'Beyond the Interregnum: A Note on the Ending of *July's People*', in *Rendering Things Visible: Essays on South African Literary Culture*, ed. Martin Trump (Johannesburg: Ravan, 1990), pp.61-67.

7.   The character is Cecil Rowe, in Nadine Gordimer, *A World of Strangers* (London: Gollancz, 1958), p.157.

8.   Nadine Gordimer, *A Sport of Nature* (London: Cape, 1987), p.228.

9.   For an illuminating investigation of this issue, see Michael Green, *Novel Histories: Past, Present and Future in South African Fiction* (Johannesburg: Witwatersrand University Press, 1997).

10.   Nadine Gordimer, *Burger's Daughter* (London: Jonathan Cape, 1973), p.127.

11.   *Ibid.*, p.16.

12.   Nadine Gordimer, *The Conservationist* (1974; Harmondsworth: Penguin, 1978), p.227.

13.   Mikhail Bakhtin, *Problems of Dostoevsky's Poetics*, ed. and trans. Caryl Emerson (Minneapolis, University of Minnesota Press, 1984), p.40.

Lemmings, Cats, Pigs: Gordimer's Women during the Interregnum and Beyond

KAREN RUTH LAZAR

The much cited epigraph to Gordimer's *July's People* comes from Antonio Gramsci's *Prison Notebooks*: 'The old is dying and the new cannot be born; in this interregnum there arises a great diversity of morbid symptoms'. Throughout the last two decades and even after South Africa's famed 1994 elections, Gordimer has shown an interest in the forms of subjectivity and action which arise in a society which lies between two orders. In her 1983 essay 'Living in the Interregnum' she comments:

> The state of interregnum is a state of Hegel's disintegrated consciousness, of contradictions ... The interregnum is not only between two social orders, but between two identities, one known and discarded, the other unknown and undetermined (1989: 269-70).

July's People (1982) and *My Son's Story* (1990) offer an interesting counterpoint to each other in that each could be said to occupy one side of the interregnum: the former offers symbolical portents of the change to come in South Africa from the urgent but fairly inchoate revolutionary perspective of the early 1980s, while the latter offers small but concrete signs that the long-awaited change in South Africa is under way, from the more definite (though perhaps more compromised) perspective of the early nineties. What the political interregnum diagnosed by Gordimer actually was, when it ended, or whether it has ended at all, are questions that have occupied the author in recent years. My aim in this essay is not to attempt to answer those questions, but rather to examine these two counterpoised texts with the help of a different set of questions: in what ways do Gordimer's representations of women shift, develop, entrench themselves or otherwise strike us during this interregnum period? I have elsewhere explored the ambivalences and tensions in Gordimer's attitudes to feminism and her related (but not equivalent) treatment of female figures in her fiction over the last two decades (Lazar 1990, 1992). In the early eighties Gordimer's attitudes to feminism waver between pronouncing it 'piffling' on the one hand and necessary on the other (necessity being the mark of a feminism which ties itself to the imperatives of overarching political change). Her attitudes towards feminism since the start of the nineties have been less equivocal, more comfortable though by no means without complication. I hope that the explorations of the two texts which follow show the subtlety, density and multivalence of her renditions of her chief women protagonists and of the complex sexual politics in *July's People* and *My Son's Story*. In particular I compare the author's encodings of the metonymic physiques of Maureen and Hannah in relation to some of her narrative strategies (such as voice and structure) in the two texts under question.

*

> When I wrote [*July's People*], we were poised like lemmings on the edge of a cliff, we were teetering ... Whether one could pull back from it seemed very difficult and unlikely at the time (interview with Clingman 1992: 139).

In the imagined interregnum of *July's People*, the white liberal Smales family flee their home in the city during a period of black revolutionary uprising and are escorted by their erstwhile man-servant July to the relative safety of his rural home. Stripped of their privilege, comforts, norms and authority, they find in their new circumstances that it is not only the larger political world that is in a state of transformation: their most intimate subjectivities have been radically destabilised. One of Gordimer's chief emphases within the novel is on the radical contingency of all meaning: things previously understood as absolute and beyond query by the Smales family are now shown to have been born in and bolstered by their previous life of power, entitlement and ease. In their situation of new and excruciating dependence on July, it is unclear whether the latter is 'saviour' or 'servant'. Maureen's deteriorating inter-actions with July form one of the chief axes of meaning in the text. (Numerous critics have analysed the complexities of Maureen's relationship with July: his relishing of his newfound power to decide on the Smales' fate yet his insistence on remaining within the codes of being her 'boy'; her attempt at setting up some equity between them and yet her reversion to 'madam-like' behaviour when thwarted, and so on.) Under the pressure of previously inconceivable circumstances, language, sex and morality also become unstable currencies. Early in the text, Maureen muses:

> We understand the sacred power and rights of sexual love as formulated in master bedrooms, and motels with false names in the register. Here the sacred power and rights of sexual love are formulated in a wife's hut, and a backyard room in a city ... *The absolute nature* she and her kind were scrupulously just in granting to everybody was no more than the price of the master bedroom and the clandestine hotel tariff. (65)

And thus Gordimer's assertion that interpretive and semiotic power are not pre-given but context-ordained. Maureen's linguistic advantages over and claims to understand July are refuted once and for all near the end of the text where he breaks angrily into his own language, and she finally understands that 'His measure as a man was taken elsewhere and by others' (152). Maureen's concept of herself as humane and liberal is shown to have been based on a staggering illusion. To July, his 'madam' partakes in a structure of massive and hurtful inequity which her minor courtesies do nothing to mitigate. Following on from the radical erosion of her certainties about self, sex and morality, Maureen – like so many of Gordimer's earlier liberal protagonists – is now also brought up against 'the final illusion of white innocence' (Smith 1984: 106).

Against this backdrop of colossal existential change, *July's People*'s famous 'apocalyptic' ending must be read. Hearing the throb of a helicopter above her in the bush, Maureen breaks into a wild and unthinking run and crosses a river in her rush towards the helicopter. Critics are crucially divided over whether Maureen's flight is an affirmative act or a final evasion of historic responsibility. To my mind the radical indeterminacy of the ending is itself a sign of interregnum thinking. Gordimer's insistence on the difficulty of fixing meanings or offering closure in this text is perhaps inevitable within a historical moment where change itself is so imminent but still so hard to envisage.

Another axis of indeterminacy runs as follows: why is Maureen's sexuality described in the terms it is? What relationships between women are depicted in the text, and how are black women and white wom(a)n differentially embodied? How does the depiction of Maureen's physique tie in with her deteriorating interactions with July?

As a self-avowed female liberal, Maureen belongs among an obvious group of figures spanning Gordimer's work who espouse a 'humane creed' and a belief in 'equality of need' (65). Elizabeth van den Sandt in *The Late Bourgeois World*, Antonia in *The Conservationist*, the mother in 'A Correspondence Course' in *Something Out There* and Aunt Pauline in *A Sport of Nature* are just a few of Maureen's many fictional cousins. There are obvious differences among these figures, but all of them are objects of Gordimer's impatience to some degree or another. Even those women who eventually commit themselves to some form of social action – such as Elizabeth, Pauline and perhaps Maureen, if her flight towards the helicopter is read as an affirmative act – appear to stand for that which irritates Gordimer most about liberalism (or her version of it): its tendency to allow rhetoric and sentiment to dominate over meaningful action, its eventual self-interestedness, its limited social vision, its capacity for self-delusion.

Bam Smales' habit of benign *baasskap* clearly has its arrogant and predatory sides but his psychology is given none of the tortured, supersubtle cruelty and guilt of Maureen's. Suffice it to say that Gordimer's pattern in her oeuvre suggests that she damns white female liberals more harshly, and scrutinises them more closely, than their male counterparts (with some exceptions). This is not to say that Maureen is only vilified. Like all Gordimer's chief female protagonists, Maureen is intelligent, vocal and capable of courage and initiative. What is striking about Gordimer's depiction of Maureen, however, is the almost obsessive and unprecedented energy given to describing Maureen's physique. This obsession with the physical details of a female figure's appearance continues a trend that is present earlier in Gordimer's fiction, and lays the ground for interesting developments in the encodings of women which follow *July's People*. Gordimer uses the physiques of her protagonists, male and female, in highly connotative ways which act to reinforce and express the values and political affiliations of the figure in question. In the case of Gordimer's less likeable women, strategically placed negative details about their bodies often hasten along the political devalorisation which attaches to the figure in each case.

At first glance, the numerous negative details about Maureen's appearance are primarily functional in indicating the breakdown in previous identity which she is undergoing. The explosive questions posed by the interregnum scenario about trust, honesty and self-knowledge, about all the absolutes and norms which she previously took for granted, are symbolised by the defamiliarisation she experiences in relation to her own body and which others notice in her. Thus, very early on in the text we are told: '[F]or the first time in her life she found that she smelled bad between her legs, and ... disgustedly scrubbed at the smooth lining of her vagina' (8). Within a short time of being in her new environment, she is rough and undepilated with the dye growing out of her hair such that July's wife thinks that her hair looks like 'the tail of a dirty sheep' (22). Maureen's rough look is apparently meant to indicate the consequences for whites of giving up their privilege: her elegance has been forcibly sloughed off along with her wealth. The numerous details about filth, smells, insects and rust in the text are an unrelenting reminder of the force of poverty.

In the grind of daily life which overtakes the Smales couple, Bam's physique also undergoes changes. He is often described as red-faced and ungainly, traits which express the floundering of his male authority and confidence. The oft-cited moment when he sees menstrual blood on his penis after sex (80) and experiences a moment of sheer castration-horror, signals the extent to which loss of political authority and 'emasculation' are two interlinked fears within the conventional white male consciousness he represents. In an interesting essay André Brink suggests that the presence of Maureen's blood on Bam's body 'affirms Maureen's physical presence as a threat to his' (1994: 165) and cites this episode as an instance of the altered and freer gender roles resulting from the interregnum. To me the episode signals more the grotesque immediacy of the physical in the new lives of both Bam and Maureen than the ascendancy of Maureen in relation to a waning patriarchy. Bam's horror has at least something to do with the de-sanitised context of his sexual behaviour.

The changes in the physical appearances and experiences of the Smales couple are more than an indicator of their newfound social debility, however. Through these changes, Gordimer is at pains to emphasise a crucial point about the nature of sexual identity itself: rather than being immanent in the individual or pre-social in kind, this identity is socially constructed and dependent on context for its particularity. Away from master-bedroom, salon and shopping centre, Maureen's sexuality becomes radically alien to her and to those who look at her (her author being one such gazer). However, if the predominant narrative stance towards the artifice and effort of Maureen's highly 'feminine' *previous* sexuality is satirical, what then is its stance towards Maureen's *current* sexuality, the dishevelled one which we get to know in the course of the narrative?

This is the point at which questions about Gordimer's treatment of white female sexuality become complicated. For it is clear that Gordimer's attitude to Maureen's new 'bush' sexuality is over-whelmingly harsh. Mentions of her feet 'dirty as a hobo's' (78) and her bare 'shallow' breasts (89) are extremely numerous. She cannot make an appearance in the narrative without some marker of her physical unkemptness accompanying it.[1] More than any other figure in the text, she is associated with dirt and odour; she excretes a 'cold-cat smell' when she sweats (151). In the course of the text she does not so much acquire a new sexuality as lose her femininity almost to the point of misrecognition:

> The baring of breasts was not an intimacy but the castration of [Bam's] sexuality and hers . . . her neck was weathered red . . . He would never have believed that pale hot neck under long hair when she was young could become her father's neck that he remembered in a Sunday morning bowling shirt (90).

Nadine Gordimer, Johannesburg, June 1968

A reading, Parktown,
Johannesburg, December 1983

Nadine Gordimer at home, Johannesburg, April 1985

Brink argues that Maureen's altered and rough sexuality allows her to '[derive] a strange new pleasure precisely from flaunting what had previously been shameful' and suggests that this flaunting is a 'significant move towards a new kind of self and a new kind of power . . . [H]here, in the interregnum, gender roles have escaped from their previous constraints' (1994: 165, 171). Given that Brink reads the ending of the novel as a 'moment of birth' (175), it is not surprising that he sees the changes in Maureen as indices of impending and positive metamorphosis. To my mind, however, the changes in Maureen are carried in a tone of overwhelming negation; Maureen's sexuality begins to be a lack, or a too-present viscerality. Gordimer seems to be implying that the sexuality of a white female figure like Maureen cannot make a home for itself away from its urban context. It has been set forward by many a feminist author that a 'back to nature' state can be a cause for celebration among women and can occasion a discovery of a more 'authentic' female sexuality free of hampering conventions of beauty. Wagner also finds evidence in *July's People* of such a discovery:

> A tentative movement towards a repossession of that body is suggested in [Maureen's] discovery of the possibility of a fierce possessive joy in it when she performs her solitary dance in the rain (1994: 111).

While I agree with Wagner on the mood of Maureen's naked shower in the rain (48), any sense of joy established here is overshadowed by the narrative's larger mood of stress and loss. Maureen's naked-ness at that one moment signals a kind of wholeness; but for the bulk of the text her bodily presence is made known to us through single aspects – her face, feet, breasts, stomach – which creates an overriding sense of fragmentation in her sexuality and subjectivity. Hillela in *A Sport of Nature* (1987) is also made known to us through parts of her body, but whereas Maureen's body parts are thin, anxious and dirty, Hillela's are smooth, stylish and voluptu-ous. Hillela's happy status as a 'new white African' is connoted through the glamour of her physique, whereas Maureen's status as an 'old' white African is connoted through the grotesqueness of hers.

For the most part then, Maureen's sexuality in the bush may be seen as a matter of degeneration rather than discovery. Gordimer seems unwilling to give narrative sanction to her chief figure's sexuality, either in its urban or its rural form. Perhaps Maureen's increasingly weatherbeaten physique is meant to signal a failure on her part: a failure to adapt to her new environment or to eschew old habits. But failure to make good under hardship, still does not sufficiently explain the obsessiveness of the detail nor the harshness of description meted out to Maureen by Gordimer. Bam, too, is not forgiven for the tenacity of his sense of entitlement but the moments which describe his disorientation in his new circumstances are relatively kind. So, for instance, 'he [takes] up the radio . . . with the baffled obstinacy of a sad, intelligent primate fingering the locks on his bars' (50). The markers of disorientation in Maureen are never conveyed in words as benign as 'sad' or 'intelligent'. The decreasing use of her name and the increasing use of *she* to describe her (particularly when she is in the narrative vicinity of Bam or July) adds to the sense that Maureen is becoming a nothing, a set of negations and dwindlings, rather than a new something in the text. The evaporation of her previous sexuality and its supplanting by a mode of womanhood that is harsh and attenuated, are the chief expressions of the denudation of Maureen's subjectivity.

If Maureen in the city possessed a dislikeable sexuality and Maureen in the bush becomes de-sexed, what about the black women in the text who have always lived in this rural environment? They, ostensibly, have no need of adaptation, since poverty and squalor is all they have ever known. But whereas Maureen moves further and further away from any recognisable indices of positive womanhood, Martha – July's wife – is associated with fecundity (she suspects she is pregnant again) and is the only figure in the very bleak language of the text about whom the word 'pretty' is used (92). Gordimer is far from unequivocally flattering about Martha, however: in body she is recognisable by 'those great hams outbalancing the rest of her' (92) and in character she is shown to possess a 'whingeing obstinacy' (83).

But the bodies of Martha and the other black women, young and old, are shown to be at one with the tasks required of them for survival and reproduction. This state of at-one-ness is mirrored in their attitudes to time. Maureen is severely disoriented in time, this being one of the markers of the breakdown in her certainties

(17, 29). Martha and the other black women, by contrast, are shown to have a stoic and anchored relationship with time and their circumstances: 'The sun rises, the moon sets; the money must come, the man must go' (83). These words suggest that, while foregrounding the poverty that these black rural women face and the effect of labour migrancy upon family life, Gordimer has a tendency to cast black female figures in a slightly static and idealising light – a tendency which we see in some of her other works as well. Such stereotypes of black women as organically connected to nature create a kind of pastoral 'soft focus' on some aspects of their lives which then leaves one with a situation in which Maureen's sexuality is shown to have been a strenuous social construct but black rural female sexuality appears to be relatively untrammelled by gratuitous social convention, and defined by necessity and 'nature'. Gordimer's attempt to establish sexuality as socially constructed in *July's People* is thus an incomplete attempt. While it is obvious that the black women's lives are so eroded by hardship and starvation that 'sexuality' in any obvious sense may be lost in them, this does not mean that their sexual behaviour is free of conventions particular to their history and context. Maureen's sexuality is clearly shown to have been *more* formulated by custom and craft than that of the other women in the text, and Gordimer seems to blame her for it. While it may be true that Maureen's wealth and situation in consumerist culture encouraged more sexual contrivance, it is puzzling why Gordimer sees fit to punish Maureen tonally to such a degree within the bounds of the narrative present.

In a reversal of imperial viewpoints about the body of the Other, July's mother finds Maureen's flesh strange and a little repulsive when she shakes her hand (22), and Martha finds Maureen's bare white calves with their 'yellow bruises and fine, purple-red, ruptured blood-vessels' shocking and ridiculous (92). The black women are shown to have an ease with their own bodies but a lack of ease Xwith Maureen's which go beyond simple explanations of their unfamiliarity with white people. Maureen's body clearly represents a site of dramatic malaise: its disjuncture from 'nature' loudly symptomatises the ontological collapse she represents.

Why, then, is Maureen the figure in *July's People* with the most distasteful, the most attenuated and the most disoriented sexuality?

Firstly, as we have seen, Maureen is the figure around whom Gordimer's political impatience centres. With the necessity of the arrival of a new order pressing down upon Gordimer in the early eighties, self-delusion and political intractability among whites was becoming ever more intolerable to her. Maureen's genteel brand of intractability and blithe self-exculpation require undercutting in Gordimer's book. Devaluing the figure sexually is one of the ways in which Gordimer devalues her politically. One brief earlier instance of this kind of procedure is the unsavoury and pathetic Mrs Palmer in 'Livingstone's Companions' (1972) whose politics – in this case blatantly imperialist politics – are helped towards damnation by the physical descriptions offered of her (filtered through the voracious eyes of journalist Carl Church):

> But this one had been out in the sun for twenty years . . . Ugly bright blue eyes, cheap china. Her dead hair tossed frowsily. He thought: . . . she's horrible (*Selected Stories* 349).

Gordimer's treatment of Maureen continues the author's well-established habit of denouncing a female figure politically through sexual devalorisation. Gordimer has also shown consistent thematic interest throughout her work in the process of human ageing. There are some male figures in her work (such as the old man in 'The Last Kiss' in *Livingstone's Companions* and the lover in 'Time Did' in *A Soldier's Embrace*) who are shown to be the sorry victims of the ageing process. But most of the figures caught in the cul-de-sac of ageing are women, and most of these women are represented in terms that can only be described as uncomfortable. There can be few portraits as grotesque and unforgiving as that of the vulgar old woman in the early story 'Enemies' in *Six Feet of the Country*:

> Fat overflowed not only from her jowl to her neck, but from her ankles over her shoes. She looked like a pudding that had risen too high and run down the sides of the dish. She was sprinkling cologne on to a handkerchief and hitting with it at her face as if she were trying to kill an insect (164).

Gordimer seems deeply to fear the prospect of the female body when it runs to seed. She herself has said: 'A woman cannot forgive herself for ageing' (interview with Rhedin 1984: 14). Even in her 1994 novel *None to Accompany Me*, which has at its centre a favoured older woman, Gordimer seems only partially to question the unfortunate habit in sexist societies of equating loss of female looks with loss of socio-sexual viability. In *July's People*, Maureen's journey towards middle age and social marginality has been accelerated by the harshness of her circumstances. The speed with which a well-groomed woman could become hairy, rough and dirty seems to emit a high level of discomfort in the text. There is, further, a faint suggestion that the prospect of *white* female sexuality running to seed most disturbs the author. July's aged, bent and wizened black mother is described with none of the squeamishness present in the portraits of Maureen. The old lady's awkwardness in relation to Maureen's white flesh is not dissimilar to Gordimer's (unconscious?) reflex away from deterioration in the white female physique.

This reflex can then be related back to Gordimer's political dislike of Maureen as a prototypical liberal. Two forms of dislike (of white liberalism, and of female ageing) are rolled into one in the representation of Maureen. Maureen is a strong central figure in the text, and an interesting, complex and lucid one, but she is pushed away from readerly sanction by the radically unappealing bodily markers slapped on her within the narrative.

∗

Critics have dealt extensively with the deterioration in the relationship between Maureen and July through the three or four confrontations which occur between them. During these confrontations, the illusory nature of the old 'trust' between them is unveiled, as well as the ludicrousness of Maureen's claims to 'know' July when his 'measure as a man is taken elsewhere, and by others' (152). The enforced quasi-intimacy between a 'madam' and a domestic servant is shown to have its cruel and explosive undersides, especially when harsh racial and economic truths about the relationship can no longer be ignored or wished away.

In one of Maureen's first encounters with July, he responds angrily to what he perceives as an absence of trust between them over the vexed matter of who keeps the car keys in the bush. Citing the Smales' numerous holidays and overseas trips, he says 'You worry about the keys? . . . Always you telling me even last minute when I'm carrying your suitcase, isn't it? Look after everything July . . . You frightened I'm not working enough for you?' (70). What July raises here is a challenge to Maureen to fault him in his work – and she cannot. In a later encounter, when Maureen somewhat sadistically threatens to tell his wife about his town woman, July again challenges Maureen to find fault with him. This time his language is bald and furious: 'What can you tell? . . . That I'm work for you fifteen years. *That you satisfy with me*' (98).

The words 'Fifteen years your boy you satisfy' recur obsessively in the remainder of the free indirect discourse attaching to Maureen, signalling the extent to which July has hit upon an accuracy. Within the terms of his employment, Maureen has nothing to complain about. But it is because Maureen as madam had, in the name of her own humaneness, transgressed the boundaries of their work relationship, because of her claims to 'know' July and to be on intimate terms with him, that so much anger and manipulation unfolds between them. The unruly truths and desires latent within the 'forbidden' zone of interracial sex have been variously probed and explored by writers as diverse as Sarah Gertrude Millin, Jean Rhys and Doris Lessing, to name but a few. Gordimer's own awareness of the many social discourses of sexual taboo and desire which overdetermine relations between black and white, particularly between black men and white women, is also not new. In the final and thematically climactic encounter between Maureen and July, the current of underlying sexual anxiety present between them surfaces in an uncomfortable scene of parody and quasi-invitation:

She lurched over and posed herself, a grotesque, against the vehicle's hood . . . sweat-coarsened forehead touched by the moonlight, neglected hair standing out wispy and rough. The death's harpy image she made of herself meant nothing to him, who had never been to a motor-show complete with provocative girls (153).

A significant feature of this passage is the sub-theme of possession.

Maureen's previous provider, Bam, has been steadily stripped of power in the course of the narrative. The two chief icons of phallic power and authority – the vehicle and the gun – have both been removed from him. He is now 'a man without a gun', a man who 'had nothing' (145). And so, Maureen, unused to providing material necessities for herself, shifts her interest to the man who does have power in the text: July. The triangle of gendered power relations in the text alters its balance. Bam is even an intruder, the 'third one' (69) whom both of them ignore. July's tacit ownership of the vehicle marks him with the sign of male identity. Maureen's grotesque draping of herself over the vehicle extends the theme of possession in that what she now offers as a thing for ownership is herself: she is 'another of the possessions that will make a *big man* of her "boy" ' (Neill 1990: 80). The crowning irony of the scene is that her gesture remains utterly opaque to July: car-shows and the sex objects metonymically associated with them are not part of his discourse. Maureen performs for herself alone.

It is clear from Gordimer's parody of the 'girl on the bonnet' image that she does not endorse the far extremes of sexist culture wherein women and objects become interchangeable. And yet, a deep ambivalence exists in the rendition of Maureen's body in this and other scenes. Maureen has already once been compared with 'a caricature of a titillating photograph in a porn magazine' (52) in the scene when Bam notices her bare pubic hair below her jersey. Considering, again, the mass of damning physical details given about Maureen, it is clear that she is continuously inscribed in the text as a recipient of the gaze: usually July or Bam's gaze, and behind it all, Gordimer's. Although Gordimer does distance herself from the more vulgar and overt aspects of sexist (visual) culture, her tendency to judge women through the look of their bodies – or to use the look of their bodies to override or frame other aspects of their being – is a habit long nurtured by patriarchal ideologies. The 'death's harpy' image attached to Maureen in the final climactic encounter with July, ironic though it is, is the culmination of a series of images in the text in which she is associated with ugliness and sexual morbidity. Her relationship with July may be the chief 'morbid symptom' arising out of the politics inscribed in the text, but Maureen's sexuality itself could also be called a symptom: of the author's own complex attitudes to femaleness as evident at this point in her history.

An important fact about this scene is that July rejects Maureen's 'invitation' or fails to be engaged by it, much as Bam gives a ' "for god's sake" look of enquiry' (52) when he notices her naked pubis. The implications are that Maureen is not accepted as a sex object – she is a *failed* 'girl on the bonnet'. This adds another aspect to the 'failures' – moral, political and familial – that have been accumulating around Maureen in the course of the text. With old power relations between white women and black men proto-typically annulled within the microcosm of the July/Maureen web, all that is left for Maureen is a parodic act. After such a gesture of extremity, it is small surprise that Maureen is ready to run blindly towards the next climax, the helicopter's arrival. Stripped of all roles, repressions, certainties that were previously known to her, an 'animal' act (160) is a logical conclusion for her. One of the curious features of the ending is that, in spite of her apparent surge of animal drive, Maureen has very little urge to save her children along with herself (if salvation is what compels her towards the helicopter). As she runs she hears 'the voices of children speaking English somewhere to the left' (159) but feels no connection or pull towards them. This factor occasioned an interesting response by Bailey shortly after the novel was published. Bailey asserts that Maureen's greatest failure is a failure of Eros:

> What Maureen runs to is a return to the illusion of identity created by a world of privilege and possession. What she runs from is a failure to find any creative source for re-birth ... Maureen is fleeing from motherhood (1984: 222).

An instinctual and loving connection with children is taken by Bailey as a sign of the 'Eros of feminine relatedness' (223), and it is this relatedness – to love, collectivity, others – that Maureen has apparently lost. Bailey then finds further support for Maureen's disconnectedness from anything meaningful in her failure to establish solidarity with the black women in the narrative, 'a connection that might have freed her from the destructive illusions of her patriarchal past' (222). Bailey's argument is useful in raising the question of Maureen's precise relation to children and to other women, and of what the significance of such relations might be.

But the terms of Bailey's outlook are too crudely binary. Evidence of any overarching scheme of feminine 'Eros' set against masculine 'Logos' is not discernible in the text, nor are these binaries mechanically attachable to either female or male figures. At any one moment Maureen does not wholly lack 'logos' any more than she can be said to fully possess 'eros'. None of Gordimer's chief female protagonists occupies a position of femininity from which reason, action and logos have been excluded. She asserts (interview with Lazar 1988: 30) that 'vitality', 'intelligence' and 'conflict' are the prerequisites which make both male and female characters interesting to her.

But it is indeed clear that Maureen fails to establish solidarity with the rural black women. Bam, by contrast, integrates more fully into the black male world of the village, and is even welcomed into its beer-drinking rituals, by virtue of his utilitarianism (Ettin 1993: 85). Bam's habituation to hard work in his former life prompts him to build, repair and hunt in his new one. Maureen, less used to hard work, is marked in the village by her aimlessness: 'She moved between them neither working as others did nor able to do nothing as others did' (28). In spite of her few forays into the bush with the black women in search of edible plants, Maureen remains largely redundant and dependent, and more of a novice in the new environment than either her husband or children. The black women, even the elderly women, are anything but redundant. Like Bam and their men, they define themselves in terms of survival, work and function, and Maureen's difference from them within these definitions comprises a large part of the lapsed solidarity between them. An old precedent for this lapse is captured by the *Life* photographer in his image of the black woman Lydia carrying little Maureen's bag home from school. The seemingly innocent bond between the two figures masks the class relations between them such that only the older/decentred Maureen can ask 'Why had Lydia carried [my] case?' (33).

Within the context of the narrative present, the linguistic and experiential gaps between Maureen and the rural women are too large to be bridged. Various opportunities for connection between the women in fact arise but are not taken: 'There was a moment when Maureen *could* have got down on her hunkers beside Martha and helped hold the baby's head while its hair was washed' (146;

my emphasis). The primary reason for these lapses in solidarity is not the failure of some essential, female principle, as Bailey's argument would suggest, but rather a fundamentally political set of reasons. As Gordimer repeatedly points out in the early eighties, possibilities for sisterhood are 'cut right through' (interview with Boyers et al. 1984: 19) by the pressing differentials of race and class experience. The weight of the long oppressive history of South African racialised capitalism does more to explain the unbridgeable gulfs between the women than any recourse to 'Eros'.

Moreover, there is little basis for Bailey's assertion that the black women exhibit an independence from July and a refusal to have their selfhood defined by him such that 'the only unqualified triumph in the novel belongs to the matriarchs' (1984: 223). While it is true that the rural black women 'sleep in their own houses' (Driver 1983: 35) and Maureen, before, had only ever known the 'master' bedroom, this invigorating fact about the black women does lie within an overarching context of patriarchy. Within rural black South Africa at the time when the novel was written, July's structural position as breadwinner and headman – albeit an absentee headman for most of the year – would have ensured him an ongoing (if insubstantial) authority to which his women remain subject. Adaptable and resourceful the black women may be; that does not make their microcosm a 'matriarchy'.

*

Published in 1990, and written in the course of the mid to late eighties, *My Son's Story* is the novel which follows *A Sport of Nature*. Whereas the latter roamed freely across Africa and other locations in its conceptualisation, *My Son's Story* has a much more localised focus, and deals initially with the life of a Coloured family[2] in Benoni and then with their life in an unnamed white area of Johannesburg which is in the process of 'going grey'[3] as the eighties advance. By the time *My Son's Story* comes out, the 'new' South Africa is already showing signs of emerging: F W de Klerk and his 'New Nats' at the helm of the South African government and Mandela and others have been released. Shortly before the novel's launch, Gordimer comments that the interregnum invoked in *July's People* had passed by the end of the eighties and a new order is emerging (interview with Dorsman and Postel 1990: 37), but then modifies this view in a later interview:

> The morbid symptoms now ... well, there's the rise of the extreme right-wing white groups, the neo-nazis, this is one of the morbid symptoms. Then there is the revival of tribalism for cynical political means; this is another 'morbid symptom'. So it gives me quite a cold feeling that Gramsci was right (with Jeyifo 1992: 923).

By the time Gordimer starts writing *My Son's Story*, she has witnessed the imposition of two States of Emergency by the P W Botha government, both of which entailed drastic harassment and curtailment of political activity. Torture, surveillance and disappearances are the backdrop against which *My Son's Story* is set: these events are so common that they form the language of Sonny's political life. Although his politics falls into the 'above board' or legal type of strategies of the Congress-aligned United Democratic Front, the presence of underground revolutionary politics (of the type associated with the still banned African National Congress at that time) is never far away in the novel.

Gordimer's use of a Coloured boy as a first-person narrator allows her a free-ranging intimacy in relation to black experience (where 'black' does not only mean African). Her interest in detailing the life of a Coloured activist also creates a continuance of her concern in *A Sport of Nature* with discovering a 'new kind of African'. Whereas Hillela is one such creature by virtue of her complete inner freedom from sexual and racial taboos, Sonny is a new kind of African by virtue of the amalgam that he represents. Says Gordimer:

> I chose somebody who was in an indefinite state in order to cover all colours and no colours. I don't know. The family's origins are ambiguous, you don't quite know the antecedents and I feel that's the way it should be (interview with Nicol 1991: 11).

Sonny's 'indefinite' state does not only invoke the pleasures of ambiguity or representivity in the text. It also causes him some worry in the non-racial politics he forms part of: he may not be 'black enough' (112) to satisfy the imperative of black (African) leadership. Cutting against Gordimer's own sentiment that 'all colours and no colours' are important in South Africa is her parallel acknowledgement throughout the text that racial divisions and an obsession with 'kind' are a powerful habit. The frequency with which the word 'kind' is invoked – 'their kind', 'our kind', 'places where our kind can go' – is very striking in the text. For all Gordimer's own commitment to a vocalised form of non-racial politics, the stubborn echo of 'kind' in both the first-person and omniscient narratives suggests that goodwill and an impulse towards non-racialism may be insufficient in contending with the ingrained habits of racism and suspicion that decades of segregation have fostered.

There are critics who suggest that there are 'submerged feminist themes' in this novel (Fritz-Piggot 1991, Wagner 1991) in that the powerful and charismatic Sonny is shown through dramatic means to be less resourceful and more dependent than his women. Indeed the structure of the text does suggest a growing descent in Sonny's power and a growing ascent in the powers of Aila and Hannah. During the period of Aila's trial (229-261), Sonny is clearly usurped as the one associated with heroism and salvation. At around the same point, Hannah simply drops out of sight in the narrative, while moving up the UN political ladder. Once closely framed between the two women, Sonny is now disaggregated from that frame and left solitary and pitiable in an empty life, an empty house with a morose adolescent son. Gordimer thus seems to suggest that, on the level of thematic meaning, Sonny is a waning force and his women are a waxing one.

But, on the level of representation, the situation is not nearly so convincing. The abrupt changes in the women, particularly Aila, suggest a writerly conflict that goes beyond a decision about dramatic technique. Gordimer clearly does wish to demonstrate that women are capable of political initiative which equals or outstrips that of men but her manner of doing so is – to my mind – uncomfortable and implausible. Aila's conversion to a life of danger and political devotion is somehow *too* abrupt, too total to be convincing. The only aspect of Aila (besides a fleeting reference to giveaway passport photos) which prepares us for the internal changes in her is her new, cropped haircut. (As in Hillela's case, her short, functional hair signals new political seriousness.) Any other signs of a growth in her motivation or her political insight are simply absorbed into that metonymic haircut, which is surely an exaggeratedly condensed image of change in an uncondensed and leisurely novel.

Hannah's disappearance from the text is also too speedy to be wholly convincing. Hannah, like Gordimer's favourite, Hillela, has the capacity to know when to 'move on' (215). But unlike Hillela, she has not previously been associated with movement in the text. On the contrary, the repeated references to the closeness of Hannah's bed 'to the earth' (173) connect Hannah with rootedness and solidity. It is hard not to feel that Hannah's timely job offer from the United Nations too closely resembles a convenient plot stratagem, a narrative 'deus', to be persuasive. Gordimer's desire to send the women in the text skipping into new lives, and to render Sonny solitary and disempowered, is not accomplished with sufficient textual substance to render it coherent.

A particularly striking discrepancy in this text is the way in which the men are constructed in terms associated with *process* while the women are constructed in terms which obfuscate process. Thus Sonny's growth towards full-blown activism is described in thorough, detailed and processive terms which cover roughly the first 100 pages of the novel. In these pages Sonny's moral and intellectual reasons for becoming politically involved are given such full airing that the logic of his choices appears indisputable. Aila arrives at activism (risky, underground activism) without any recorded process such that her conversion seems almost whimsical. We are given very little insight into the interiority or path of her reasons besides the epigrammatic statement 'I understood' (239). Hannah's process of politicisation is given slightly more attention but the terms in which it is described are likewise problematic. Hannah's interest in politics arises as follows:

The fascination came to her in the mud-brick and thatch of the mission ... from her grandfather's commitment to struggle against evil in men, for God (88).

And that is all we are told. Given what we know about Gordimer's own relationship with religion ('I'm someone without a religion', interview with *The Bookseller* 1990: 2033), the tone in which Hannah's political motivation is described appears more condescending than the tone through which Sonny's is conveyed. Hannah's last name, 'Plowman', reiterates the mood of faithful and pedestrian goodness which attaches to her. The truly lofty, the truly heroic ideals belong to Sonny. The Hannahs of the world – do-gooders and hard workers all – have their place in the struggle, but they are not Gordimer's first choice of hero.

In short, a familiar ambivalence exists in Gordimer's rendition of women in this text: while wishing to construct women in terms associated with power, autonomy and effectiveness, her actual modes of representation seem not to complete the project. Where male consciousness is described through detailed interiority and process, female consciousness is depicted through exteriority and lacunae. Even the taciturn Will is made more fully known to us as a psyche, through our sheer contact with his voice, than his belatedly powerful mother or Hannah.

There is a further dimension which undercuts the status of the women in the text, whatever their putative power. At the end of the novel, Sonny has lost all 'his' women, has been marginalised within his political organisation and, in a final instance of textual negativity, has his house burned down by right-wing whites. The reasons behind his political decline are never fully explained, a fact which gives the movement which ousts him a supremely powerful but inscrutable aspect. Likewise, the whites who raze his house are a faceless, sinister mob. At the end of the text Sonny the hero has become Sonny the victim. And in a certain way, his women *en bloc* have contributed to his persecution: Sonny feels 'resentment . . . [of] women, these two women with their capacity to wound, to threaten' (130). However much Gordimer attempts to set up Aila, Hannah and Baby's aims as laudable and justifiable, another set of messages comes through: the women have *left* Sonny, and that in itself adds to the overwhelming punishment he faces. He clearly remains her favoured figure in this text. In her own words:

I am very fond of Sonny, I think he's a very sympathetic character. As is the boy (interview with Nicol 1991: 11).

There are various readings one could thus give of Sonny's women. They all become free, autonomous, politically viable and vehicles for admiration. *Or* one could say, especially bearing in mind the persecutory atmosphere which governs the text's denouement, that they are punitive and unreliable. On this last point, the representation of Baby in the text has obvious significance. Her decision to become a revolutionary follows hot on the heels of descriptions of her as confused, 'hyped' (61) and mentally unmoored (120). If her father's decision to become politically engaged is born out of honour and outrage, hers is born out of instability. Female actions in the 'public' world thus appear to arise out of private hurts and instabilities. Male actions arise out of seemingly 'purer' motives.

※

The structural tensions and lapses in Gordimer's presentation of her female figures' trajectories are compounded by the complexity of narrative voice in the novel. Critics of *My Son's Story* have shown curiosity about who the 'my' of the title is, whose story is told and who does the telling. While it is clear that there are two dominant voices alternately narrating the text – a sardonic, adolescent first-person voice and a more formal, removed third-person voice – it is unclear whether both these voices 'belong' to Will (Sonny's son). At the end of the novel Gordimer ensures that the two narrative voices converge. Will has been narrating the text all along – his is the 'will' that has made the story happen:

> In our story, like all stories, I've made up what I wasn't there to experience myself . . . I am a writer and this is my first book – that I can never publish (275-7).

Some critics suggest that, indeed, Will is the text's sole narrator in fluctuating guises, and what gets seen and known throughout the text is filtered through his limits (King 1991; Boyers 1993). Others suggest that, while the first-person sections must be read as the particular viewpoint of Will, the third-person sections display an omniscience that could not possibly be attributed to him (Coles 1990; Hotz 1990; Kossick 1991). Gordimer's own overt authorial voice would thus play an active part in shaping the reader's understanding. The matter of whether a shaping Gordimer-like voice is present in the text or not is important to a feminist reading of the novel. The numerous portraits of Hannah, Aila and other women are sometimes clearly transmitted with a male adolescent bias, but there are other aspects of female portraiture in the text which remind one immediately of Gordimer's familiar renditions of women in her previous work. The author's closing narrative sleight of hand will have us believe that the narrator is Will, all Will. But there is a clear margin of difference between their voices which makes the gender encodings in the novel a more than usually complex and multivalent affair.

Hannah and Aila are continually juxtaposed with one another beginning within the first five pages of the novel, and this procedure entails a minute attention to their bodily differences. Will's obsession with his mother involves a fascination with her 'elegant legs on high heeled shoes', her 'sleek shiny hair', her 'lovely teeth and lips' (7) and so on. Aila's immaculacy of appearance symbolises for Will the perfect incarnation of womanhood. His indignation at his father's betrayal of this perfect woman finds form in a very strong repulsion towards his father's chosen object: Hannah.

Passages describing Will's sexual nausea when thinking about Hannah and his father are too numerous for mention. Will's apprehension of Hannah as the sexual Other who breaks up the family nucleus is compounded by his acute awareness of her as racially other. She is 'his father's pudding-faced blonde', a 'pinkish . . . blurred' (15) woman. His constant comparison of her with a pig links Hannah in the narrative with taboo and uncleanliness (an association Will would have had through some Muslim aspects in his family history, 93). Hannah is thus not only profoundly ugly and clumsy to him: she is also racially distasteful and illegitimate in her very body. In *My Son's Story*, Will's rage at his father involves a transgression of his father's non-racial codes of behaviour, such that sexual distaste for his father's beloved takes the form of a brazen and provocative racism.

At times Gordimer tempers the viewpoints offered of Hannah by Will by inserting some gentler portraits of her into the third-person narrative, so that the excesses of revulsion towards Hannah can be attributed to Will's blunt Oedipal disturbances and teenage immaturity. The basic features of Hannah's physicality remain the same in both narratives: her stockiness, pink skin, soft body and blue eyes are indices of 'Hannah' which connect the two narratives. In a kind moment when Gordimer is wanting to highlight the erotic and emotional delight which Sonny and Hannah take in each other, these same indices find mention as Hannah's 'soft pastel cheeks' and 'the brilliant blue chips of her eyes' (174). And yet, in spite of these moments when Hannah's physicality is described forgivingly, the majority of the descriptions of Hannah *in the third-person narrative* share at least some of the distaste of Will's first-person narration. Gordimer's own clear authorial presence appears to sanction descriptions of Hannah as 'heavy', 'plump', 'fleshy', 'freckled', 'swollen' and as having 'repaired teeth' and 'shaking thighs'. Again, a veritable catalogue of negative physical features exists about a woman which answers to no such catalogue – negative or positive – about her male counterpart in the text.

The (partial) physical devalorisation of Hannah can be related to Hannah's characteristic dress sense, her sloppy, 'layered' look. Hannah appears to be the type for a sexual aesthetic that Gordimer associates with left-wing women, apparently based on some of the women she might have observed around her in political circles in the eighties. She comments:

> These are things that come from observation. I think we all fall into some kind of uniform (interview with Lazar 1997: 158).

Some female figures who appear earlier in her work – Clare in *Burger's Daughter* and Joy in 'Something Out There' – also fall into the same recognisable family of clashing, gypsy-style dressers. Aside from their dress sense, these women have two other features in common: their political earnestness (a lacklustre quality to be distinguished from the more vibrant dedication of a Sonny) *and their feminism*. Of Hannah we hear: 'She was a feminist, careful of genders' (88). Gordimer's partial derogation of Hannah seems to me to have more to do with residual conceptions the author holds about 'feminists' than to do with conceptions she holds about adultery.

In *My Son's Story*, Gordimer seems unwittingly to collude in the popular stereotypical views about feminists which a great number of her fellow South Africans hold: that they are physically ungainly and earnest to a fault. Of course there has been a brand of 'feminist chic' in Gordimer's texts: Hillela embodies it, and so, in the end, may Aila. But Hannah and her predecessors are members of a recognisable species or 'kind' in Gordimer's work: feminists who are associated with do-gooding rather than heroism, with plodding rather than soaring. Aila and Hillela have in common a quick and marked ascent in standing and power. Hannah and her kindred are 'ordinary' (89), and their overt association with feminism makes feminism seem lacklustre too. The author's tendency to endorse the politics of selected glamorous women through a textual foregrounding of their bodies, and to devalorise their plainer counterparts along with their plainer politics, appears to be again at work here.

I would not, however, like to suggest that Gordimer's presentations of feminism are wholly negative in this text. On the contrary, *My Son's Story* demonstrates a greater absorption of feminist ideas and a greater relish of them than any previous work, factors extended in the more recent *None to Accompany Me*. One of the features of the relationship between Sonny and Hannah which is most foregrounded in the omniscient narrative is the equity between them:

> They had never seduced one another. What were known as feminine wiles and male deceptions were denials of equality, an ethic of the wide struggle for human freedom they belonged to (201).

This credo is linked to other aspects of balance in their relationship: they are lovers and comrades, private and political beings, and so on. Sonny and Hannah's intense mutual interest in things intellectual and aesthetic occasions Sonny to experience the following:

> Seeing Hannah's fair eyelashes catching the morning sun . . . he understood why, in the reproductions of paintings he had puzzled over in the days of his self-education, Picasso presented frontally all the features of a woman – head, breasts, eyes, vagina, nose, buttocks, mouth – as if all were always present even to the casual glance. What would he have known, without Hannah! (102).

Sonny's apperception of Hannah as 'always present' is not accidental here. At its height, the bond between Hannah and Sonny is
total, an integration of public and private, as enjoyed briefly by
Whaila and Hillela but by very few other couples in Gordimer. By
the late eighties, Gordimer's view of favoured heterosexual relationships insists upon equity and multidimensionality as primary
ingredients, and in these relationships 'feminism' is not an eccentric
component but a central one.

In short, the text's partial *physical-metonymic denigration* of
Hannah the feminist is rerouted through its *endorsement of feminist
ideas*. The fact that the male figure of whom Gordimer is so fond,
Sonny, can love a woman who is 'heavy' and 'pink' with such
fervour suggests that Gordimer herself is now more ready to forgive
some imperfections in the (white) female form. The denigration
she permits of Hannah is altogether less absolute than renditions
of Maureen and other women in her earlier work. Also of significance is that Gordimer makes room in her text for a gaze which
does not belong to men. Thus Hannah gazes ruefully at her own
'pudgy familiar face' (201) in the mirror but Gordimer is quick to
point out that she would not regard herself as a 'pig' and that
such a term belongs in a (male) repertory of insults towards women.

Turning again to the other (unlikely) 'feminist' in the text: Aila.
As in Hannah's case, the indices that mark Aila in Will's narrative
reappear in the third-person narrative, but in Aila's case Gordimer
does not temper these indices with kindness because they are already
very favourable. Nor does she temper the crude idolising edge of
Will's Oedipal depictions of his mother with consistent realism.
Gordimer and Will seem to see Aila with a fairly similar gaze
throughout most of the text. Aila's elegance is a feature of sexuality
which Gordimer has always endorsed in women: we see this as
early as the fifties in the figure of silk-clad activist Jessica Malherbe
in 'The Smell of Death and Flowers' (*Six Feet of the Country*) and
on several other occasions. Often in Gordimer, elegance is not only
an index of sexual desirability and authorial sanction; it is also an
index of class. From the start of *My Son's Story*, Sonny and Aila
are set apart from their racial 'kind' by virtue of their surpassal of
'silly, sugary, cheap lower-class sentimentality' (83), their self-
education and their air of being destined for greater things. Their
move into a white suburb is as much a sign of upward class mobility

as it is of racial defiance. Where Sonny is distinguishable from the wily, crass humour of Uncle Gavin by his reading of Shakespeare and Kafka, Aila is distinguishable from 'factory girls' by her poise and grooming. Although Aila performs work – lots of it – to keep the life of her family going, its status as work is obfuscated by her ardent maintenance of the softness of her hands (40). As can be seen in Gordimer's early depiction of the lofty Mrs Hansen in the earlier mentioned story 'Enemies' (*Six Feet of the Country*), she seems to have a certain impatience with excessive hauteur or class pretensions. But there is little doubt that, in the final analysis, the author finds Aila and Mrs Hansen's class markings attractive rather than repellent. A female sexuality which speaks of time, money and attention from its bearer is more readily endorsed by Gordimer than a careless sexuality like Hannah's or an unkempt one like Maureen's.

Gordimer does, however, seem to be more forgiving than Will of the eventual physical changes in Aila which connote her political transformation. Where Will finds his mother's haircut 'ugly' and 'dull' (205), Gordimer seems to wish to give Aila the space to drop the trappings of femininity in favour of a life of meaningful action. As in the case of Hannah, Gordimer's representation of Aila is less absolute than her renditions of comparable figures in earlier work. Where the much earlier Jessica Malherbe would not have had a single proverbial hair out of place, Aila's physical appearance is allowed to reflect her newfound political stresses. And indeed, it is not as if Gordimer lets Aila turn into Hannah: her beauty and slimness (like Hillela's) do not desert her, and she still manages to 'smell of perfume' (194)!

And so, in the end, Maureen's 'cold cat smell' bars her from full political endorsement and ensures her textual defeminisation, while ten years later Hannah's apparently piglike appearance is shown to be a perceptual matter, and not a matter of truth or a cause for political condemnation. Aila stays glamorous but moves from marginal silence into revolutionary significance, and is one of the chief 'black feminists' behind whom Gordimer has thrown her authorial weight to date.

Interregnum? Perhaps. Gordimer's depictions of her women and their textual-political functions may be seen as a concurrent submerged path within the author's larger political and intellectual trajectories during this time. This is a path towards less categoric renditions of women, a less tenacious habit of damning (white) women through the metonym of their disfavoured bodies, and an ever more centric inclusion of (select) women as political agents and feminists within a revolutionary scheme. Her more recent public utterances bear this out. Her insistence on the incorporation of women as agents and citizens in the post-1994 scenario takes the form of a congratulation of the civic and governmental strides she believes have been taken in the area of gender equity (see interview with Lazar, 1997). It also takes the form of a worry about the extent to which South Africa's new regime will make any difference to the majority of marginal black women. She comments:

> While women are taking part in the momentum of political action, and a growing feminist movement among young black women is adapting feminist issues, common to women all over the world, to the particular ones of South African black women in the liberation struggle, the load of firewood on the back and the jar of water on the head have not been cast off . . . If the lives [of rural women] do not change in the new South Africa to which black women, and some of their white sisters, have contributed so much sacrifice, even the presence of women in cabinet positions . . . would not mean that justice for women has been achieved (in Magubane 1993: 5-6).

And so, the black rural women who were cast in semi-soft focus in *July's People* now come into relatively sharper focus in Gordimer's recent observations. It remains to be seen how the concept of 'justice for women' will play itself out in Gordimer's writing in the coming years.

Endnotes

1. Both Lars Engle (1989) and Sheila Roberts (1993) comment on the presence of elements of the uncanny or 'unheimlich' in *July's People*. Engle defines the uncanny (following Freud) as 'moments of breakdown that occur when an interpretative scheme encounters a particular object or event that it cannot satisfactorily interpret' (1989: 112) and argues that *July's People* is full of such moments. Roberts argues that the

'unheimlich' or uncanny is inscribed in the descriptions of the unhomely and dirty rondawel that the Smales family inhabits, and suggests that Maureen's repulsive sexuality is associated with this dwelling in highly metonymic and negative ways such that she too is inscribed as 'unheimlich' (1993: 80 -81).

2. I use the term Coloured rather than 'Coloured' (or so-called Coloured) in this essay in accordance with Alex La Guma's questioning of the political coyness implied by the inverted commas. In a letter to *Sechaba* in the early eighties, La Guma comments:

> I am now a 'so-called' Coloured – when did Congress decide to call me this? It makes me feel like a 'so-called' human, like a humanoid. (Quoted in Frederikse 1990: 186.)

Matthew de Bruyn's comments are also useful:

> A number of radical intellectuals attach the cumbersome 'so-called' to the word Coloured. It is understandable why they are so anxious to escape the stigma of all which has taken place in the past. However ... Coloured ancestors were the first enslaved and what we have today is the living offspring of miscegenation. Despite the obsession of the South African regime with colour and race purity, there are in fact no reliable methods of classifying people in racial compartments. The use of the term 'so-called' in the case of the Coloured and the non-use of the term in the case of other racial groups implies that the others are pure. Whilst the Coloureds are a greater mixture than most, there is really no such thing as race purity (1984: 29).

3. 'Going grey' was a term used in the eighties by political organisations and the press to specify previously white residential areas (such as Mayfair and Yeoville in Johannesburg) that had begun to house black residents. Blacks moving into these areas did so principally out of an urgent need for housing, but in some cases as a deliberate anti-racist political strategy. While this process was initially informal, the repeal of the Group Areas Act in 1991 made it formal.

References

Bailey, Nancy. 1984. 'Living Without the Future: Nadine Gordimer's *July's People*'. *World Literature Written in English* 24 (2): 215-24.

The Bookseller 1990. 'Interview with Nadine Gordimer'. 29 June: 2031-3.

Boyers, Robert et al. 1984. 'A conversation with Nadine Gordimer'. *Salmagundi* 62: 3-31.

Boyers, Robert. 1993. 'The Art of Nadine Gordimer'. *Salmagundi* Winter: 188-202.

Brink, André. 1994. 'Complications of Birth: Interfaces of Gender, Race and Class in *July's People*'. *English in Africa* 21 (1 & 2): 157-80.

Coles, Robert. 1990. 'A Different Set of Rules'. *The New York Times Book Review* 21 Oct.: 1, 20-21.

De Bruyn, Matthew. 1984. 'Coloured Role in the National Democratic Revolution'. *African Communist* 97: 28-38.

Clingman, Stephen. 1992. Interview. 'The Future is another Country'. *Transition* 56: 132-50.

Dorsman, Robert and Postel, Gitte. 1990. Interview. 'Nadine Gordimer – Johannesburg, 10 July'. *Between the Lines II* 1993: 37-52.

Driver, Dorothy. 1983. 'Nadine Gordimer: The politicisation of Women'. *English in Africa*. 10 (2): 29-54.

Engle, Lars. 1989. 'The Political Uncanny: The Novels of Nadine Gordimer'. *The Yale Journal of Criticism* 2 (2): 101-28.

Ettin, Andrew V. 1993. *Betrayals of the Body Politic: The Literary Commitments of Nadine Gordimer*. Charlottesville and London: University Press of Virginia.

Frederikse, Julie. 1990. *The Unbreakable Thread: Non-racialism in South Africa*. Johannesburg: Ravan/Popular History Trust.

Fritz-Piggot, Jill. 1991. 'Son and Lover'. *The Women's Review of Books* 8 (4): 8-9.

Gordimer, Nadine. 1956. *Six Feet of the Country*. London: Victor Gollancz.

Gordimer, Nadine. 1966. *The Late Bourgeois World*. London: Jonathan Cape.

Gordimer, Nadine. 1972. *Livingstone's Companions*. London: Jonathan Cape.

Gordimer, Nadine. 1974. *The Conservationist*. London: Jonathan Cape.

Gordimer, Nadine. 1975. *Selected Stories*. Harmondsworth: Penguin.

Gordimer, Nadine. 1979. *Burger's Daughter*. London: Jonathan Cape.

Gordimer, Nadine. 1980. *A Soldier's Embrace*. London: Jonathan Cape.

Gordimer, Nadine. 1982. *July's People*. Harmondsworth: Penguin.

Gordimer, Nadine. 1985. *Something Out There*. Harmondsworth: Penguin.

Gordimer, Nadine. 1987. *A Sport of Nature*. Cape Town/Johannesburg: David Philip/Taurus.

Gordimer, Nadine. 1989. 'Living in the Interregnum' in *The Essential Gesture: Writing Politics and Places*. Ed. Stephen Clingman, London: Penguin. 262-84.

Gordimer, Nadine. 1990. *My Son's Story*. Cape Town/Johannesburg: David Philip/Taurus.

Gordimer, Nadine. 1994. *None to Accompany Me*. London: Bloomsbury.

Hotz, Paul. 1990. 'Gordimer's latest offering interesting and readable'. *The Daily News* 1 Nov.: 13.

Jeyifo, Biodun. 1992. 'An interview with Nadine Gordimer: Harare, February 14'. *Callaloo* 16 (3): 922-30.

King, Bruce. 1991. 'South Africa: Nadine Gordimer – *My Son's Story*'. *World Literature Today* 65 (2): 351.

Kossick, S.G. 1991. 'Nadine Gordimer: *My Son's Story*'. *Unisa English Studies* 29 (1): 54.

Lazar, Karen. 1988. 'Interview with Nadine Gordimer, Wednesday 27 January' *Between the Lines II. Interviews with Nadine Gordimer, Menan du Plessis, Zoe Wicomb, Lauretta Ngcobo* eds. Eva Hunter and Craig MacKenzie. Grahamstown: National English Literary Museum: 21-36.

Lazar, Karen. 1990. 'Feminism as "Piffling"? Ambiguities in Some of Nadine Gordimer's Short Stories'. *Current Writing* (2): 101-16. Modified version in King, Bruce (ed). 1993. *The Later Fiction of Nadine Gordimer*. London: Macmillan.

Lazar, Karen. 1992. '*Jump and Other Stories*: Gordimer's leap into the 1990s: Gender and Politics in Her Latest Short Fiction'. *Journal of Southern African Studies* 18 (4): 783-802.

Lazar, Karen. 1997. 'An Interview with Nadine Gordimer'. *Salmagundi* 113: 150-65.

Magubane, Peter. 1993. *Women of South Africa: Their Fight for Freedom*. Boston: Little Brown and Co. Introduction by Nadine Gordimer: 1-7.

Neill, Michael. 1990. 'Translating the Present: Language, Knowledge and Identiy in Nadine Gordimer's *July's People*'. *Journal of Commonwealth Literature* 25 (1): 71-98.

Nicol, Mike, 1991. 'Mike Nicol/Nadine Gordimer'. *South African Literary Review* 1 (2): 4-10.

Rhedin, Folke. 1984. 'Exiled In Their Own Country: Three White South African Writers'. Trans. Rose Pettersson. *Bonniers Litterara Magasin* (Sweden) 53:14.

Roberts, Sheila. 1993. 'Sites of Paranoia and Taboo: Lessing's *The Grass is Singing* and Gordimer's *July's People*'. *Research in African Literature* 24 (3): 73-85.

Smith, Rowland. 1984. 'Masters and Servants: Nadine Gordimer's *July's People* and the Themes of her Fiction'. *Salmagundi* 62: 93-107.

Wagner, Kathrin. 1991. 'Credentials for Interpreting the Struggle'. *Die Suid-Afrikaan* Feb./March: 44.

Wagner, Kathrin. 1994. *Rereading Nadine Gordimer: Text and Subtext in the Novels*. Johannesburg and Bloomington: Maskew Miller Longman, Witwatersrand U.P. and Indiana U.P.

Hillela and the Whale

RONALD SURESH ROBERTS

Introduction

Her turn has come.

The Australian novelist and Nobel Laureate Patrick White; James Stern, short story writer and translator of Franz Kafka's *Letters to Felice*; the recently departed Trevor Huddleston – as these friends and others each turned seventy-five, Nadine Gordimer sat down to write the sorts of pieces that now fill this volume, for her. In these, she celebrated enduring human and artistic qualities, not the accident or accomplishment (call it what you will) of physical survival through three score years and fifteen. In the case of Pablo Neruda who would have been seventy-five in 1979 had he not died in 1973, her 1979 offering was not so much posthumous as an acknowledgment of the deceased's continuing vitality, his artistic liveliness from beyond the grave. He was proof, she said (quoting Neruda himself), that 'poetry has a cat's nine lives'.

Gordimer's real tribute to these friends and colleagues is the careful thought and craft that she invests in writing about them: a thing of large importance for one who dislikes writing non-fiction and who guards her time jealously. Not only were such people important to her, she clearly felt some additional obligation *to say so*, in print, as a writer.

Perhaps predictably, the novelist in Gordimer frequently leaps alive in this non-fiction, enlivening with anecdote some or other sonorous conclusion. Thus, upon Huddleston's seventy-fifth in 1987, she expounded for five pages his immense awareness of black people, his immersion in the townships, and his apartness from the vanities and courtesies of white suburbia. Then, the following story lightheartedly summed up much of the sober analysis that preceded it:

> A party for Anthony Sampson [the British journalist] was held in my house [in the fifties]. While my husband, Reinhold Cassirer, and I were still preparing food and drink, the first guest arrived. It was Huddleston, and he and Anthony settled on the verandah. Our son, taking on hostly duties for the first time, kept offering a plate of stuffed eggs, and to his dismay the guest never refused, but kept absently reaching out and eating them. The small boy came rushing indignantly into the kitchen: 'Mum, the man in a skirt is finishing all the eggs.'

Over decades, Nadine Gordimer has developed a minor sub-specialty in elegant tributes to septuagenarian friends and colleagues. And now, her turn has come. It must be both familiar and discomfiting – like a veteran stage director, accustomed to guiding on-stage events from the off-stage shadows, now flung under the spotlight herself.

And what protocols bind the biographer, among the celebrants, in a book like this? Must he bring to the feast that fussy chaperon, objectivity, to deflate the riper flights of hyperbole? Must he bring impertinence, vinegar to season the homage? How to maintain, amidst the *Festschrift*'s loving momentum, the biographer's requisite coldness?

Fortunately, we are celebrating a genuine *artist*, which eases matters a little. Arriving at the age of seventy-five, the businessman with a self-styled Midas touch, the politician sure she is the second coming of Solomon's wisdom, even a certain kind of megalomaniac artist – these all will expect and probably receive fluent confirmation, from polite acquaintances, that they are indeed the selves they have always taken themselves to be. (Some such acquaintances doubtless snicker privately afterwards.)

By contrast, in Gordimer's life and work we see that true intimacy can disrupt, can challenge and change us, in large and small ways. 'The atmosphere was not one in which kindly lies were necessary' notes the narrator, looking over the protagonist's shoulder in *A Sport of Nature* (1987), as she finds a new self,

wish I'd written that!

among true friends.

Conversely, what creates *A World of Strangers* (1958) is not only the mutual self-regard of township and suburban Johannesburg in that novel, not only the apartheid laws that separate the white and black social worlds; it is also the British protagonist Toby Hood's prim reluctance to challenge his suburban friends by disclosing his township ones. Hood attempts to run parallel lives – township friends kept secret from suburban ones – in a situation where the gist of each life is a renunciation of the other. More than disingenuous, this is a dereliction of self, a failure to choose who really he is. His polite intimacies estrange him from both sets of friends, suburban and township alike. His peculiar sincerity – his good faith attempt to live lies – eventually dies with a whimper, not even a bang. Here is evidence of what Gordimer noted in a different context nearly four decades later (quoting Claudio Magris): that 'the lie is quite as real as the truth, it works upon the world, transforms it'.

Letters written during the final stages of its composition reveal that Gordimer toyed with calling the 1958 novel *A Grin for Anger* (instead of the eventual title, *A World of Strangers*). The rejected title, echoing a phrase that occurs late in the book, captures how lies work upon friendship, invert it, transform it into something odd that we might call cordial enmity. Suddenly distrusting his own ability to distinguish a black friend's smile from its angry opposite, Toby Hood finds that intimacy itself is hostage to the web of lies that he himself had tried so energetically – and with the best of intentions – to live out. 'We page through each other's faces/we read each looking eye . . ./It has taken lives to be able to do so' wrote Gordimer's close friend Mongane Wally Serote in 1987. This passage, which Gordimer has cited approvingly, is a fitting epitaph for the spoilt lives in *A World of Strangers*. We look in vain for the true pages of self in Toby's hooded being.

So in Nadine Gordimer's world, the white lie is not trivial; honesty is not optional; courtesy seldom trumps truth. It is striking to see this principle upheld – and reciprocated – in her correspondence with editors, colleagues, true friends. They inhabit an almost brutal ethos of frankness, of sharp criticism amidst manifest affection. Polite praise or euphemism are the real betrayals. Again and again one sees, in her life, that nothing so deepens a Nadine

Gordimer friendship as a volley of well-informed criticism, incisively expressed (whether or not she happens to agree). Around her, celebration and sincerity become one. The biographer may loosen his tie.

The Importance of Being Earnest

Where exactly is she taking us with all this sincerity? Is it a purely personal trait, arresting but irrelevant to her art? A device that authorises cruelty in the guise of unswerving integrity? Or simply the kind of affectation – 'truth though the heavens fall' – that a good spin doctor would swiftly prescribe for a Great Artist?

Answer: none of the above.

A passion for truth both *animates* and *organises* Gordimer's writing. Truth *animates* her fiction in that, for her, art is never instrumental. The artist does not aim, in the process of creation, to produce calculated outcomes in the world beyond. Art is not propaganda and truth can be ugly, she frequently insists: 'the truth is not always beauty, but the hunger for it is'. The search for truth – including the challenge of its indeterminacy – is why this artist gets out of bed in the morning. She has said that 'The truth is the real definition of "home": it is the final destination of the human spirit beyond national boundaries, natal traditions.'

Truth *organises* Gordimer's work in a very particular sense. Among the several meanings of this fertile verb, the *Oxford Paperback Dictionary* (1994) teaches that to organise is to 'make organic, make into a living tissue'. Whatever the place of realism in Gordimer's fiction (a debate for another day), her goal has never been the static representation of prevailing realities. 'This is the song of what is happening and of what will be,' she writes, quoting Pablo Neruda. Her art is a living tissue, rooted in the present but also challenging it, and reaching out towards a future pregnant with both hope and dread, unconsoled by assurances of Utopia.

When Gordimer writes – in a phrase we might hang like a banner across her career – that 'the *transformation of experience* remains the writer's basic essential gesture' (her emphasis), she places herself within the most demanding of the tributaries that feed the turbulent mainstream we call art. The writer neither flees from social engagement nor becomes the mere instrument of some contending faction:

52

'Writers who accept a professional responsibility in the transformation of society are always seeking ways of doing so that their societies could not ever imagine, let alone demand.' If the writer's task is the enlargement of perceptions, of society's ways of seeing, then to propagate in art perceptions around which whole factions of society already are mobilised is to squander the opportunity of art.

Such ideas place Nadine Gordimer squarely alongside the late Austro-German Nobel Laureate, Elias Canetti, who had more than a passing interest in Africa. For Canetti, the British missionary H Callaway's transcription (from indigenous experts) of the details of Zulu ancestor worship is 'among the essential documents of mankind'. He saw it as a book that enlarged the common inheritance of readers and writers. And Gordimer herself took excerpts from Callaway's book, *The Religious System of the Amazulu* (1870), as the textual backbone of her novel, *The Conservationist* (1974).

Behind the coincidence that Canetti and Gordimer both used Callaway's transcriptions stands a more basic twinship: each is what Canetti calls a *Dichter*. As Canetti tells it, this German word for the writer is beleaguered on two sides. First, by the hubris of those writers who believe that writers *really are* the unacknowledged legislators of the world, with straightforward power to impact directly on historical events. Second, by the perception of non-writers that to be a writer is inherently escapist and unserious, a flight from past and present. Whether as a reckless Pontiff, warlike despite lacking the battalions that history-making takes, or as an effete Marie Antoinette, seeking diversion among ivory turrets while the peasants eat imaginary cake, the *Dichter* walks a fine line in seeking a lively compact with reality.

But the true *Dichter* – and here the term becomes comfortably honorific, not beleaguered – is an essential cultural figure, says Canetti, because s/he is '*the keeper of metamorphosis*'. (Emphasis added.) Practising the gift of metamorphosis, the true *Dichter*

> ought to keep the accesses *between* people open. He [or she] should be able to become *anybody and everybody*, even the smallest, the most naïve, the most powerless person . . . It would require an ever open ear, but that would not be enough, for a majority of people today are scarcely able to speak, they express

themselves in the phraseology of newspapers and public media and say the same things more and more without *being* the same. Only metamorphosis, in the extreme sense in which the word is used here, would make it possible to feel what a [person] is behind his [or her] words; the true existence of whatever there is of life could not be grasped in any other way. It is a mysterious process, its nature has scarcely been examined, and yet it is the only real approach to another human being. (Emphasis original.)

Nadine Gordimer's artistic fingerprints – her distinctive moral and aesthetic insistences – converge around this idea of metamorphosis. This idea captures and clarifies: her view that writers have a monster-like ability to project themselves into the existence of others; her insistence that blacks can and must write about whites and vice versa; her belief that men can and must write about women and vice versa; her rather controversial withdrawal of *The House Gun* from the women-only Orange Prize shortlist in London in 1998; the idea she compulsively repeats of her own 'second birth', out of whiteness and into humanity; her view that the writer inhabits a creative tension between belonging and standing apart, in personal and societal relations; her rejection of the idea that her non-racialism springs from her Jewish cultural heritage rather than her broader humanity; the fact that she was led out of white supremacy by Kafka (savant of metamorphosis and author of *Metamorphosis and other stories*) rather than Marx.

Canetti suggests (but does not develop the point) that metamorphosis is 'more demanding' than empathy. Others have noted that where there is empathy, a stable self extends itself in sympathy, magnanimously, towards the less powerful or secure other. Empathy is the benevolence of the unruffled personality; it can become a form of emotional or existential empire-building. The empathiser can become an expansionist sensibility, acquiring emotional terrain at the expense of the dispossessed other. One United States literary scholar has commented that toleration increases in inverse proportion to there being anything at stake. Much the same could be said of empathy, which will thrive once its demands remain within the empathiser's pre-established comfort zones. Empathy can be a fickle moral, political and existential resource, serving foremost the vanity or self-image of the empathising self.

By contrast, metamorphosis places the self in chaos, as others are not patronised but actively internalised. The *Dichter* is thrown, says Canetti, into 'constant internal motion, which he cannot weaken or terminate' and which is fuelled by 'the force of the characters who have come to tenant him, who do not abandon the space they now occupy in him. They react out of him, as though he consisted of them. They are his majority, articulated and conscious, they are – since they *live* in him – his resistance to death.' (Emphasis original.)

Last year I asked Gordimer what she thought of the film, *Surviving Picasso*, a rather harrowing depiction of that artist's emotional abuse of women. She replied that although the film had little to do with the real Picasso – devilish grin – 'I enjoyed it with the *worst* part of myself.' Even this demonic faux-Picasso, so at odds with her own notions of emotional fidelity but compellingly presented in the film, could find tenancy in (admittedly a louche district of) her writerly persona.

For the *Dichter*, metamorphosis expands writerly being, even (or especially) in ways that contradict the writer's real-life persona and real-life relationships. This is explicitly the subject of Gordimer's Charles Eliot Norton Lectures (1994), where she characterises the novel as an art form possessed by a 'bundle of transformations'.

Metamorphosis and the Abolition of Whiteness

Now this South African *Dichter*, this keeper of metamorphosis, this one for whom a self tenanted by unruly others is integral to art and life – she came of age in a cultural unmelting pot, a system madly separating cultures and frantically purifying bloods (or so it thought). What to do?

The tension between expansive white artist and constrictive white culture meant that something would have to give way – either art or whiteness – and whiteness did. 'As long as you think you're white there's no hope for you,' James Baldwin admonished Americans in 1985, by which time Gordimer had written nine novels and numerous stories that can be read (among other ways) as a sustained critique of whiteness.

Gordimer says that she began writing as part of a 'clumsy battle to chip my way out of shell after shell of ready-made concepts and make my own sense of life.' This contrasts with Sarah Gertrude Millin, de facto novelist laureate of apartheid, whose post-war art embodied apartheid concepts and unrepentantly promoted whiteness.

The apartheid legislature manufactured whiteness in ways both brutal and subtle. Now those laws are gone, but apartheid whiteness – both handmaiden and product of those laws – is not. I emphasise: whiteness is not just apartheid's material legacy (the loot) of privilege, about which much is heard in media and political debates. It is the dried cement of concepts, habits, intuitions and expectations that still bind white emotional responses and ways of seeing, although the legal scaffolding of apartheid is gone. Whiteness is the existential fabric, the flesh and blood, the captured hearts and minds that energised apartheid's laws and institutions. And it is not dead yet. It lives as a form of what Franz Fanon called 'affective ankylosis', an artificial stiffening of the emotions, a hardening of the heart against the injustices that underpin privilege.

For instance: if apartheid policy dictated inferior health care for blacks, whiteness gave this policy a seeming backdrop of common sense. As a Red Cross volunteer in 1950, Gordimer served at a first aid station on a mine in Springs, where she lived. 'There I once saw the mine's white Medical Aid worker stitch, without anaesthetic, the gaping wounds black miners had suffered from a falling rock underground. He grinned and told me, "They don't feel like we do." ' *He grinned*, believing himself, not merely placating a young woman. Whiteness gave apartheid's anti-black brutality its seeming *naturalness*, in the eyes of the apartheid privileged. Whiteness lives in the unintended irony of the medical worker's comment – they don't feel like we do. Indeed. How exactly is it that this peculiar white 'we' feels? Does it feel at all? Does it feel in human (inhuman?) ways? And towards what, or whom?

So the abolition of apartheid is not the same as the abolition of whiteness in South Africa, any more than the abolition of slavery (or of Jim Crow) was the same as the abolition of whiteness in the United States. In her contribution to what is now an influential reassessment of Herman Melville's *Moby Dick*, Toni Morrison suggests that the book is best read not (in the various traditional ways) as an allegory of the state, capitalism and corruption, of God and man, the individual and fate, or of brute indifferent nature. Such interpretations, she says, place the book under 'house arrest'.

Properly read, *Moby Dick* is consciously immersed in mid-nineteenth century American conflicts over politics, slavery and freedom. But unlike those revisionist readers (with whom she broadly agrees) who see the book as an anti-slavery allegory, Morrison finds in the extremity of Ahab's quest an unprecedented attempt to go beyond even the relatively comfortable camp of antislavery activism. Since there were many white Americans speaking, writing and legislating against slavery, Melville's 'attitude to slavery alone would not have condemned him to the almost autistic separation visited upon him'. Morrison instead reads Ahab as the only white male American heroic enough to try to slay the monster of whiteness:

> if, indeed, a white, nineteenth century, American male took on not abolition, not the amelioration of racist institutions or their laws, but the very concept of whiteness as an inhuman idea, he would be very alone, very desperate, and very doomed. Madness would be the only appropriate description of such audacity.

And what would it mean for a white South African under apartheid to take on not the amelioration or abolition of its laws, but the very concept of whiteness? 'It will take another kind of being to stay on, here. A new white person. Not us. The chance is a wild chance – like falling in love.' This now is not Melville's Ahab but Gordimer's Sasha in *A Sport of Nature* (1987), a novel that, as no other that Gordimer has written, remains under the house arrest of traditional critics: misunderstood, underestimated, inappropriately construed. (The novel is discussed in some detail below.)

To free Melville from house arrest, says Morrison, is to see that he was not so much transcending politics and race as 'transforming' them 'into intelligible, accessible, yet artistic modes of discourse'. As what we may now call a *Dichter*, a novelist of metamorphosis, Melville may be contrasted with Harriet Beecher Stowe, whose *Uncle Tom's Cabin* is a classic novel of empathy: it activated white anti-slavery support by simplifying black personality to satisfy white tastes (creating the Virtuous Childlike Black Victim). Thus a certain kind of political gain was had at the expense of the critique of whiteness itself. Whiteness was validated even as those in its grip were aroused to a certain form of revulsion against slavery. Slavery was made to seem a 'peculiar institution' – a deviation from white norms of freedom – rather than an iteration of the brutality of whiteness, which would be differently iterated in the post-slavery period, and in today's America. As Stowe's biographer, Joan D Hedrick, puts it, 'Stowe's political achievement was to make a national audience see the subjectivity of black people, but what she herself saw was filtered through a white woman's consciousness.'

As Melville may be contrasted with Stowe, so Gordimer – as a novelist of metamorphosis – may be contrasted with Alan Paton, a novelist of empathy. Paton's *Cry, the Beloved Country: A Story of Comfort in Desolation* (1948) aroused white anti-apartheid support as no other novel before or since, but again did so by simplifying black personality to satisfy white tastes (creating the Virtuous Tribalised African versus the Nihilistic Urbanised One). Within the old discourse of 'the native problem', whites are urged to see the uses of measures to ameliorate the specific laws and policies of white supremacy. 'Our natives today produce criminals and prostitutes and drunkards, not because it is their nature to do so, but because their simple system of order and tradition and convention has been destroyed. It was destroyed by the impact of our civilisation. Our civilisation has therefore an inescapable duty to set up another system of order and tradition and convention.' This is a voice from the files of a good white man, a reformist, who was killed by a nihilistic urban black. He is the martyr-figure of the novel. And in his pivotal voice, white personality un-ashamedly construes blacks as passive beneficiaries of white moral obligation. Whiteness is so far from being the disease that whites are called upon, as whites, to 'set up' the cure.

Throughout apartheid, Gordimer sought out – and she wrapped words around – the elusive aspects of what she called the 'white tribal morality' that upheld Southern African white supremacy. In this period, her critical and artistic energies went far beyond the specific laws and policies of apartheid; she addressed its theology: 'We have created our own sense of sin and our own form of tragedy.'

Within these prevailing white mores, whole novels (like Sarah Gertrude Millin's *God's Stepchildren* (1924)) could for instance be written on the premise – the premise was like normal to enough whites – that a mixed marriage is a sin, requiring sustained religious atonement by the generations of its progeny. These mores pre-dated – and now their avatars post-date – apartheid.

In 1982, Gordimer told an interviewer that South African whites 'have developed a totally unreal idea of how they ought to live . . . Consequently, they must undergo a long process of shedding illusions', which she acknowledged would be painful: 'it's very hard to peel yourself like an onion, without producing a lot of tears in the process.'

The hallmark of Gordimer's critical engagement with white -ness is the rejection of glib solutions. 'We do know what's cheap, what's stupid, what's *shit*,' Pauline, a white liberal parent in *A Sport of Nature*, tells her more radical son, back home from his non-racial school in Swaziland. 'We've spent our lives finding out how to live in the midst of it, part of it, and . . . and behave as decently as one can . . . until it's changed . . . it's not a clean process . . . getting out of shit . . . it's not going to be for you, either, don't think it can be.' (Emphasis and ellipses original.)

The tenacity of whiteness, its ability to reinvent itself and pop out of boxes, leering, when least we expect it – this theme has received its most nuanced treatment in Gordimer's novel, *A Sport of Nature*.

A Sport of Nature and the Anatomy of Whiteness

This novel has been read, by certain complacent admirers and hostile critics alike, as a straightforward revolutionary fairy tale. To both these ostensibly warring camps, the main character, Hillela, might well belong in one of those multicultural Benetton clothing advertisements, which juxtapose grinning faces across racial and ethnic spectrums. Such critics and admirers alike think that Hillela heroically converts racial *angst* into multiracial fun.

In this picture, Hillela flees apartheid suburbia, embraces revolution and establishes a rainbow family with a black freedom fighter. He is assassinated but she fights on, marrying yet another black freedom fighter, who goes on to become President of his country. The curtain falls happily, as the second husband, President of the Organisation of African Unity, presides over the inauguration of a new South Africa. It is in this vein that the publisher's blurb on the back cover of my 1988 Penguin reprint sees Hillela evolving through personal 'tragedy' into 'a heroic role in the overthrow of apartheid'. What complacent critics praise as healthy agitprop, hostile ones deride as mawkish.

What all miss is the ironic sensibility that brackets this misleadingly bare plot summary. It is dangerous to take this (or any) Gordimer novel at face value. She has said that one of the 'secret locks' of personality lies in what is ironic to us. The *Dichter* needs more than an open ear, needs to see what people are *really* saying, behind the automatic vocabulary that they regurgitate, without really *inhabiting* it. Late in the day, at the height of her powers, Hillela herself 'had learnt to read more in the ellipses than the dictation' we are told (by a narrative voice which itself constantly shifts in tone, degree of omniscience, and reliability throughout the book). Gordimer is a novelist who relies as much on the unsaid, on oblique revelation, as on the explicit.

It is also dangerous to overlook Gordimer's understated but persistent gifts of satire, even parody. The attentive reader will notice that the narrative voice consistently distances Hillela's second husband as 'the General'; that his current foes are not imperialist baddies but those (including his son) who have deposed him in a post-independence coup; that on his return to power he implements one-party rule; that in the book's supposedly happy-clappy closing scene, 'cannons ejaculate from the castle' and the new South African flag is 'smoothed taut by the fist of the wind'. This muscular and patriarchal imagery ironises the denouement of *A Sport of Nature*. The novel's end is mock-Utopian, not Utopian. Indeed, it implicitly alludes to the kind of potentially violent post-revolutionary rivalry that Gordimer explored in *A Guest of Honour* (1970).

Furthermore, the idea of the 'rainbow family', product of Hillela's interracial marriages, is itself jostled by sardonic subtext. Hillela's Benetton rainbow child, in whom Hillela is proud not to have reproduced another generation of whiteness, is nevertheless 'over-indulged by everybody, precocious and spoiled. The brat already knew how to exploit being black.' This child of revolutionary passions, named after Winnie Mandela, grows up to become a *supermodel*, trading on the eighties market for black ramp girls. When Hillela tricks her first revolutionary husband, Whaila Kgomani, into conceiving a second child, he lapses into didactism, calling her 'a spoilt little white girl without proper responsibility to the discipline of the struggle'. She laughs 'at the pomposity so alien to his nature. – The struggle in bed? –' The book's irreverence allows no sacred cows.

No sacred cows. The epigraph of *A Sport of Nature* is a definition of the book's title, taken from the *Oxford English Dictionary*: 'Lusus naturae – Sport of Nature. A plant, animal, etc., which exhibits abnormal variation or a departure from the parent stock or type . . . a spontaneous mutation; a new variety produced in this way.' This is metamorphosis at its most serious. Yet this solemnity (Latin tag and all) receives an unobtrusive but pivotal touch of the parodist's brush half-way through the novel: a mid-level British diplomat shows up at Hillela's wedding to Whaila. In another country, this Brit was Hillela's platonic 'public partner', camouflaging her decidedly unplatonic affair with a married diplomat. 'We had a lot of fun together. She's a really good sport.' This was a term that – our narrator assists – 'in its particular British sense, was a high compliment'. But it is a compliment – attributing to Hillela the virtues of the clubbable, reliable British mandarin – that specifically inverts the unruliness of the sport of nature, as defined in the title. The *discretion* with which Hillela consents to camouflage the affair qualifies the unrestrained recklessness of her title role.

Those who (in delight or disgust) view Hillela as a kind of Rosa Luxemburg in stilettos, or who veer towards hushed tones because of high seriousness of the critique of whiteness at the book's heart, will misunderstand the heavily ironised strategies that Gordimer deploys. Even irony itself receives a satirical lash (it is portrayed as a Eurocentric sensibility), when the narrator describes Whaila Kgomani's charming way with Western diplomats: 'Here was a black man with whom one could talk of contentious matters in the European mode of scepticism and irony that makes communication possible between the social irreconcilables of power and powerlessness.'

In *Notes of a Native Son* (1964), James Baldwin identifies as a hallmark of whiteness the unshakeable confidence in one's own innocence, and comments that 'anyone who insists on remaining in a state of innocence long after that innocence is dead turns himself into a monster'. When this weighty theme appears early in Gordimer's novel, it is again in parodic form. A girl in Hillela's class at school tells a black servant not to lean his 'smelly arm over my face' and, Hillela continues, 'when we had to draw a self-portrait in the style of a famous painting, she drew herself as the Virgin Mary, blue veil and all.'

As an adult, Hillela finds that being white, stubbornly white during apartheid, made all manner of doctrinal debates, imported from elsewhere, self-deluding. To debate the fine points of political doctrine while ignoring the gross force of whiteness was to enact a rarefied form of white innocence: like arguing over the blueness of the veil, rather than discarding it. 'White made it impossible to understand. For me, anyway. Everybody talked and argued, and I thought about other things. And whenever I heard them again, they were still talking and arguing, living the same way in the same place. Liberalism, socialism, communism.'

This is an important point – that no political camp, however conceptually radical, offers its white members automatic exemption from the pitfalls of whiteness. Despite her unambiguous real-life admiration for Afrikaner revolutionary Bram Fischer, despite her authorship of *Burger's Daughter* (1979) as sincere homage to people like him, the Gordimer of *A Sport of Nature* remained aware, in the words of an important character at an important point towards the end of the novel, that 'even the white communists, people like Fischer and Lionel Burger . . . they'd always at least told blacks how they thought it should be done; and even the ANC in its mass campaigns had responded [before the tectonic shift of 1976 boosted black political agency] to what whites had done rather than forced whites into situations where they were the ones who had to respond.'

The accuracy or otherwise of these remarks (they belong to Sasha, Hillela's earnest but rather erratic cousin) is less important than the fact that they confirm Gordimer's objective as novelist: her concern is not to applaud or condemn particular anti-apartheid camps or sub-camps. Like Herman Melville, who looked beyond slavery to its existential engine room of whiteness, so Gordimer looks beyond the ranks of the apartheid battlefield to portray in

62

detail, as Melville in his different historical moment could not, how sensibility curdles where whiteness reigns.

Look for instance at Hillela's liberal aunt, Pauline, keeping in mind Gordimer's well-known and often severely stated real-life criticisms of most South African liberals. Consistent with her intention to foreground whiteness rather than political camps, Gordimer's treatment of Pauline is markedly sympathetic. Pauline is not an untroubled liberal, effortlessly reconciled to fighting a lawless system through its own laws. She taunts her husband (a liberal anti-apartheid lawyer): 'everything's going to come right through the loopholes you manage to find in disgusting laws. The government stops up one mouse-hole, you find another. You work yourself to death, but what's changed? What will you be at our Nuremberg? – In her face was the cruel pleasure, already distressing her while indulged, of turning her fears for Joe into hurt inflicted on him. – The one who tried to serve justice through the rule of law, or the one who betrayed justice by trying to serve it through the rule of unjust laws?'

Pauline cherishes her audiotape of Mandela in the dock at the Rivonia trial, attends protest meetings and organises anti-apartheid petitions; she even falteringly (once she refuses, another time accepts) harbours black fugitives. She has what Gordimer calls a 'revolutionary temperament' with which her liberal half-self is locked in battle. 'Not lawyers' houses,' she says in liberal mode, rationalising her initial refusal to take in a family on the run. If her husband were accused of being involved 'any way other than professionally' he would 'never be able to take on such cases again'. Pauline possesses fully fledged anti-apartheid commitments, within a certain paradigm: the failed paradigm of whiteness, whose stopping-point is the safety of the self. Ultimately hers is a 'professional' engagement with societal injustice; the more intimate vulnerabilities of the self are kept apart, at a safe remove.

Gordimer has said that to risk is to live. And she portrays whiteness as fundamentally risk-free: a walking death. In Pauline's household and among her extended family, 'newspapers are horror happening to other people'. When the black consciousness movement in the seventies makes it impossible for Pauline to continue her anti-apartheid activities in collaboration with blacks, she and her lawyer husband decamp to London, where he takes up the legal problems of soccer teams with energy matching his previous defence of South African detainees. Meanwhile, Pauline's stridently suburban sister Olga ('If you live here you must abide by the law of the country') has a double-mastectomy and stays on in her house filled with 'antiques – that selection from the past only of what is beautiful, lifted cleanly from the context of its bloody revolutions.'

In this secure white milieu, anti-apartheid activism itself becomes suburbanised. Living in Pauline's house, Hillela and Sasha 'were absorbed into activities in which a social conscience had the chance to develop naturally as would a dress-sense under Olga's care.' Far from a disruptive influence triggering transformation or metamorphosis, suburban activism, in South Africa and elsewhere, can become what it is for Bradley Burns, a member of the Washington elite whom Hillela almost marries, whose grandfather was an editor of the then venerably left *New Republic* and a victim of the McCarthy hearings, so that 'the leftist tradition was a family heirloom sufficient in itself; a claim to a way of life that no longer actually need be practised, just as the painting of an ecclesiast ancestor in ermine on the wall is prestige enough for descendants who never go to church.'

As a spontaneous mutation, a sport of nature, Hillela impulsively disrupts each situation of beckoning security that visits her. But she is such a good sport that the visitor's queue seems infinite: she always lands on her feet, cosseted by new mutations of whiteness, even when she seems to have placed immense distance between herself and apartheid suburbia. '*Hadn't she always lived in the eye of the storm? That eye that meteorologists say is safe, a ball of security rolled up in fury, that eye that was whiteness. Pauline, given away by wild-blown hair, put her head out into the cyclone briefly. Others went out and did not come back. But fixedly, the white eye was on itself.*' (Emphasis added.) Hillela's global whirlwind of political exploits amounts to a genuine – and partly sucessful – effort to flee whiteness. Her relative success in abandoning aspects of whiteness is a large part of her importance in the novel. But as the hurricane cannot outrun the calm of its own eye, so she carries some core of whiteness with her always. In similar fashion, Rosa Burger in *Burger's Daughter* leads a charmed existence in Europe (with its anti-black immigration ethos) that clearly eludes her black childhood friend Baasie, in his London exile.

When Hillela tells her black co-revolutionaries that 'there are people who have given up being white', they laugh in friendly mockery. Hillela here betrays a hint of what American critic Patricia J Williams calls the 'I think therefore it is' school of idealism: 'I don't think about colour, therefore your problems don't exist.' This is the final hubris of whiteness: to announce its own demise, its own cessation to be a problem. It is a hubris that underlies the insistence, by many privileged South Africans, that 'we are all colourblind now' and so can stop talking about race, despite apartheid's glaring legacies.

Gordimer (as opposed to Hillela) has long seen through such pretensions. In the short story 'Home' (1991) she struck a satirical note on this theme, writing of a black South African *émigré* and her 'Swedish husband, living in this backwater coastal town in the company of marine biologists who were content to believe all species interesting, and enquire no further into questions of equality.' And towards the end of *A Sport of Nature*, whiteness is palpably thrown into crisis, not because of Hillela's declamations but because of the initiative of black schoolchildren in 1976 and the consequent revival of non-racial politics within the United Democratic Front in the eighties.

Gordimer's treatment of whiteness avoids the criticism that some have made: that the emerging critical study of whiteness is just another way of placing whites at the centre of race issues. By bracketing Hillela's self-portrayal with critical (but sympathetic) irony, and by placing the momentum of history in black mass action, Gordimer the artist (as opposed to Hillela the character) intricately evades a stubborn recidivism, a well-meaning white egocentrism, that traps many earnest but lesser talents. She avoids the classic flaw of the novelists of empathy, who place black dignity under the house arrest of white moral initiative.

By looking beyond the moving parts of South African politics to address the stubborn blight of whiteness, Gordimer has produced a body of work that is of primary relevance to how we live now, not only in South Africa, but the world. Her work is a safe house for a decades-old brand of South African wisdom, more honoured in the breach than the observance, that stretches back to the William Plomer of the 1920s. 'I am much too humanitarian to be colorblind' says a character in Plomer's novel *Turbott Wolfe* (1926), published at the height of America's Jim Crow era, two decades before the apartheid government took office in 1948, and fully five decades before the false hope of 'colourblindness' (a self-righteous euphemism for whiteness) gripped the imagination of white Americans in the 1970s (and continuing) backlash against affirmative action.

South Africa has a lot to teach, the country's literature is a good place to learn it, and Gordimer's work is the best place to start.

References

Canetti, Elias. 1962. *Crowds and Power*. London: Victor Gollancz.

Canetti, Elias. 1979. *The Conscience of Words*. London: The Seabury Press.

Gubar, Susan. 1997. *Racechanges*. Oxford: Oxford University Press.

Hale, Grace Elizabeth. 1998. *Making Whiteness: The Culture of Segregation in the South, 1890-1940*. New York: Pantheon Books.

Haney-Lopez, Ian. 1996. *White By Law: The Legal Construction of Race*. New York: New York University Press.

Hedrick, Joan D. 1994. *Harriet Beecher Stowe: A Life*. Oxford: Oxford University Press.

Morrison, Toni. 1992. *Playing in the Dark: Whiteness and the Literary Imagination*. Cambridge: Harvard University Press.

Roediger, David. Ed. 1998. *Black on White: Black Writers on What It Means to Be White*. New York: Schocken Books.

Roediger, David. 1994. *Towards the Abolition of Whiteness*. New York: Verso.

Spelman, Elizabeth V. 1997. *Fruits of Sorrow: Framing Our Attention to Suffering*. Boston: Beacon Press.

Williams, Patricia J. 1997. *Seeing a Colour-Blind Future: The Paradox of Race*. London: Virago.

The Critical Reception of Nadine Gordimer

DOROTHY DRIVER

Nadine Gordimer is the first South African writer to win the Nobel Prize for Literature. Characteristically for a writer who has consistently spoken out against censorship, and who has seen it as one of her tasks to help place the work of aspirant or unrecognised writers before magazine editors and book publishers, she took care in her acceptance speech to draw attention to those South African writers who have suffered banning or imprisonment. She has long been aware of her own relatively privileged and secure position. In her acceptance speech she also drew attention to the conflict she has felt to be an increasing part of her writing since the start of her career – between her responsibilities to political change, on the one hand, and what she called 'the word', on the other. Although she tried to resolve this conflict by quoting Gabriel García Márquez, 'The best way a writer can serve the revolution is to write as well as he can', the particular way she negotiates 'politics' and 'art' in her writing gives it its distinctive flavour: the signature by which her work has come to be known.

Since the start of her writing career in 1937 until the time when she was awarded the Nobel Prize in 1991, Gordimer had produced ten novels and over two hundred short stories. She has also collaborated in various television films and two photographic studies of South African life, has produced a considerable amount of literary and socio-political criticism, and has always been generous with interviews and talks. Since she has been the subject of more critical analysis than other South African writers, it seems worth while looking over certain aspects of her critical reception, partly to assess what has been said about her responsibilities to politics and to writing.

More than any other South African writer, Gordimer has been the subject of intense critical scrutiny, both local and abroad: seven critical books, by Robert Haugh (1974), Michael Wade (1978), Christopher Heywood (1983), John Cooke (1985), Stephen Clingman (1986), Judie Newman (1988), and Andrew Vogel Ettin (1993), nearly two hundred critical essays – some of which appear in Rowland Smith's *Critical Essays on Nadine Gordimer* (1990) and Bruce King's *The Later Fiction of Nadine Gordimer* (1993) – and nearly fifty academic theses. She has given over one hundred interviews, a large selection of which are reprinted in *Conversations with Nadine Gordimer* (1990), edited by Nancy Topin Bazin and Marilyn Dallman Seymour, and has written nearly a hundred and fifty magazine and newspaper essays, the most substantial of which are gathered in *The Essential Gesture: Writing, Politics and Places* (1988), edited by Stephen Clingman. 1993 also saw the publication of a bibliography from the National English Literary Museum (NELM), which lists all her work, in English and translation (including talks, films and so on) and all known criticism of her writing, along with a large amount of occasional comment.

Much of the critical work on Gordimer is written either by outsiders, unfamiliar with South African history and politics except in its broadest strokes, or by South African critics offering an introduction to her work. Essays on her have recently started appearing in overseas books and journals not solely devoted to South African writing, sometimes written by overseas critics with reputations already established in work other than South African. An essay by Homi Bhabha on *My Son's Story* is a case in point.

In part, this trend signals a shift in the commodification of South African writing, which has begun to enter world literature through current interests in colonial and post-colonial discourse. Although it is still too easy for overseas critics to reproduce Gordimer as representative of white South African writers – 'We read her for a progressive white's view of "the situation", ' says one American critic (Ettin 1993) – the intellectual level of critical work on Gordimer is tending to rise.

The placement of Gordimer as the white South African writer/

spokesperson appears to be one of the reasons for the cooler welcome given her work by South African readers (her seventieth birthday on 23 November passed unnoticed, for instance, in the South African press). Some readers wish not to be represented by a writer so antagonistic to all that surviving South African liberals hold dear, some object to her betrayal of 'art' through political 'axe-grinding', and some feel detached from a white writer who speaks from a secure upper middle-class position. Moreover, Gordimer has never provided an easy read for an audience not noted for its intellectual tastes – 'a nation of philistines', as Olive Schreiner once called us. Her local sales are not high.

Certainly her texts can by no means speak for all South Africans, not even for all white South Africans. Yet her now famous insistence on the relation between herself and her work – 'I have to offer you myself as my most closely observed specimen' ('Living in the Interregnum', 1982) – points to a way in which she *is* representative of white South Africa, just as her very different characters – Mehring, Rosa Burger, Maureen Smales – may be taken as representative. In the most influential of the books on her so far, *The Novels of Nadine Gordimer: History from the Inside*, Stephen Clingman takes his lead from Gordimer's insistence, and thus examines the characters and the writer/narrator herself as 'typical', in the Lukácsian sense, of this time and place: as figures in whose lives some of the major currents of history intersect.

Clingman's contribution is crucial. No doubt because of the political demands of the time, to say nothing of the 'spectacular' nature of apartheid (to use Njabulo Ndebele's well-known term), criticism of Gordimer has tended to engage with the historical and political dimensions of her fiction. But Clingman takes sociological criticism to its limit by seeing Gordimer's writing as 'history from the inside' – history as experienced by individuals who are products of a contradictory and fraught social and political history rather than just actors in and observers of that history. Gordimer writes not just of the events and movements of South African history, but also of what it has been like to live through them.

Thus Clingman suggests that the writer's own consciousness is open to scrutiny in the fiction as part of the texts' literary production. This is an interesting move for him to make, not least since some South African readers of her work have judged it harshly for the way it reproduces the dominant stereotypes of white South African thinking. If Clingman sees Gordimer as vulnerable to these stereotypes in her early fiction, he also watches her rise above them, for he develops a thesis regarding her changing consciousness through contemporary history. Again, he is close to what Gordimer has said, notably in the oft-cited preface to her first *Selected Stories*.

Early critics saw Gordimer's development in different terms. Robert Haugh, in the first book on her work, has been the only one to see it negatively, arguing that Gordimer's primary interest in the personal was increasingly awkwardly integrated with the political themes she felt obliged to explore. In contrast, Michael Wade looks at her work in terms of its progressive turn to 'Africa'. Unusually among her commentators, John Cooke focuses on individual psychology, addressing the importance of Gordimer's childhood and adolescence to her writing. He argues that the novels may be seen in terms of an increasing liberation from the mother's confining world. Thus for Cooke, too, Gordimer's development is positive, moving from a private to a public frame of reference. Finally, where Clingman sees South African history as the conditioning force behind Gordimer's fiction, and thus relates her work to a realist tradition, Judie Newman argues from a post-structuralist perspective that Gordimer's writing produces a highly self-conscious reassessment of narrative realism. For Newman, Gordimer's development involves an increasingly sophisticated narrative technique which interweaves racial, colonial and sexual themes.

Newman argues that Gordimer's deconstruction of realism as a way of knowing South African reality opens up a route to cultural and political decolonisation. Her reading is not entirely new. It resonates interestingly with that offered five years earlier by Abdul JanMahomed in *Manichean Aesthetics* (1983), whose interest is specifically in the deconstruction of some of the binary oppositions that underpin the colonial enterprise. But unlike JanMahomed, Newman gives space to textual presentations of gender, looking at the precise narrative structure of each text – the discontinuities with which the *Bildungsroman* must be infused in depicting women's lives, for instance, or the particular relation in apartheid society between race, politics and female desire, or the ways in which the concept 'woman' works in the white South African subconscious as a symbol on to which political and sexual conflicts are projected, as well as the ways in which gender is constructed as a function of economic existence.

One of the questions that critics keep coming up against – but not fully resolving – is the relation between author, narrators and characters. Of *Burger's Daughter*, Newman writes that Gordimer employs the terms of the white racist subconscious in an attempt to free her art from the complex of racial and sexual projections that dominate life under apartheid, and to direct it towards a world where a white is able to address a black not as a 'fantasy projection', but as 'real'.

In his later book, *White on Black in South Africa* (1993), cultural psychology is taken up more emphatically by Wade, though more simplistically. On the assumption that there are a set of mythic structures which have been used to maintain white South Africans' visions of themselves as part of a 'classic neurotic structure' of defence and denial which often turns into 'a psychotic perceptual world as the price they pay for power', Wade sees Gordimer's early work in terms of an authorial entrapment within this 'perceptual system' or 'mythic structure', whereas her later work offers a more detached address. Gordimer's project is increasingly, then, to try to adjust those mythic structures quite as much as it is to record and judge them. (Wade's reading also resonates with JanMohamed's, but – in what must be a gesture of Jew-Muslim antagonism – Wade refers only once (rudely) to JanMahomed's book, and then obliquely, refusing to give it scholarly citation. So much for political reconciliation!)

Although Wade's book was not finished at the time of his death, and although he tends to generalise 'the' white South African psyche, some key parts of his chapter on Gordimer are well-developed and others are suggestive. In one instance of close reading, he notes Gordimer's early recognition that the myths white South Africans construct of blacks as sexually threatening function as a denial of their real threat to white ownership: 'the prescriptive relationship between white and black in South Africa is based on property and territory, on power, not sex.' He thus begins to adjust the 'classic neurotic structure' he derives from Octave Mannoni and Frantz Fanon by placing it in a political, historical and economic context.

Wade sees Gordimer as capable, then, of standing outside herself, as Clingman does, in the sense that she recognises something about the way white South African thinking works. For Wade, she offers no revolutionary gesture: the fact that she recognises neurosis as neurosis is the first and only step to change. Some of the very recent work on Gordimer will suggest a different relation to the future than this.

But first let me turn to an argument made by a relatively recent critic probably unknown to most South African readers, David Ward, whose book, *Chronicles of Darkness* (1989), is devoted to various writers on Africa. He argues that her writing produces a recognition not simply that there is always another way of seeing or experiencing the world, but, more emphatically, that seeing and experiencing the world is necessarily 'other' to itself: flawed, contradictory, not after all in command. Again, I see this as a crucial moment in Gordimer criticism, for it addresses with intelligence and tact what has hitherto been pejoratively regarded as detachment or coldness in Gordimer's art. Ward quotes a comment made in 1969 by Dennis Brutus, that in Gordimer we find 'how dehumanized South African society has become – that an artist like this lacks warmth, lacks feeling, but can observe with a detachment, with the coldness of a machine.' Numerous other critics have called Gordimer 'cold', Alan Paton among them. For Ward, Gordimer's detachment is a fault neither of the writing nor of the writer, but an aspect of her ability to produce her narrator as 'other', alienated not just from the presented world but also from pre-existing ways of seeing reality.

Ward's focus is very much on the techniques of Gordimer's fiction. One of the limitations of critical work on Gordimer has been the tendency to see her writing in stark contrast to Coetzee's. Although there are differences between them, criticism has tended to place the two writers in such radical opposition to each other that the opposition keeps mindlessly reproducing itself rather than being offered up for interrogation: she is concerned with 'politics', he with 'art'. But it seems, looking at very recent work, that critics are starting to feel emboldened to turn more decisively to close textual analysis of Gordimer's writing in such a way as to see beyond this opposition, and thus also to see more complex ways in which Gordimer's writing deals with South African history.

Again, one turns first to Clingman's work here. His book on Gordimer has recently been reprinted in a new edition which adds a prologue on her later work. Clingman keeps to his historical focus. But he also argues that we now need to start reading her writing not simply in terms of a 'rising historical curve' (as he previously did) but also in terms of 'an equal and opposite curve beginning to arc downwards'. Upwards, for Clingman, means 'commitment and engagement'; downwards means an interrogation of this political development. Gordimer's recent work manifests not just the 'graph of history' but a 'double graph', which affirms the political at the same time as the need to question it. Clingman uses Bakhtin's term 'dialogic' for this double movement, and suggests that the dialogic might be found in all her work if one re-read it, though he is hesitant enough to add, 'especially her later fiction'.

Clingman recalls that in his earlier work he was interested in the ambiguities and contradictions in Gordimer's writing, what he termed 'splits' in the writer's consciousness – between an African and a white identity, between the personal and political, for instance. He offers the 'double graph' of history as a means whereby Gordimer has raised the configurations of her 'split position' to a 'higher historical level'. She now finds a crucial division within the longed-for moment of liberation: *A Sport of Nature* and *My Son's Story* offer ambiguities regarding the 'currencies of power' and the idea of nation, for instance. But the interesting truth is that Clingman's earlier work did not foreground the splits in her narratorial consciousness nearly as much as he intends to now. His current reading of Gordimer amounts to a re-reading, then, and one which to some extent closes the distance between Gordimer and Coetzee, though Clingman still takes care to note Gordimer's political involvement as a difference between them. For Clingman, Gordimer is now to be read as a writer whose fiction always 'asked questions, relentlessly and in every direction'. This seems to produce some unease, for he hastens to say that Gordimer's interrogation of current history does not amount to a betrayal of the liberation movement: 'we should not forget that in her personal life Gordimer's commitment is as strong if not stronger than ever.'

Thinking about what Clingman said – and didn't say – about

betrayal, I turned with particular interest to another recent book on Gordimer, Ettin's *Betrayals of the Body Politic: The Literary Commitments of Nadine Gordimer*. Admirably, Ettin tries to forge a new path by breaking with chronology, by dealing simultaneously with the novels and short stories (virtually all other critics separate them), and by treating her writing as 'one book' (this at Gordimer's own invitation, for she often remarks on her obsessive return to the same themes). But by 'body politic' Ettin simply means the South African 'police state', and his book fails to break new ground. Moreover, considering current readings of Gordimer, his use of 'body' is odd.

More interesting, in terms of re-readings, are some of the essays gathered by King in *The Later Fiction* (later means *The Conservationist* and after), several of which are implicitly based on the notion of 'split' in Gordimer's writing. Susan Greenstein argues that the dual narrative structure of *My Son's Story* combines not the voice of Will and an unnamed third-person narrator but Will's two voices, as in 'double agent': 'each voice endlessly reflects, refracts, incorporates, and produces the other, in infinite regression or unending dialogue.' Lars Engle re-reads *The Conservationist* as a deconstruction of the oppositions it examines: not simply 'authenticating black claims and denying white ones', as Clingman and others have argued, but as 'mapping subtle and largely unseen axes of similarity' between black and white, including similar and ethically possible desires to possess the land. Brian Macaskill identifies a 'dialogic interruption' which creates a new space where 'politics' and 'art' can no longer be polarised, a space for what he calls 'political aesthetics'. While these three see contradiction or duality in positive terms, the other essays which foreground splits of one kind or another see them at the level of unresolved conflict.

In his otherwise plausible preface, King sets up a new dichotomy in Gordimer's writing: the feminine – 'the instinctual, the personal, the socially and morally conscious' and the masculine – 'public, rational, dominating, distinguishing between public politics and personal possessions'. Even Gordimer's feminist detractors know that her work refuses categories as crude and essentialist as these.

In feminist criticism, Gordimer is sometimes praised for producing female characters who break stereotypes of femininity and sometimes accused of an uncritical use of sexist ideology, especially regarding the representation of women's bodies. Karen Lazar's essay in *The Later Fiction* usefully notes that Gordimer's apparent antifeminism is often simply an antagonism to 'liberal feminism', which separates issues of gender from those of race. Indeed, as the interview with Lazar attests (as does her recent refusal to write for the South African *Playboy*), Gordimer is now making a new space for herself: by defining feminism as narrowly as she does, she may now respond to the revolutionary potential of (another kind of) feminism which sees gender, race and class as intersecting forces in people's lives. The most interesting feminist discussion about Gordimer is in fact concerned with these intersections (following Newman): in an essay not gathered in the King collection, Louise Yelin reads *Burger's Daughter* as a feminist contribution to dialogical criticism, for it makes visible the terms 'race' and 'gender' occluded in Bakhtin's work (see *Feminism, Bakhtin and the Dialogic*, 1993).

Significantly, in an implicit address to the ubiquitous topic of 'art' versus 'politics', Yelin argues that dialogism in Gordimer's writing should not be identified with indeterminacy or with carnivalesque transgression. For Yelin, *Burger's Daughter* insists on moral responsibility. This concurs with Gordimer's own insistence in *The Essential Gesture* that her project is not to 'transform the world by style'.

Still, at a certain level style and content are inseparable. Also included in *The Later Fiction* is a new essay to this effect by Clingman. Here Clingman reads the anti-realism of *A Sport of Nature* as an act of political transformation, so that Gordimer's ironic vision is elevated to the status of political strategy. And he makes the kind of space Macaskill makes for the concept of 'political aesthetics', though their two arguments are very different.

Clingman also produces the concept of the 'organic body', derived from Hillela's 'bodily intelligence', 'bodily instinct' and 'bodily politics', in order to suggest that Gordimer *repairs* splits in consciousness. Thus he buttresses Gordimer's project against any accusation of irresponsible interrogation which might otherwise linger after his use of the term 'double graph', with its implications of irony rather than resolution.

For Clingman, then, not only is Gordimer's moral responsibility bound up with the idea of resolution, but it is also his responsibility as a critic to assert resolution in her work. As regards the 'organic body', he argues that each of Gordimer's characters (he means central characters) 'has searched for this kind of unity with varying degrees of success, and that it is always involved with a larger political context.' Thus, despite his interest in interrogation and despite his claim that his earlier work noted splits in Gordimer's consciousness, his critical thrust is always towards unity and resolution. On one occasion he spells 'double graph' with a hyphen as if to insist on wholeness rather than rupture. He also offers a reading of *A Sport of Nature* in which Gordimer's fictional and non-fictional works are no longer to be seen in opposition but in more intricate forms of negotiation.

What is happening in recent Gordimer criticism, then, in Clingman's work and in that of others, is that a tension is being set up between 'art' and 'politics' at an entirely different level than the more conventional and banal one deployed earlier. Now 'art' and 'politics' exist in dialogue with each other rather than in opposition, the two terms sometimes in harmony ('political aesthetics') and sometimes not. True to the spirit of the times, dialogue suggests negotiation: Gordimer's critics, quite as much as her characters, thus stand as 'typical' figures of contemporary history in the sense that they express current historical desire. Wade suggested that Gordimer helped create her own readership by opening a space for herself within white South African society. Certainly the work of her most substantial critics has been extremely responsive not just to the leads given by the writer herself but also to the adjustments advanced from one novel to the next. Perhaps most significantly, one of her early antagonists has now publicly changed his mind: this is Lionel Abrahams, who confessed in a recent issue of *New Contrast* that what he saw earlier as a dishonest contradiction in her work between 'politics' and 'art' (where 'politics' won) is now to be read as a tension 'born of deliberate, difficult choices'. It stands 'challengingly', he says, in the centre of her consciousness as yet another example of the 'morbid symptoms' of political interregnum her writing has been shown to depict.

Gordimer's challenge is this, then: to depict a world where 'art' and 'politics', like 'body' and 'mind', 'black' and 'white', 'betrayal' and 'commitment', have separated as binary oppositions, and to reconstruct a world where they need no longer do so. The challenge is an intellectual and artistic as much as a political one.

As Gordimer's most perceptive critics have seen, addressing the challenge demands a certain kind and degree of detachment: not only is a distance set up between observer and observed, but the observer is also seen to be placed at one remove, as are the strategies or ways of seeing which the observer employs.

In my own reading of Gordimer, I would stress that such detachment belongs to a writer who is always watching her language, always aware that *she* is being written even as she taps the typewriter keys. Thus, paradoxically, given what has been said about Gordimer's development, and despite her insistence that in fiction 'the inhibitions go', the critic needs also to be on the lookout for signs of increasing vigilance, even repressiveness, in the very texture of the prose. Bodily knowledge and sexuality have, as critics are now suggesting, always played a part in Gordimer's fiction. In her best writing (in my view) they have been wrought into the texture of the prose as part of its imagery and rhythm, and as a way of fusing the splits produced elsewhere: *The Conservationist* is the most complex and successfully sustained example. In Gordimer's very recent fiction, though, the body and sexuality, having surfaced from the repressed of the characters' consciousness, seem to be increasingly placed at the level of plot; that is, as part of the 'telling' rather than the 'showing' (to adapt an old-fashioned distinction). In interviews Gordimer has suggested that the short story form permits her more play in writing. Without wishing to qualify the homage being paid, perhaps it is time for Gordimer to re-think the distinction set up in reference to writing short stories and novels, and to return to the powerful, lyrical quality that marks her best writing. And perhaps, since Gordimer is re-thinking her attitude to feminism, she might also consider the political project implied by *écriture feminine*, writing from a body that refuses old social and cultural distinctions.

A question must also still remain about the relation between author, narrators and characters. The relations Gordimer sets up in her fiction are complex, and always interesting. There is no reason to believe – and no justification for insisting – that Gordimer's fiction should be quite free of the specific neuroses which make up white South African thinking, however much her writing has developed and however much it strives for detachment. She has rendered white South Africa visible to itself – and, perhaps, she will render black-and-white South Africa visible to itself: as she said in recent interviews, she will continue to pose questions under a new regime. She offers scepticism but also an ethics, envisioning a world that glimmers irretrievably beyond doubt.

TRIBUTES TO A WRITING LIFE

Troubled Enchantments:
A Tribute to Nadine Gordimer

ALBIE SACHS

It was in the busy seaside town of C—— that a young man discovered that he was addicted to nineteenth-century novels. Not any novels, they had to be translations into English, set in far away landscapes and peopled with characters with names that could be read but not easily pronounced. The rushes of excitement started with Russian writers. Then it was the time of the French novelists. When the nineteenth century was exhausted, the young man ventured cautiously into early twentieth-century Russian, French and even German books. The important thing was that the land of the imagination had to be an entire one and totally exotic. If one's emotions and experiences could be surprisingly revealed in the lives of characters in other places at other times, by authors who knew nothing about oneself, they had to be true and they had to be universal.

The influence of literature on this young man was strong. He once observed about a vivacious friend that she had so much energy and was so full of surprises that she was almost as real as someone in a novel! The two characters with which he identified himself existentially were Fabrice from the Charterhouse of Palma and the Idiot of Dostoevsky. It was not that he modelled himself on them, but that he recognised himself in them; their physical and cultural remoteness meant that his identification could only be based on pure emotion, and not on superficial points of biographical or contextual resemblance.

Novels written in English in an English setting just could not reach that world of imagination. They could never engender the same excited sense of discovery and recognition; their universe was too familiar, too pale, too factual. They depicted what he thought he already knew, through points of entry which to him were banal. What was even less acceptable was any fiction located in South Africa itself. Familiarity bred imaginative revulsion. Who wanted to read about the landscape through which one actually passed? Who wanted to know about the lives and passions of persons with the names of those one knew in school? Why bother to read about settings which one experienced directly?

It was then that he read *The Lying Days*. Today, older but no wiser, he thinks of the book as having had the yellow dustcover of a Gollancz publication. It was important then that it had been published in England, and that it looked and felt like 'a real book'. But what really mattered in this case was its content. The setting was South Africa, the names were familiar, the landscape recognisable, but it had a glow of imagination which encapsulated all. For the first, time this young man found himself transported into a fictional South African world which seemed more real than the world in which he actually lived. He could hardly believe that he actually existed in a psychological landscape as magically interesting as the world of nineteenth-century novels. The repudiation, embarrassment, almost revulsion that he had until then felt about attempts to locate South Africa in a fictional universe, were instantly dissolved. He felt like a discoverer of his own continent, all the more amazed because what he was viewing was a continent behind the continent in which he lived, one that had always been there, but which had been blocked out from him by the surfaces of its familiarity. The way to Alex La Guma, Oswald Mtshali, J M Coetzee, André Brink, Breyten Breytenbach, Njabulo Ndebele, Jeanne Goosen, had been opened up to him.

Years later when he was living in exile and visiting the United States, he found that nearly all his friends there were reading *Burger's Daughter*. So he too decided to read it. Strangely, while he found it complex, they said it was most accessible; for them it was a real novel set in a strange land with characters having names that were difficult to pronounce in physical settings that were remote, but who experienced emotions and had insights that were instantly recognisable as their own.

When some time later, Nadine and that now middle-aged man met for the first time in New York, there was great mutual curiosity and instant sympathy between us. I didn't tell her about the impact that the *Lying Days* had had on me, but I spoke about moments connected with the death and burial of Ruth First. I felt great relief at being able to impart to a totally honest hearer all the little details associated with the departure of someone I had loved as a friend, details that had had no overt political significance, but great private emotional meaning to me. She was the insider writing for the broad world outside, eager to connect with the exile. I was the physical outsider, longing to re-establish intimate contact with the person from inside.

Much has since happened to our country, to her and to me, overwhelmingly, I believe, to the good. Inside and outside have become blurred. Our encounters are occasional, but always intensely affectionate. I want to hug her, to get close to that head that has thought so much and to feel direct contact with that body that has experienced so much. I'm proud to live in a country that has produced someone of such sensibility and intellectual and moral purpose. May she long carry on entrancing young and old readers in foreign lands with the troubled enchantment of South Africa, and may she long continue to help me in the ongoing discovery of my own reviving continent.

On Nadine Gordimer

PER WÄSTBERG

The house dates from 1910, and is one of the few in South Africa that have never been broken into. It is open and quiet. A dog shuffles around, a cat scratches at the door. The windows, which have been left ajar, look out on an old cherry-tree. In the neighbour's garden a raven is visible among the tropical plants which the neighbour brought with him from Mozambique. Birds resembling goldfinches and wheatears dart and wheel through the air.

I hear an utterly uninhibited laugh from the direction of the road. No white person can laugh that way, and I am almost envious: the strange consonants, a lexicon that is not mine. People are demonstrating. Further off, the hooting of sirens. But these bursts of laughter are primeval explosions, like the sound of schoolgirls on their way home. Could they suddenly modulate into bloodthirsty curses?

'I'm a little envious of my friend Joseph Brodsky,' says Nadine. 'He's a Bohemian, flitting from town to town, a summer here, an autumn there. I'm rooted in family, friends, the social milieu I live in and have wanted to influence. I can't go in for serious travelling. I try to take off, living with my daughter in France, visiting my son in New York. I give lectures in Europe and the USA. But I always come back to Johannesburg. Even during the worst years of the seventies and eighties it never crossed my mind to stay away, and now I know I'll always stay here.'

In Reinhold and Nadine's home one hears clicks and creaks. In the floorboards. But between nine and one silence reigns, for then the lady of the house is in her study. The brown-panelled interior is full to overflowing with books, photographs of children, souvenirs. The eye strays ineluctably over the deposits of a lifetime.

Nadine types on an old machine. Thomas silently sets down trays of tea and biscuits for all of us in our different rooms. Reinhold takes the dog for a walk, reads *The Star* in the garden, listens to the radio. The routine is the same decade after decade: the livelier the imagination, the calmer the daily rhythm.

Staying with Nadine and Reinhold in 1959, I had my first inkling of the South Africa which is only now being born. So it was a strange feeling to come here again and see how unchanged everything was on the outside, while realising how much construction and renewal had taken place. The trees have become thirty-five years higher and thicker. Thomas, like me, has become greyer. The children are grown up and have children of their own. Todd Matshikiza and Bloke Modisane, Helen Joseph and Bram Fischer, Can Themba and Nat Nakasa are dead.

One of Nadine Gordimer's themes is leaving the parental home, and the need to find a place where one can feel truly at home. For the blacks, 'Homeland' has the same ring as 'Siberia' for us. A place of exile.

Nadine talks about 'the country that owns me, for I don't say "my Africa" when it's exactly the other way round.' She disapproves of the term 'Afro-Americans' for Americans who happen to be black. 'Anglo-Africans' for the whites in Africa? In that case: white and black Africans. She has remained a South African patriot in a way that the forces of the right are unable to understand. Three of her books have been banned. She has advocated boycotts and sanctions when it was illegal to do so.

But she has refused to become a self-appointed voice of conscience, as a means of scoring moral points. She knows that the truth perhaps does not set us free, but there is no personal or political freedom without the attempt to find and express the truth. This demands an honesty and candour which is not always appreciated.

In her Nobel speech, Nadine warns that an author risks both the state's condemnation of him as a traitor, and the freedom movement's complaint that he fails to demonstrate blind loyalty. But, she explains, 'the author serves humanity only as long as he utilises the word against his own loyalties too.'

'Give yourself the freedom to write as if you were dead,' she often says. 'Do it without regard to your family, friendship, politics, critics. You can't do it one hundred per cent, but you can try. The novel I'm writing is my reality and my only responsibility. I am ruthless when I write. Nothing I say in interviews and articles can be as true as my novels.'

Her characters are often recognisable middle-class people who have been forced to break with the lifestyles sketched out for them. She is attracted – she says – by experiences which lie outside what you thought you were intended for. For Nadine, the novel has been a tool for the moral examination of a society which for long enough resisted any form of scrutiny.

Bray in *A Guest of Honour*, for example, makes a choice which, in a way, changes and redefines his environment. It can be a question of the revolutionary aspect of a new view of Africa's history, such as that which one of the characters in *Occasion for Loving* is in the process of developing, or it can be a guerrilla who knows what he is doing, even if death is the only reward.

How does one break out of those roles and expectations that hold one captive? Which events stand everything on its head – like when the middle-class housewife becomes an underground agent, the lawyer offers his life for a future that is not his, a young career architect hides a resistance fighter?

'The episode in my books that readers protested about most,' says Nadine, 'was when the mother in *July's People* leaves her children for a man she is madly in love with. It's a sacred taboo that a mother, unlike a father, never abandons her children. Although I've seen it time and again. But even if it does happen, these people who write to me want it hushed up.'

Nadine Gordimer's novels delve into the most intimate aspects of people's lives – in order to show how they were violated in the South Africa of race-registration and informing. To then write from a personal standpoint and make it public was the opposite of the police's method of tramping in at any time of the day or night and confiscating letters and diaries. In Nadine's work – and *My Son's Story* is a good example of this – apartheid is what shapes people's entire existence, a sickness that infects both the rulers and the freedom fighters.

The moral corruption that makes betrayal possible is one of her central themes. She can reproduce the pathetic over-simplifications of political rhetoric while still managing to convey its appeal for the mob, thanks to the affecting experiences of the speaker. She seeks out those unexpected moments when the revolutionary spark ignites, but at the same time she has a keen eye for the average day when internal dissension is rocking the upper reaches of the movement.

My Son's Story and her latest novel[1] *None to Accompany Me* are part of an ongoing chronicle reflecting South African society over a fifty-year period. Continuity, inheritance, historical interpretation are ever stronger elements in it. What history consists of is not the great events which become clearer in retrospect, but rather countless small episodes which gradually form a pattern. In these two novels the main characters think they are actors in a historical drama, but they seldom see what is happening in the room where they are with others.

Despite the contributions of André Brink and John Coetzee (Coetzee's centre of gravity lies elsewhere, besides the fact that he is the most original writer of them all), it is to Nadine Gordimer's works that one has to go to find South Africa's archivist and lighthouse-keeper.

The light sweeps over her collective experience, illuminates parts which otherwise would have lain in darkness, and helps us navigate towards a South Africa which, far from being geographically and politically cut off, is a wide, more universal landscape that could bear a quite different name.

On Nadine Gordimer's background and books

When Nadine Gordimer taught herself how to write and how to read the classics, at the end of the thirties, she fell from the pinnacle of South Africa's arrogant upper crust down to its lowest depths. Her books and her writing helped her to navigate her way out of the typical girl's colonial existence, which led from boarding-school to engagement, from home-town wedding to motherhood. No

---

[1]As of March-May 1994 when this was written. Nadine Gordimer's latest novel *The House Gun* was published in February 1998.

blacks were allowed into the library in the little mining town of Springs. Jane Austen, Dickens and Conrad, Trollope and Rider Haggard were all to be found there. Without that library Nadine would never have become an author.

Maureen Smales in *July's People* regards life from the same point of view as the fifteen-year-old Nadine. You might happen to find a job after leaving school, but the object was to get married, and soon. To Nadine's mother it was a social disaster if the woman had to work: an indication that the man could not provide for his family.

Nadine's parents were immigrants. Her father was a small-town watchmaker and jeweller who sold trophy cups to shooting clubs, as well as engagement rings and canteens of cutlery. He read nothing. Her mother read aloud. They were quick to adapt to the reality of white South Africa. To avoid being conspicuous they turned a blind eye to every reminder of the oppression they had once been subjected to themselves. Nadine did not turn a blind eye. Her début novel – which she wrote when she was twenty-eight – was entitled *The Lying Days*.

Her father fled from anti-Semitism in Lithuania at the age of thirteen. Nadine's grandfather was an assistant to a shipping agent in Riga. Her mother came from a more secure English background. She realised that the blacks were like herself, but put up with the race laws. Nadine wanted to be a dancer, but an enlarged thyroid gland gave her mother an excuse to withdraw her from school and deny her any further physical activity. Nadine realised later that her mother wanted her for company in an unhappy marriage.

Nadine stayed at home more than other girls did, had lessons from a private tutor for several years, read a great deal and had a fairy tale published at thirteen, a short story at fifteen. She learned how to interpret subtexts: her mother's tone of voice, imperfectly hidden secrets, familial hypocrisy, the gulf between public behaviour and private reality.

'People were buried alive under our feet, and we cheerfully picnic on their graves,' she wrote. Hence that uneasy mixture of naivete and hysteria that characterised her formative years. The mood lingered on, acquired a historical dimension, and came to embrace the dilemma of liberalism and the failure of humanism.

The feeling of falling through different layers of illusion in order to land finally among some truths has followed her throughout her life. It comes about as a result of being brought up in a society where, from childhood onwards, one contents oneself with excuses.

'When I went to school, I took it for granted that black children didn't want to go to my school. It didn't occur to me that they were banned from there, just as they were from the cinema and the library. The blacks didn't need all the things we were dependent on, was what we were told.'

Nadine says that she had wanted to write as if she lived in England, beyond racism, but she has a share in a fearful inheritance which she has to refashion. Thus her novels and short stories form source texts for our understanding of the atmosphere, psychology and behaviour patterns of an epoch. Here is a society which for a long time has hidden itself in censorship, hypocrisy and topsy-turvy concepts and this has fostered a grammar of lies with which to root out 'the unknown history'.

'Loneliness is living without social responsibility. I've come to realise this in later life. When a baby is being born, its head is formed in the birth canal. Anyone born into the apartheid society is only formed afterwards.'

Nadine Gordimer has shunned political parties, but she joined the ANC as soon as it was possible to do so. She takes a lot of practical initiatives within her own domain: part of her Nobel Prize money went towards bursaries and writers' workshops. But as an author she belongs on the world stage, and she is better known there than in South Africa.

Nadine belongs among those whom Seamus Heaney has dubbed 'the guerrillas of the imagination'. When she joined the ANC in 1990, she issued an explanation of her action in a bid to avert misunderstanding.

'As a South African and a lifelong active opponent of racism, and as a sympathiser with, and now a member of the ANC, I have both in my behaviour and my actions voluntarily and at no cost to my self-respect submitted myself to the discipline of the liberation movement. In my writings I have asserted and put into practice my right to freely interpret reality in whatever forms and modes of expression I have thought necessary.

'. . . Writers have contributed to the struggle, but it is time to throw off the uniform. Some of us, of course, have never worn it in the first place. The days when a black writer had to describe the struggle in terms of clenched fists and powerful black mother figures, and when every policeman had to be a monster, are over.'

She has seen it as her mission to raise the consciousness of the whites and to inform them about what went on. Her individual language and fearless demeanour have made her a counterbalance to the propaganda of a mendacious regime. She has written as if the censorship did not exist, and as if there were readers willing to listen. Early on, she created a free zone where it was possible to try out, in imagination and in one's thoughts, what life beyond apartheid might be like.

Nadine believes that sex and politics are the strongest driving forces in people's lives. The political activists she has known have had no time for family life. They have been in and out of prison and exile, their families have been abandoned for years at a time, and new relationships have been forged. The choice between the movement and one's own emotional life has meant victory for the movement – until now. Apartheid thought only in terms of groups, and had to be fought in groups. Democracy means that the individual counts.

'I'm no hero, far from it, but it's wonderful to live in a country where there *are* heroes, and it's a privilege to have got to know them. In lots of countries, no huge demands are made on people. One doesn't know who might turn out to be an exceptional human being when the need arises. But in South Africa, when some have disappeared into prison or been murdered, others have continually come forward. There are people I feel great reverence for, and I wonder if I would do so in America or Europe.'

The Nobel Prize, she says, involved a kind of retrospective exhibition in which she was forced to think back over what she had done. She was surprised that her black friends and colleagues were so happy on her account. She belonged to them. And the world had taken notice.

Many people ask what she will write about when apartheid is defeated. She replies that she began to write because of the mysteries of life, and in order to create a structure of her own and to call out, 'I'm here!' She continued with literature, with fiction, which embraces what is articulated between people and within oneself: all the complicated stuff that we never produce in a conversation or in a factual summing-up of a situation.

'There is a freedom in literature that is lacking in facts – because inhibitions are released. A lecture has to have a point, a moral, a purpose. Fiction is open-ended – the story continues inside the reader; there is no final page. It doesn't matter if people ask what I'm getting at. There are twenty different interpretations of the ending of *July's People*.'

It's Good Friday. Nadine's children phone her from France and New York, and Betty du Toit calls from Cape Town. A neighbour comes in to borrow a roasting pan. Lists of chores to be done before Easter are drawn up. I have never met a major writer who is quite so un-neurotic, practical, rooted in the here and now.

'I'm an author who happens to be a woman. Authors who happen to be men are never cross-examined about whether there is something special and limiting about being a woman, or the opposite. Centuries of slave mentality have led to liberating rebellion among both women and blacks, but they also deposit strange sediments. The blacks here are amazingly tolerant. They have kept their dignity better than the Afro-Americans, who perhaps are more aggressive because they are more powerless, despite their rights.'

Nadine believes that popular South African literature will come to be written largely in African languages. There are few blacks who, like Salman Rushdie, were brought up on English and who at the same time have another cultural perspective. The schools in South Africa have been poor, with the result that English-language writers have been read by few blacks or Indians.

'There should be anthologies published for the young. COSAW (the writers' union) has made the mistake of printing whole collections of poems where only one poem in ten was any good. Nobody buys them. The most important thing is to make people realise what fun reading can be. Then the rest will follow of its own accord.'

When COSAW was founded, it was for everyone who wanted to write and not only for those who had already been published. In a period when every political association was forbidden, COSAW became an umbrella under which people gathered to discuss politics. Before long they had to reduce the absurdly high membership numbers and exclude those who took no part in the writers' workshops.

'We gave them a number of words to write a story about, e.g. termite-hill, sleep, teacher, doctor, goat, smoke, bricks, twins. This resulted in short tales which they read aloud to each other. Sometimes they were silent and gripped, for they recognised themselves; sometimes they laughed so much that they broke the chairs.'

Nadine Gordimer's *None to Accompany Me*

In *None to Accompany Me*, the central character is called, with rather obvious symbolism, Vera Stark. Some readers will find her irritating. She is wracked with guilt because she is white, but she has sufficient insight to feel ashamed of her guilt, which in a country like South Africa after all is just a white person's luxury.

The novel is set 'in that year when the old way of life came to an end', three years after *My Son's Story*, and about a year before the free elections. Political and personal destinies are interwoven. Those who had fled the country are returning, most of them are without a job, and they are being forced to settle on land whose ownership is disputed. Some are being taken on by anti-apartheid organisations and are sleeping in apartments whose owners have left. The leaders of the ANC have come back from France, the Soviet Union and Libya, and their children speak none of the languages of Africa. They are setting up committees and negotiating with the government. They are educating the uneducated for trades that no longer exist. Relations between those who stayed on and those who fled are wary, occasionally strained.

'I read the proofs and move in and out of the novel, for those who have returned keep turning up at the house in Parktown West, saying their hellos and smiling, with an unspoken question in their eyes. Someone stays overnight, then moves on. People are phoning all over the place, to townships and committees, to Human Resource Centres and other places with Human as the first word in their name.

'Rebecca opens the door with a yellow watering-can in her hand, and her face lights up when she sees that it's Ronnie Kasrils, long South Africa's most wanted "villain", but, since the election, Deputy Defence Minister. And one morning F is standing there, smiling sheepishly and asking humbly for a handout. Once he was an occasional activist; now he is a secret drinker, a self-flagellant – and a metaphor for the frightening unpredictability of existence.'

In *None to Accompany Me* we meet two couples. Both consist of a strong woman and a man who has retreated into her shadow. The lawyer Vera Stark has long been committed to the cause of freedom. Her husband Bennet's role has been to attend to the business matters that provide the family with a good living. Sibongila and Didymus Maqoma have spent years in prison and exile. Sibongila has been allotted an important role by the incoming government. Her husband Didymus, as a former hero, has been forced to give his consent.

Vera is tormented by the weight of Bennet's love, which remains the same, without taking in everything that has happened around them: the births of children, the disappearance of friends, the deaths of parents, a whole country in upheaval. He is besotted with her, and for many years she has felt an intense love for him.

But his constant assertion that he cannot exist for a minute without her begins to feel like an imposition. His love has failed to move on, Vera complains to her son. And to her daughter: 'I can't live with someone who can't live without me.' There is both resignation and coldness in that remark. The distressing thing is that Vera feels his devotion to be demanding, a form of self-pity or self-importance which excludes other people.

Vera wants someone who is committed to what she thinks is important. Whoever loves her must also love what she does. She finds in work a defiant independence which she has perhaps experienced earlier in her erotic life. In becoming free she has at the same time locked herself out from most of what other people want their freedom for.

Vera proceeds on her lonely path towards a chilly truth, with a profane, desperate hope in her heart of hearts that the death of the old regime will make it possible for her to bring her old personal life to a close. But she knows that the country's needs and her own are not the same. Or is she – Vera, Nadine – trying to imply that the end of the longstanding public lie may be the beginning of the private truth?

In the end, Vera persuades herself that only without Bennet can she become a genuine and independent human being. She suffers pangs of conscience because he, in his uninvolved innocence, cannot understand her rebellion. But, in these late years, her foremost responsibility is to the liberation struggle and her own sense of self.

But perhaps Vera has always been looking for a kind of solitariness, a lack of dependency. 'None to accompany me on this path: Nightfall in Autumn', goes the haiku which gives her novel its title. It is this solitariness in the midst of her community activism, her work for victims of persecution, which is the paradox in Vera's life. She is looking for a combat-free zone on a battlefield. This makes her more complex than engaging. Is she freeing herself from the nasty old world only to simultaneously repudiate love, family, the loyalties of everyday life?

Politics closes in on non-political people like a sea of mud they find it hard to move around in. Vera claims to detest power, since her own people have abused it, but her black friends assure her that what she is doing is giving our people power: 'our' meaning the blacks. In her comradeship with those who are risking their lives Vera becomes closer to her black colleagues than she does to Bennet. She survives an assassination attempt, but her friend Oupa dies slowly and painfully as a result of it.

Politics gives rise to ethical conflicts. Didymus was once forced to work in a camp for informers against, and traitors to, the movement. Terrible things took place and he succeeded in escaping from the camp. One problem that concerns both himself and Vera is how to keep one's own hands clean while working against a dirty regime which does not shrink from using any means at its disposal.

It is Nadine Gordimer's strength that she engages with bold and dangerous questions and gives them form without offering a ready answer. One question is: Does freedom consist in losing the past bit by bit?

Nadine knows what she is doing as a writer, and what she is not doing. There is something in the middle that she can't define, and she knows that too.

In this novel she is gripped once again by what history makes of certain people; both those who side with history and those who try to forget it. And then there is always someone who cannot afford to remember, and some who are incapable of forgetting, however much they want to.

Nadine Gordimer and the Afrikaner

AMPIE COETZEE

In the past, before the beginning of the beginning of the end for apartheid we used to be very sensitive about what other people thought of us, the Afrikaners. Especially what the English speakers thought about us; and particularly what English writers said. But now one realises that identity – ethnic identity – although it exists it is not an absolute. Now that, it seems, the concept 'Afrikaner' – through the inquisitions of the Truth and Reconciliation Commission – finally may have become a signifier for something evil; as Antjie Krog's dedication in her indictment *Country of My Skull* confirms: 'for every victim who had an Afrikaner surname on her lips'. Now that one's sensitivity is questioned, one is tempted to recall that sensitivity.

I remember reading Nadine's description of the Afrikaner family, the De Beers, in *The Conservationist*. These Boers are, of course, seen through the eyes of the main character, Mehring. But nevertheless.

The entourage of Boere visits Mehring on a Sunday afternoon: a whole delegation: '. . . the whole family expects to go along if there's an outing of any kind on a Sunday afternoon' (Penguin Books, 1975, pp. 50-52). Then *they* are described, in a style close to ridicule: Old De Beer and young De Beer and young Mrs De Beer, a child, and a girl looking like young Mrs De Beer. They all stand behind old De Beer, they hide behind him. They don't speak, the child clings to 'her mother's thick knees-together legs'. The patriarch is the spokesperson, he with the thick body, and bunch of balls '. . . to wear your manhood, fatherhood like that, eh, stud and authority'. *Their* children are often beautiful, but what happens to them, the girls for instance, when they grow up? 'Vacant turnips . . . To go into one of those women must be like using the fleshy succulent plants men in the Foreign Legion have to resort to.'

The 'bywoners' in the old Afrikaans farm novel were often described in similar manner – although not quite that basic!

At the time this seemed to us typical stereotypes of the Boer, written by someone without empathy for 'them'. But who could criticise that? In the seventies the Afrikaner Nationalists had divided the country, were resisting decolonisation, were instituting racism. And, of course, whether you had anything to do with that or not, whether you were nine years old when they began their apartheid – you were still 'one of them'. But not only did they humiliate and oppress black people, they also practised thought – and creativity – control, especially through the Publications Control Board; and writers – also white writers – became vulnerable. On the 11th of July 1979 they banned Nadine's *Burger's Daughter*.

In the mean time three of us, academics attached to the Department of Afrikaans at the University of the Witwatersrand (John Miles, Ernst Lindenberg and myself) had organised a protest meeting to vent our anger at the banning of *Kennis van die Aand* by André P Brink in 1974. When Brink's publisher refused to publish his next novel, *'n Oomblik in die Wind*, the following year, we decided to start *samizdat* publishing; publishing clandestinely and distributing through mail order. Brink's novel was the first book of our venture, Taurus. We gave writers the assurance that we would publish any manuscript of value without any form of pre-censorship.

Nadine had heard about us. We made lots of noise. I suppose the fact that one of 'our people' had been banned opened our eyes and compelled us to act. She approached us to publish a document on the history of the banning of her book. *What Happened to Burger's Daughter or How South African Censorship Works* was published, in a limited edition, in 1980. Thereafter we published jointly with her South African publishers, first Ravan Press and then David Philip, *July's People* (1981), and then *Something Out There* (1984), *The Essential Gesture* (1988), and *My Son's Story* (1990). She wanted to be associated with our active protest. To us it was an essential gesture: support from a writer and intellectual activist of her standing could only strengthen our little attempts at subversion.

Nadine and I became friends. Perhaps I was the first Afrikaner she really knew? Perhaps the first she trusted?

But she had experience of some other Afrikaners, and I had the opportunity of observing her in the midst of the real 'boere' – on their farms. Her husband Reinhold had a passion for hunting wild geese and guinea fowl. He is a gentleman hunter – and an excellent shot. He had heard that I also hunted sometimes; and invited me to go with them on an outing to a farm somewhere in the old Transvaal, where he had excellent relations with the Afrikaner farmers. They were flattered to have 'Oom Reinie' shooting a 'kolgans' or 'tarentaal' whenever he wanted, in season.

My shooting was bad that day, probably because I had no experience of shooting Egyptian geese in flight. When we were hunting for guinea fowl I said to Reinie, jokingly, that we Boere don't wait for birds to fly away: it's easier to shoot them while they are still running! We don't believe in fair play! He was not amused. I shot no guinea fowl.

Afterwards we had drinks with the boere; but Nadine spoke very little. She sat quietly: a tiny figure in a corner, observing and listening. I know she loved the veld and the countryside – but what she really felt about these people one has to surmise, or attempt to interpret where they figure in her books.

After I left Johannesburg we lost contact, although our left-leaning sympathies remained intact. When she received the Nobel Prize for Literature I received a gift on congratulating her, with a note attached (dated 16.1.92). It was a book on the life of Georg Lukács by Arpad Kadarkay; a wonderful book, and with it she said: '. . . you are the only friend I know who would share that interest to the extent of wanting to read this long work'.

Then our Democracy came, and freedom from political oppression, and, ultimately, of racial discrimination. But with it the Truth and Reconciliation Commission and its revelation of atrocities; many – the most? – committed by Afrikaners who believed that their government was right, although they had been warned by writers, and yes, by their own Afrikaans writers, of the injustices of that government.

When her novel *The House Gun* was launched in Cape Town some time at the beginning of 1998, I had to see her. For a few brief minutes we could talk. So much had happened, what was there to say? There was, however, time for her to voice her one concern then.

With her characteristic intensity she said that she was very upset about the terrible things being said, by implication, about 'all Afrikaners' through the testimonies at the TRC. In some manner she felt a balance had to be restored. You know, Ampie: they aren't all evil!

Even though we should avoid thinking ethnically; nevertheless, thank you, Nadine.

Nadine Gordimer
and South African Politics

ANTHONY SAMPSON

Any future historian of South African politics over the four decades of apartheid will find it hard to do without the novels and writings of Nadine Gordimer. She has never been a political novelist in the obvious sense: her books have always revolved round very individual people interacting in intensely domestic situations behind private doors. But her writing career coincided almost exactly with the rise and fall of apartheid; and over that forty years the challenges and storms of the growing political crisis loomed darker and closer outside those doors. Her presented moral choices lit up her characters like lightning, throwing sudden shafts of light on the shadows. And they also presented precious insights into the human side of the political struggle, giving a much subtler social background than the broad generalisations of political scientists and historians, and reflecting the crucial stages of the darkening political scene.

I have always seen South Africa partly through those flashes of light. When I first met Nadine in Johannesburg in 1951 she had just written her first novel *The Lying Days* where black life was still in the background; but over the next years she came much closer to the vibrant world of African writers and politicians, first through her friend Es'kia Mphahlele and then through the *Drum* writers to whom I could introduce her: like Henry Nxumalo, Can Themba, Nat Nakasa, Todd Matshikiza, Bloke Modisane. She could convey better than anyone the spiky frontiers between the white and black worlds – whether in her novel *The World of Strangers* in 1958 or her short story *Which New Era Would That Be* – with none of the sentimentality or paternalism which afflicted so many white liberals at the time. But she also vividly conveyed the buoyant optimism and creativity of Soweto and Sophiatown – the world in which the young Mandela moved – of which most white politicians and commentators were completely unaware.

It was her individual friendships and loyalties which led her into political stories, rather than theories and preconceptions. During the long-drawn-out Treason Trials of the late fifties she came to know and admire Albert Luthuli, the President of the ANC, who briefly stayed in her house when she was writing a long profile of him. When the Sharpeville massacre of 1960 was followed by mass protests and mass arrests, Nadine's friend Bettie du Toit was taken to jail; and for the first time she abandoned her strict regime as a morning writer, to take care of Bettie and other prisoners. When Mandela and his colleagues were prosecuted in the Rivonia trial she became friendly with their defence lawyers, particularly George Bizos, who has been close to Nadine ever since, and Bram Fischer who would later become the subject of her book *Burger's Daughter* – a favourite novel of Mandela.

In the grim years after 1964, when all overt black political expression was suppressed, Nadine's role as a writer became more lonely, while her ability to reflect the changing mood became still more valuable. She had always refused to emigrate despite her hatred for the regime, while her husband Reinhold, who had already escaped once from Nazi Germany, was painfully aware of the symptoms of tyranny. Nadine had many friends in America and Europe and loved the luxuriant culture of the South of France – whose contrast with the growing harshness of South Africa is so marvellously described in *Burger's Daughter*. But she had seen how other *émigré* writers had dried up without the inspiration of their home soil; and she knew that her creativity depended on her roots within South Africa. She stuck it out, with a diminishing group of white friends and with more obstacles on the road to blacks. But when the militancy of Black Consciousness discouraged many white writers from building bridges Nadine still kept her lines open, with her rare ability to encourage and exchange advice, as a patron without any patronising instinct.

The bleakness of those years was vividly reflected in her novel

July's People in 1979, where a white family seeks refuge from a black revolution. But Nadine always retained a basic optimism about the African instinct for survival, and adaptability, which came through in her light-hearted picaresque novel *A Sport of Nature* in 1987 whose heroine Hillela roves through Africa and ends up prophetically in the victory celebrations of a black government in South Africa.

The release of Mandela in 1990 suddenly brought that fantasy into a possible reality; and it also marked Nadine's release from her isolation. When the news came through, when I was staying with Nadine, she quickly wrote an article for newspapers round the world which eloquently described that sense of liberation. Mandela himself, as he wrote in jail to a friend, had been deeply grateful to Nadine for helping to keep his struggle in the world's eye; when I saw him a week after leaving jail he insisted: 'I must see Nadine.' Their two paths came closer as the barriers broke down, and they expressed different aspects of the liberated South Africa. After Nadine had won a Nobel Prize in 1991, he invited her to join his own party to Oslo where he uneasily shared his own Nobel Prize with De Klerk, wryly observed by Nadine. At his last election rally in Johannesburg she was a favoured guest below the podium; and since becoming President Mandela has treated Nadine as a trusted friend.

'What to write about after apartheid?' Nadine like other South African writers faces the stock question. It is hardly a problem for someone who has always been primarily concerned with the human condition: and South Africans still face the special opportunities and dangers of a uniquely multiracial society, and further problems of violence and alienation – which her last novel *The House Gun* describes against the background of more subtle and complex relationships across the rainbow.

Her extraordinary consistency and sensitivity through the apartheid years has given her a precious continuity through the country's discontinous history, maintaining a golden threat of integrity through all the brutality and hysteria of that time: she kept her head through the 'collective madness' as she called it, and distilled her sanity into her novels. Like Mandela on the political front, she provides a crucial link between past and future, through which the New South Africa can see its problems more clearly in a long perspective.

Nadine Gordimer
at Seventy-five

LEWIS NKOSI

If we begin at the beginning as Beckett's narrator advises: we will begin essentially with the body, at least with the face. Every time I think of Nadine Gordimer as a young writer in the opening years of the 1950s emerging, improbably, from the numbing somnolence of the white suburb to assume, gradually, the status of a national symbol, I return again and again to that face as it invariably appeared to us in private and on the jackets of her books. It is a small face with the chiselled features of a classical model, a face not so much calm or peaceful as confoundingly tormented and tormenting: the eyes are unvaryingly alert, watchful, almost discourteous in their intentness, and finally unbelieving. It is a beautiful face in a head which is fixed on a long elegant neck with a strong nose which seems already to be scenting trouble. In the photographs which appear on the covers of her books the expression is disconcertingly prim, even frigid, reflecting a sharp intelligence which is determined to leave nothing to chance. In private, at a party, a kind of fractious wintry smile fleets across the mouth, all the more welcome for the relief it brings to the interminably cold rigour of that face.

Nineteen years ago Diana Loercher of *The Christian Science Monitor* produced a profile of Nadine Gordimer whose main traits have changed little over the years: 'A tiny woman,' she wrote, 'with the carefully cultivated fierceness of the fragile found in Joan Didion and Oriana Fallaci, she is a commanding, even a theatrical, presence. Her features are sharp, her face etched with lines of humour and indignation.' Phenomenally, freakishly, the purity of line in her face is matched only by the stylish purity of the prose as if one was the isomorph of the other. When I first met Nadine Gordimer it was the face, its sharply edged classic features, which seemed the very embodiment of the meticulous precision of the prose, born of what she herself has referred to as 'an acute sensibility'. It was as the best critic of her own work when she described her style as formed by an 'acute sensitivity . . . I mean the acuteness of catching nuance in behaviour.'

My own introduction to Nadine Gordimer's fiction occurred with a contradictory double movement of South African history of the 1950s, when government attempts to regulate every aspect of our lives was being met by increased defiance, and the private and public domains came to seem inexcusably entangled. Paradoxically, increased efforts to keep the races apart produced among us, the young, an accentuated desire to breach every apartheid wall. Thus, when we met young social rebels from the white suburb we tended to romanticise life on the edge – that is to say township life – as beyond the capacity of any white citizen to imagine which, as to be expected, provoked the desire among white youth to penetrate the township. It was Gordimer's attempts to imagine this life which was both captivating and perplexing. But in exchange of recitals of shebeen life, gang warfare, political strife, murder and rape, Gordimer suddenly appeared on our social horizon with a fresh consignment of family secrets about the white suburb, written in assiduously polished prose, which no white writer before had offered us; certainly not Alan Paton in *Cry, The Beloved Country*, whose vision was paradoxically restricted by its own epic pretensions.

While at school I had gorged myself on the classics of nineteenth-century realist fiction. Of our local South African writers Pauline and her representations of the stunted arid lives of *The Little Karroo*, was my favourite. Of Gordimer I knew but very little beyond the fact of her existence. That I came to learn more was through Janet Jaff, then a seventeen-year-old student at the University of the Witwatersrand, a precociously well-read Jewish girl with whom I fell madly in love. Janet and I had quickly become friends after a fortuitous meeting at one of those clandestine mixed black-and-

103

white parties common in the fifties, this one thrown by Frances Suzman (Helen Suzman's daughter), though I forget now what the pretext was. The late Nat Nakasa and I were driven by wayward anarchic impulses which, had we remained in the country long enough, I am sure would have pushed us to some quite unforeseeable end. That evening, as I recall, Nat had crept into Helen's bedroom in order to find out, as he put it 'how the other half slept'. Later, we discovered Nat quietly asleep under the bed from where, with Janet's assistance, I extracted him. Janet and I talked a great deal that night about literature. Subsequently, we arranged to meet for lunch at the *Drum* office, presumably to continue this discussion, and she it was during that lunch who enthused endlessly about Gordimer's fiction until I was persuaded.

As a young black South African learning to write, I began to read Gordimer's stories, then the novel *The Lying Days*, with immense pleasure and surprise. Here was an 'acute sensibility' on display, matched only by stylistic control and precision which to this day still rings many changes. Later, she would refer almost apologetically to this fine filigree of prose: 'I couldn't have gone on writing quite like that. It was a conscious change . . . because the vehicle was too delicate to carry what I had to say.' That, of course, is partly the trouble with the later Gordimer. But she did say in that same interview: 'My struggle has been not to lose precision and intuitiveness and a certain delicacy even though dealing with harsh themes.' In pursuit of the grander themes of the South African revolution the precision has sometimes appeared to split off from her fine intuitive power. At the time when I first read her all I could think was: here, indeed, was 'the voice of the world that speaks from its cage'.

Later we met and we became friends. Once I heard her speak at Wits on South African fiction. Commenting on Paton's second novel, *Too Late the Phalarope*, she criticised the novel's moral viewpoint as 'off-centre' because it was not lust it condemned but the awfulness of the object of that lust. Gordimer was right, of course; her own critical intelligence has rarely been 'off-centre'. Only sometimes. Another time she invited me to lunch to which I brought along Nat Nakasa, who was like a young brother to me, and Nat played his township card to great effect. Gordimer has written amusingly about the incident. After leaving the country we continued to meet, frequently it was in London when one of her books was being published. At the beginning of the 1960s she came to give a lecture at Harvard's Radcliffe College and we were invited to dinner at the home of the revered American critic Edmund Wilson, who astonished us by his erudition. Before he passed out at table his discourse ranged widely from Russian, European, Australian and Haitian negritude poets. Later, we went to hear Miriam Makeba who was appearing nightly at Storyville. When she joined our table during the break it was like a miniature South African mixed party of the 1950s. During one stay in London I remember arriving at a party at Anthony Sampson's when *Playboy* magazine was being passed around in the crowded room. The buzz of interest was not the infamous centrefold but an article on the new generation of black South African poets Gordimer had recently published, accompanied by a selection from the work of some of these poets. So, in no time at all, Gordimer and I were on the floor, with *Playboy* magazine spread in front of us. Those days she always seemed to arrive from South Africa like a thief in the night, bearing news of activities from the cultural front. In the middle of the 1980s, when I was teaching at the University of Zambia, we met at a dinner in the residence of the American ambassador to Lusaka, a personal friend of Nadine Gordimer's. I took this opportunity to invite her to speak to our students, who were prescribed one of her texts, at the very unsocial hour of eight in the morning. She drew a huge grateful audience of students and faculty.

As we celebrate her seventy-fifth birthday I cannot think of Nadine Gordimer as what is called an 'old lady'. Her mind is at its most agile, always so creatively engaged that we can sympathise with the foreign interviewer's hyperbole who wrote: 'Her intense concentration smolders, and seems to burn a hole through my notebook.' The face had been young once, of course; but even in old age it is still entrancing in the deliberately exact articulation of its features; at social gatherings, its expression of a deeply engrossed concentration, is what I chiefly remember about Nadine Gordimer long after I had left South Africa.

On the eve of my departure from the country for what was supposed to be permanent exile a gigantic farewell party was held for me somewhere in the northern suburbs of Johannesburg in the stately home of the scion of one of the oldest South African families: a venue far enough, we had thought, from the prying eyes of the ubiquitous police patrols. From many walks of life and from different political parties that made up the extra-parliamentary opposition to the apartheid regime, friends turned up to wish me well; they included members of the ANC, liberals, communists, writers and musicians, and members of the professions. Although it is now nearly forty years since, I still distinctly remember that party as if it was only yesterday, how during this maelstrom of socialising Nadine Gordimer was standing quietly by the door to one of the rooms, perfectly calm, perfectly still; but this stillness was not blankness; beneath the calm exterior there was on her face an expression of rapt attention to what was going on around her, an expression I had seen many times before of a curiosity of almost startling voracity. Gordimer was looking, studying, observing other faces; people got drunk, people danced, cuddled, knotted into gossiping groups; and unperturbed, Gordimer remained standing by the door, watching, studying, observing. Later during the evening there was a police raid which was deftly handled by Joe Slovo, one of the lawyers present; we blacks were breaking the law after all by consuming what was then called 'European alcohol', but the host was equally guilty of illegally supplying it. In addition, there were racially mixed couples wandering drunkenly around the extensive grounds that resembled a 'Deer Park'. To say the very least, this was Gordimer territory; the mixing across the colour-line, the subterranean confrontation between the white suburb and the black township, only to be interrupted by an untimely police raid. 'I've written about the borderland,' she had told Studs Terkel, 'the kind of frontier where black and white do meet, to a certain extent, and more or less as equals, though you can never be equal in an unequal society.'

Later, when as a teacher and critic I began to read Gordimer's fiction for more serious purposes, I gradually began to see how much of it was based on close observation, on the precise, even fastidious, transcription of the minutiae of the everyday as well as the contingent. Indeed, she is a collector of contingencies out of which grow unexpected plots. In Gordimer's fiction even the chance appearance of an insect can trigger off a tiny seismic shift in the psyche which may be a prelude to emotional catastrophe so

106

effectively demonstrated in her early short story 'The Soft Voice of the Serpent': 'One day a big locust whirred dryly past her head, and she jumped up with a cry, scattering her sewing things.' In that famous denouement to the story the false identification between a crippled husband and a crippled locust is shattered by the sudden flight of the insect. 'They had forgotten that locusts can fly.'

One thing is clear. Gordimer's insects are not remotely like Kafka's insects which, from the very beginning, are already endowed with the aura of symbolic meaning; on the contrary, it is Gordimer's careful accumulation of detail which restores to the trifle, when set among other trifling details, its ponderance and symbolic weight, and finally has the power to startle. After the mention of some small incident, in itself unimportant and usually never much fussed over, we usually know we are in for very nerve-racking internal voyages. And just as one is fascinated by the configurations of the novelist's facial expressions, intense, rumi-native or suddenly splitting up into a smile, Gordimer is herself the most supreme physiognomist of modern realist fiction: 'The pretty, narrow, self-possessed face, which might have been rather frightening and haughty towards an old lady, dropped its look of aloof reserve, as if the girl had been unconscious of it, and opened into a smile of such warm pleasure and charm that the old lady was quite bewildered.' ('A Bit of Young Life')

Critics like to refer to the posture Kafka's characters often assume and the significance such posture – a head bent over the breast – can have for our interpretation. In Gordimer's stories it is often the face, and what the face conceals rather than shows, which provides a fetishistic lure to an internal drama that is taking place. A smile in Gordimer's stories is likely to open up to some private, carefully camouflaged hell or, at the very least, to some awkward revelations. 'In "A Bit of Young Life" the smile is so insistently dwelled upon that our suspicion grows that something lies behind that smile; and this is soon confirmed: "But suddenly he saw that the smile was merely something done with her face, and that, really, she was about to cry. It was incredible –" The face is the sleeve where Gordimer characters usually wear out their hearts.' These fleeting facial expressions are hardly to be passed over as stop-gap realistic descriptions, mere filters in the narrative. Stories like 'Friday's Footprint' provide sufficient evidence of what such expressions may presage: 'There was something about Johnny, his mouth slightly open, the glimpse of saliva gleaming on his teeth, his head thrown back and his eyes narrowed while his body snaked on stooping legs and nimble feet, that couldn't be ignored.' In one of her stories, 'The Rain Queen', set in the Congo, the young narrator describes an Italian woman with 'her pile of dark hair tinted a strange tarnished marmalade colour that showed up the pallor of her skin – all [was] arranged like a still-life.' During a game of squash the narrator notices that the face of the Swede goes all 'red and blotchy'; and when Marco the Italian pants he grins, 'showing white teeth and one that was repaired with gold.' The young girl concludes: 'It seemed to me that all adults were flawed in some way.' In South Africa, whose white society was so inflexibly resolved against self-examination, observing and detailing the flaws of this society, seemed then Gordimer's most rewarding vocation. As the diagnostician of the white South African psyche under pressure she has no equal. When discussing the wonderful South African climate, she had told Studs Terkel: 'There are people who live only on that level. Who don't come off it; who never look around; who happen to be white, and so don't feel. They only get the advantages – the so-called advantages – of the colour bar and nothing else.'

Significantly, these few examples are drawn from the earlier fiction, before Gordimer abandoned what had seemed to be her main project so spectacularly displayed in the early story 'Is There Nowhere Else Where We Can Meet?' or in that magnificently condensed, briefly encapsulated inquest into racial pathology, 'The Train from Rhodesia': then her concerns seemed to be the articulation of the psychic damage incurred by the white South African subject in its monopoly exercise of power which in turn requires a constant, wearying vigilance against any attempts to snatch it away by the black majority. Increasingly, in her later fiction, as Gordimer moves gradually to assume the mantle of poet laureate of the South African resistance, a role sometimes exorbitantly imposed upon her by the kind of critical reception her work attracts from foreign publications, she is now frequently tempted into the uncharted waters of the pullulating life of the black township.

Quite frankly, I think she has been set up by foreign critics and she has bought into their sales pitch. In a 1990 collection of interviews one reads in the introduction: 'She clarifies to her interviewers that she is a radical, not a liberal.' This will come as a surprise to some of us. Again we learn that: 'From early on, she wished to disassociate herself from liberals.' Paradoxically, it was precisely out of her liberal humanism that she produced her most effective work. In her later work even the swarming details of the domestic interiors of a township household, crowded into the first pages of 'A City of the Dead', can be read more like a carefully researched report prepared for Amnesty International than her earlier intuitive insights: 'The house provides the sub-economic township planner's usual two rooms and kitchen with a little yard at the back, into which his maquette figures of the ideal family unit of four fitted neatly. Like most houses in the street, it has been arranged inside and out to hold the number of people the ingenuity of necessity provides for.' The mimicry of the township voice, so egregiously spurious, is often one unhappy result of Gordimer's attempts to appropriate a social experience of which she is ignorant. In 1972 she had told Stephen Gray and Phil du Plessis: 'When there are certain experiences that are outside your potential, that are inconceivable and could never happen to you, then your subject matter is restricted to some extent; and it's restricted in this country with its colour bar more than in any other. White writers are cut off from the proletariat. There is no getting away from it.'

By 1989 when we were jointly invited to appear before a television audience in Amsterdam she was telling Adriaan van Dis, the interviewer, that she had no problem representing township life. In an angry exchange Gordimer countered with a long explanation about the vastly superior, imaginative reach writers enjoy, citing for her example Joyce's handling of Mary Bloom's menstruation episode in *Ulysses*. She concluded her riposte by announcing: 'I'll let you know that I have in fact visited the township and have even spent a night there.' I started to laugh at this. What Gordimer's example slides over is the fact that whereas all bodies, black and white, menstruate the same way, or more or less, the collective lives of segregated communities sometimes beat to a different drum.

In an introduction to a collection of essays published in 1993 under the title *The Later Fiction of Nadine Gordimer*, Bruce King writes that: 'Her recent fiction has evolved so rapidly in new directions that there is considerable puzzlement about what she is doing and why. Many readers feel her later fiction has a prominent place among the classics of our time; others do not like it or became lost along the way.' I confess to be among the latter readers. It is no secret that I am one of those who have expressed reservations about her later fiction. The status so often claimed for Nadine as some Diva of South African history, able to produce a novel with the cut and fit for every twist of South African politics, has an alienating effect that is hard to describe. At her level of maturity it is of course inconceivable that Gordimer can produce an entirely failed piece of work; but the intricate rococo style of her later fiction, with its too many ellipses and syntactic torsions, is too self-consciously laboured and yet along the way seems to have lost that 'emotional genius' once described by *The Village Voice* as 'so palpable one experiences it like a finger pressing steadily upon the prose.'

In some uncanny fashion, without even being directly aware of it, I find that my own friendship with Nadine Gordimer has undergone subtle changes over the years almost parallel to her evolving writing practice. In my jokey moods I like to put this down to something perilously close to the sort of reaction in reverse that whites sometimes display when they encounter a literate native whom they suspect of laying claim to some dubious 'Western' sophistication, and quite frankly, my negative response to her later work has probably been mildly corrosive to what was once a warm relationship. Neither of us has openly admitted to this subtle transformation. My devotion to Gordimer's earlier fiction in direct proportion to my distrust and suspicion about her later productions probably irritates her just as much. But what South African, black or white, cannot be grateful for Nadine Gordimer's immense contribution to South African life and literature, for her unfailing generosity and support for black writing.

Letter to Nadine

GÜNTER GRASS

Lübeck, 7 May 1998

Dearest Nadine

I have to write to you in my own language, hoping at the same time that your husband will translate for you every word of the outflow of enthusiasm and admiration which your novel, *The House Gun*, evoked in me.

What a daring theme. None the less, you succeeded in shaping, with inexorable precision: the changes of all acting persons; the remoteness and the closeness of the married couple; the isolation of the perpetrator as a personal and social process. As far as the end of the story is concerned, the not so serious problem is apparently pitilessly exposed, yet the inexplicable, the 'dark rest' remains unlit by explanations.

Besides, I admire the way in which you succeed in sketching the development of the South African society after the end of apartheid. Thrifty accents, yet clear indicators that this process, so well and broadly elaborated by you, limited to a few characters, none the less engages the whole society.

Just one question lingers. I therefore ask you: why do the father, mother and son speak rather soberly and without telling uniqueness, and why, on the other hand, is the lawyer provided with a manner of speaking expressing this uniqueness?

This, of course, is just a side aspect, and in the process of translation these telling nuances might have been lost.

I am stuck deep in manuscript work, yet I want to participate in three or four activities during the election campaign of next autumn. After an April spoilt by too much rain, May now is also draped in grey. Yet – and perhaps it is out of defiance – our fruit garden is blossoming.

Be greeted and embraced

Yours

Günter Grass

A Slip of a Girl

GUY BUTLER

The invitation to congratulate Nadine Gordimer arrived when I was immersed in a complex nostalgia for the forties, fifties and sixties, induced by attempting to select the best poems I had written during those years for the eyes of Lawrence Wright, who is editing them.

1946. Half-way through my stint at Oxford, I was briefly back in South Africa, in Johannesburg. I sought out the company of Uys Krige, whom I'd met in Florence, hoping he would publish some of my poems in his bilingual journal *Vandag*. I was twenty-eight. I had dreams of becoming a writer. I had had a handful of poems published in university and army magazines. Uys Krige was putting an enormous amount of hard work into *Vandag* . . . mostly at parties, where, as one of the regulars said, 'Minerva and Mercury vied with Bacchus and Venus' for attention. Jack Cope talks of a 'blur of good fellowship among a crowd of enthusiasts'. Among them, bright and contained, was a slip of a girl called Nadine Gordimer. 'Watch her,' said Uys. 'A real talent.' (*Local Habitation*, p.142) She was twenty-three, I think.

Eglington, another ex-serviceman, played an important role as gatherer-together of writers and artists. I remember Nadine at one or two of these. We always talked about writing in South Africa.

As early as 1950 (in collaboration with Professor Greig) in an article *South African Literature in English*, 'I hailed the short stories of Herman Charles Bosman and Nadine Gordimer' (*Local Habitation*, p.101) as cause for hope.

I left teaching at Wits for Rhodes at the end of 1950, by which time I had already started making louder noises about the virtual

113

absence of South African writing in English in South African schools and universities. 'I played a leading part in setting up a conference, held from 10-12 July 1956 at Wits, of publishers, writers and teachers of English' to discuss this question (*Local Habitation*, p.170). For the stand I took I was attacked and pilloried by nearly everyone, except the head of the English Department of UCT, an Australian.

I think it was during this visit that my wife Jean and I were staying with her parents in Melrose with our adopted son Patrick, a toddler. We had Nadine to tea. I remember two scraps of conversation. First, about our curly headed Patrick: 'What a lovely Botticelli child!' Second, about the recent conference: 'Do you think that they (universities) will ever take South African writers seriously enough to prescribe them?' After the treatment I had just received, all I could report was that we were already trying to do so at Rhodes, but much against the grain of some members of staff.

During a subsequent visit to Johannesburg, she invited me to a *soirée* the like of which I had not experienced before. The slip of a girl had become a superb hostess in a wonderful house full of original Impressionist paintings, and the guests seemed mainly cultivated refugees or exiles from right-wing European regimes. There was an interlude for a Spanish dancer and singer, and I found a visiting American girl almost irresistible. The evening resulted in a poem called *Keeping a Distance*, the first and last sections of which I quote:

I

Over such comforts –
good food, good wine, a companionable room
lit gently
a dozen voices in various accents
conversing politely –
beat broken laments for intricate gardens
bell towers and squares in old-world cities
curtained in iron, raped by guns.

O lost Eden,
childhood before the deluge rose,
before the exile,
medievally far in time and place
you press as close
as these originals on the walls:
dandelion Degas dancer, an acid
Lautrec, a cool scene by Cézanne.

No exile, and yet
to capture trembling in webs of words
my childhood remote
among shrubs, birds, granite and storms
I must take all
as lightly and as tenderly as these
proud Spaniards, gentle Viennese
their childhood in forbidden cities.

What beauty, what virtue
flower in clean-kept distances!
Artists and exiles
disciplined by fate and choice
may learn how to master
their times by Time, their places by Space:
without strict distance, no clear vision:
Babel breaks from a voice too close.

V

Cold clocks will strike.
The guitar must go sleep on the wall.
It's easy to get fixed
in the acids of Lautrec.

So I hold back to keep
your listening form and face
in the pastels of Degas.
How could the dance go on?

Don't move, don't end
deliberate distancing;
keep out of time, avoid
starting a history,

permit each form, each face
apparently at ease
to relax for a space in Space:
with no future, with no past,

only a perfect present,
impersonal, perpetual
held by the discipline
of Paul Cézanne.

In the delicate shell of your hand
let the pearl of your world spin on.

I quote these passages not merely to evoke Nadine's social milieu at the time, but because as a writer she displays the talents which I ascribe to the masterly painters on the walls.

I can recall a conversation with her at her home in Frere Road, Parktown, some time in the sixties, in which she raised the ongoing question of 'which English'? Like myself, she received for comment pieces from aspirant writers in which there was no doubt about the authenticity of the experience but insufficient control of that apparently simple but devilishly difficult vehicle, the English sentence. I had nought for her comfort.

In 1969 she attended and read a portion of a current work at a conference in Grahamstown entitled 'South African Writing in English and its Place in School and University'. By this time the climate was changing, rapidly, and continues to do so. The more things change, the more they stay the same.

One of my greatest lifelong handicaps is the slowness with which I read. This may account for my preference for plays and poems to novels, of which I read very few, and am not qualified to speak of Nadine on the world stage. I did, however, in 1974 review *The Conservationist*, was very impressed by it, and was pleased to learn that it was a joint winner of the Booker Award. I ended my review (*EPH*, 23 November 1974):

> When a South African writer of the calibre, skill and integrity of Miss Gordimer produces a provocative parable such as this, and frames it in this way, it should be read with care, particularly in South Africa.
>
> One can contest many things, e.g. the notion that South Africa is 'Black' or 'White'; or that Africa 'asserts' this or that; but one ought to listen to what this articulate voice is saying about the nature and cost of belonging here, or anywhere.

Uys was right. The slip of a girl is now a Nobel Prize Winner, and academics the world over study and teach her as one of the major novelists of our time. Bravo!

POETRY FOR A WRITING LIFE

An Image From Beowulf
for Nadine Gordimer

SEAMUS HEANEY

Sootstreaks down the pointed granite, a hole
Blown in the slates, the rafters in the rain
Still smouldering:
         when I heard the word 'attack'
In St Columb's College, Derry, in nineteen fifty
Whatever, and probably because
The courthouse was the target, it left me winded.
From my boarder's dormer, I watched the big sky move
The way it would have moved the morning after
Savagery in Heorot, its reflection placid
In those waterlogged huge pawmarks Grendel left
Down the boreen to the marsh.
                      Beowulf
Was a closed book to me then, but something still
Made its break for the open, as giddy-headed
As clan-chiefs galloping the sandy paths
At dawn,
        in awe of the talon Beowulf tore off
And nailed to the gable underneath the eaves,
The sky still moving grandly . . .
                Every nail
And spur and claw-spike, every nail-curl
And hackle and barb on that heathen brute
Was like a steel prong in the morning dew.

Two Oblique Salutes to Nadine Gordimer

LIONEL ABRAHAMS

1

Praise Singer
to Nadine Gordimer

All the blood-polluted seas of history
and daily tides of sour dismaying news
that we dilute with sugared slimes of fashion
have not yet sluiced away Earth's loveliness.
Easy to find for praising is grandeur
of deserts, mountains, oceans, living forms,
the moon and constellations.
Cloudscapes and beetle-patterns, stones,
children at play who dance an undesigned
pavane can catch the breath.

But there's another kind of excellence,
not bestowed by Earth or chance or God,
but earned on purpose – then, rarely, attained
in acts and works of human hands and minds.
These the chancy justice of posthumous time
may well, or not, call to remembrance
and accord consensual praise.

But while the authors live, their present gifts
lie all too readily neglected, dully wasted
through our taste-corrupted ignorance
and hourly rubbish-cluttered time.
Or worse, we turn on them blind-folded with our vanity,
or deafened to them by our envy's noise.

Your own gifts have been nobly honoured,
yet there's one I think has not been sung
or sung enough:
                        I mean your passion to confess
your admiration for the mastered word,
the philharmonious prose you lift in praise
of late and living peers
who offer us soul sustenance, largesse
in art and vision, and their truths' defence
of humankind's humanity.

2

That Symmetry
(considered by the light of several conceits)

No human soul's a single seamless piece.
Dicotyledonous, the split each one betrays,
though it define our undivinity,
need not deny one one's identity.
Common morphology presents odd halves:
one plump with hopes and causes we   confess,
and then a shrivelled second pip, stained dark
where one secretes defensive enzymes –
doubts, defections, fears, disloyal dreams.

Your rarer conformation,
double-centred Sport of Nature,
occupies a symmetry of lobes,
each entire, disclosed, immaculate,
a balanced twofold wholeness –
but one spliced across a breech
I gauge as perilously stressed.

Yet your potent germ thrusts forth
its fold of leaves and spiking radicle
as though immune to mutual toxins
spewed from fiercely guarded spheres; –
as though the ichor of your limpid faith
(strict for art, as strict for righteous war)
pulsates all through a grafted circuitry of veins
to rinse away the rumoured venoms,
or, mixing with them, blend the antidote.

Nadine

SIPHO SEPAMLA

They saw her flitting about for butterflies
   Their eyes were on gold
They must have thought her kinky
   When her sights flew all over the veld

Now she celebrates life evermore
   In search of a vision
She's confirmed the sweetness of dreams
   In the many faces of her creation

Of her we say the mountain speaks
   truths showered like rain drops
Of her we say the lion speaks
   wisdom heard far and wide

We salute you lady of South Africa
And as they say grow till you winter
You whose feet could never be of clay
You whose heart is of steel

Two Poems

DENNIS BRUTUS

February Saturday

It is Saturday night over there
the summer smoulders down to shadow
the Saturday summer games are over
time to replay them, in success or failure
time to talk, to speculate, to dream:

flickers of hope, speculative murmurs
firefly in the dusk, trill like birdcalls
in the sudden twilight hush:

all human aspirations are valid
all can hum through the heart,
no pain, no desire, is trivial
when its urgent pang transfixes:

the young, energetic and ebullient,
the mature, mellowed in victory and defeat,
all reach beyond the darkening horizon
yearn to the crimson glimmer that holds
splendor and wonder and hope

Silence in the still warm room

Silence in the still warm room
stillness pressured from the silent street
snow-muffled, traffic deserted:
the self, in the stillness, poised,
a pivot around which nothing revolves
looks inward, finds itself in flight
from itself and the inexorable demand
for surrender to the ocean of selflessness:
this is what love is about:
and it resists, hugs fiercely
its self to itself: is doomed to loneliness
and still it cries out against aloneness.

From *The RDP Poems*

ARI SITAS

Unlike
> *the policy, these poems are*
>> *meant to be*
>>> *delivered.*

Black Mamba Rising

I

Walked

past Clairwood
and the back road
by the railway track
where the Local met
to change the world
and count who was alive

the building:
dirty-white as
dilapidated as it should have always been
the clothing sweatshop on the second floor
still, uncleaned windows from 1966
and the bare staircase

where we had to negotiate a wheelchair – three flights and a
twisted back
and a goat –
to cut its throat for protection
and eat it with the guys
the goat: still owns a stain
in the emptied hall
with its leaking lavatories

from the fire-alarm exit
the eye sees the only change:
a dozen women and their stalls by the
railway entrance:
one tomato, two orange and a piece of cloth

II

What happened to Qabula?

It is hard to get news, about Qabula.

The walk to the taxi rank, past Clairwood
to Mobeni might help:

asking his nephew, does not help.
He stares at you, and you can see the gun
on the inside of his leather-like, almost grey-jacket
surrounded by the guys who bleed the line from
Pondoland to the factory-gates
who serve the line, from the dagga plantations to Bambayi
taxi warriors who char the backs of Hiace scabs.

Tell the *umlungu* he says, that I know nothing.

I drop the right names – his father's from Port Shepstone
his uncle's who died of the virus in Umzumbe
his friends' who fought the zombie-keepers at Kokstad.
Sitas, he says, I used to know you
through your words
but we do not know you, now
Qabula is my father now, since my father died
and he has the say of our inheritance
he is finished with your nonsense.

I lie about a film and money and
possibilities!

Capetown, he says,
looking for a job, you will find him
in Pondoland this Christmas
Now go to Hell.

III

Spoke to Mattera and he said,
let's speak to Mzwakhe
and to Kunene
you heard, we need to do something about Qabula
he has had a stroke. Paralysed.
Holy Cross Hospital. Bitter. Angry.
Nise said, we need to do something about his wife
she is on the brink of despair.

I push the CD inside the machine
and there is Mbuli's voice declaring
peace on KwaZulu Natal; but the real
voice? Vodacom. cell-phones
Walkietalkies – Mzwakhe-man
you have been stealing sugar from our tea, man?
Redistributing cash from our democratic Banks?
We need cash for Pondoland, man. Could you help
at least for now man? No chance – they froze me up!

IV

Telephone wire.
My words faster than the people cutting it
off the phone-line, copper wire good for trade and craft!
My words make it, survival of the swiftest –
'Hello. U Mi,lo?
– Excuse me sir, I do not understand
U Mi,lo?
Your director, U Mi, man
You mean Mr Michael Sidumo Hlatshwayo!
Yebo.
He's busy. Phone again, next week
Can I leave a message?
I am afraid, I do not have a pen handy sir
To use a Zulu expression: Fakofu.

V

'Hello, ma'
quick word past the copper pliers
uNise, she's there?
No she's gone.
Where?
Dead.
What dead, are you crazy?
She was on hunger strike and died of complications
What hunger strike? I was with her yesterday!
We were all together, yesterday, sir, but today?
Why didn't she say to me she was on hunger strike?
Oh she left a note with your secretary sir.
Why was it not in the Press?
You tell me sir, you are the intellectual, after all.

VI

U Mi, man
quick word past another set of pliers.
Yebo, mfo.
We need money for a coffin and money to get to Qabula in
    Pondoland
We are frozen man.
There is an investigation
into 3 million unauthorised cash
I don't even have a salary for this month.
We only have a small budget for Tourism

VII

Hello, Sawubana, Dumelang
Welcome to Durban
We are here to please and smile
we can do poetry in your room
give you souvenirs of our smiles and scars
we can dress dashiki or leopard leather
to maskanda or mournful howls
show you our lovely teeth
our words can gumboot
our mambas rise or crawl at your wish

I will personally take you past Clairwood
where we used to meet and count
who was alive!
Love you all, love you all
– this is the graphic of the mamba
rising at St Anthony's, the mamba that lived
inside the songs, others risked it in the trees
that's me there – with the funny hat
and the toy sickle.

Childhood on Stilfontein Mine

INGRID DE KOK

Safest white childhood of the fifties
if your father didn't beat you.

Cricket pitch creasing the veld,
constructed by somebody's boys.

Wheeling your bike up the only hill
to mebos at the Greek café.

Salt, mustard, vinegar, pepper:
skipping on hot cement.

Waiting for the ice cream van
to ring its Saturday bell.

'Afrikaner, vrot banana:
rooi-nek, rooi-nek'.

Slimesdams: for safety's sake
forbidden to go near them.

Minedumps: for safety's sake
forbidden to play on them.

Men's compounds: for safety's sake
forbidden to hang about them.

Your Name

MORAKABE RAKS SEAKHOA

After the handsomeness of your brother,
Down from the heights of his making others merry,
Through to his Herculean arms that pre-empt us splitting
    asunder
What shall your name be?

Shall we name you after eve?
For you are about to arrive just before another storm, another
    war?
A different world that glorifies separateness over togetherness?
Where there is not even a moment's respite to wish your journey
    smoothness?
An expectancy that sorrows your mother's heart?

Shall we hope to call you nadine?
For in there lives hope far from feigned barrenness of
    parenthood?
Home to our everlasting togetherness, so when your hour of
    womanhood strikes,
Yours will be the strongest of spines?

Spreading out

LISA COMBRINCK

I am numb. He says I am numb with desire. He believes what he says. I am hungry but I cannot eat. He says that it is not food that I seek. This too he believes. I am numb from the aftermarks of too much pain, the aftermath of too many submissions, too few gains.

Maybe I am like the moon. Numb and cold. But unfortunately inherently seductive. Always beautiful, wounded yet beautiful. Always screwed senseless by the sun. We are too dumb to understand that our suffering makes us seductive, alluringly beautiful. No-one sees beauty in strength. It is our capacity for suffering that damns us. Our faces that remain mute, white-powdered masks, hiding our wrinkled wombs that have been pulled this way and that, torn apart, misshapened, anaesthetised.

No-one sees beauty in the brownness of my skin, the wanton wildness of my curly black hair. They see what they want to see. And their vision damns me. I am desperately chipping away the mask which they made for me. This is what the story is about. Freedom that comes from complete nakedness, when one has been clothed in shrouds for so long.

flowering

CHENJERAI HOVE

we were young once
our realms: mud and torn flowers,
             sometimes torn butterflies
               or fireflies in the dark night.
but as weave words, years later, on the page
memories of butterflies give us fireflies of words
reminding us:
             novels are only butterflies, flying,
             poems are eagles, roaming the sky.

time is a friendly bird
that refuses to perch,
with a flower in its beak.

A Meditation
for Nadine Gordimer's 75th birthday

C J DRIVER

Action is deceit; what one needs most of all
Is to sit still, to wait and to look –
One might even want to call it *Being* patient
If one wasn't so busy with the detail:
Four figures in a landscape; three poplars
Positioned in a quarry; two pied crows;
And Mohammed Ismael's general store
On a roadside in the middle of nowhere.

That's what novelists do. As Auden said,
Art makes nothing happen, so to be old
Becomes an advantage. One sees further;
Oh, the broad brushstroke, the sweep –
                                        well, call it
'History' if you really must, but it's more . . .
What makes this entirely this, and not that:
And one notes it down, unreservedly,
Telling lies to make imaginary truth.

And the people too, poor forked beings,
Whom one thinks one sees so clearly, until
They do something odd, as in eating apples,
And one's surprised, even though one made them.
What they should see is what one lets them see,
But then they see much further than one thought
And they add a sentence that's not one's own –
Almost, sometimes, at dictation speed.

And the desire for change? One has that too,
Though to confuse what is with what should be
Is dangerous romance, enemy of art,
And time will sort that out, quickly – or so
One has to hope, or else there's not much point
In all this striving, hours, and days, and months
And then years, and tens of years, piled up high
Like a builder's yard, all the bits and pieces

Which may one day make – who knows? – a palace.

My hands ache sometimes, and when I look up
From the keyboard even the wall is blurred.

Beyond Transitions

LESEGO RAMPOLOKENG

I
every tom dick a jericho wall
no ball bounce where it viagra fall
in a mist-pool of fears
a fistful of years
from here to the lenin plan

II
head to the moan & the rotten meat
in the stagnant street
live waters crumble
fallen from spring to crawl
no birth-toll
just death call-
up pregnant corpses from festering tummies
play-ketchup-with-blood-armies
(gory sport cinema
short glory enema)

III
now the black lash culls pink from patriot
we are open mouth & deep-throat
but who's hand-job-judas iscariot
for the baas-hole down south

IV
since paradise burnt down
there's no rubber in heaven
we drip-dry seventy times seven
                              forgive
suck the past's pustule to reinvent the anger
for mister slow bile

V
all praise to the human-hole
separates cream from clenched fist
leaves the other hand to the devil
with less skin to wear than history
now power's knob rides our poetry
to a mother-sies-father-pooh-catharsis
flesh stink where soul sink into paralysis

VI
'too many words running past too many heads too fast'
'give me a freudian line & a piece of the action
& none of that pre-fabricated subversion'

VII
the order is celebration lament transgression
celebration's in the control dungeon
locked in latex dreams
rocked by latent domination screams
revelation's an armageddon amen
a servitude affliction
the genesis WORD the first destruction act
the bark of the covenant
interstellar flight grounded in mud
fraternal spite sounded in blood
flush nothing plush squashed against whiteness
scratching the struggle itch
longing for black moments

VIII
we bake & break red inside promises
we bear the naked weight along groaning roads
to desolation's cities
our deliverance to mourning feasts
analysis burns to blabberashes
we missile up to re-globalisation
& torch the skies with pain enough to lick the lies
unfolding septic swinging up from barbaric thighs

IX
the bowl moves its bowels
the drums have grown breasts
we suck on silence
ripped from here to hell
stripped to a cell
brainswell we strum veins
hear strains of the salvation virus
rot floating off its tongues
buried in the throat
where we dig for birth-breath

X
mutation's blood-stream rises
& drowns palpitating memories
bursting out of brain-cells

XI
fly righteousness in the mind & conscience dies
no allegiance to caress we cross over to sole-sale-sacrifice
we bomb the edge to erase the core
put the debris centre-stage
nude-parade it as the art/heart
& kill with praise

XII
we're riding on HIS story's back
'dear god rein in the bleed to the tip of my pen'
schemespeak lift our sins to heaven in pigstock prayer
our crooked paths spread thrashing
across the bowed earth
we lay down more/law
& things contra-edict
(it's a fool moon smiles
when sky-juice drips)
we march out in nemesis dress
faces of the apocalypse
but press & the gore recedes
into celluloid decadence
now the rage is miracles
this age hyena geriatrics
profess innocence
holding up placentas
against rebirths

'love dispels the stench of death'

MBULELO VIZIKHUNGO MZAMANE

for chris and limpho

i was the moth
you were the light
our lives a macabre
dance with death
lived so close to earth
we could kiss worms
in those cold days of june
our sole source of warmth
heat radiated from
rocks and sods
we shared intense
interludes of guerrilla love
in a life blighted by
loss of loved ones
shed off like leaves in winter
gathered into compost heaps
to fertilise the future

our world was ravenous
ready to sight scandal
in a speck of dust
we swore then
to sink or swim
locked in tight embrace

we knew we were products
of a resilient culture of resistance
we knew we were beneficiaries
of the accumulated wisdom
of generations of creative fighters
raining rocks down the precipice
from the mountain of the night
upon the enemies below
who dwell on lush plains
appropriated from our forebears
with sticks that hiss death
cause carnage
and turn fields into
wastelands

sometimes you came on a starless night with
blistering winter winds
mountains casting shadows over you
the town's wary mongrels
too weary to keep vigil or
wag their tails in welcome   ·
we woke up next morning
our world again aglow
and the birds singing

    umdoko . . . umdoko
    amabele . . . amabele
    avuthiwe . . . avuthiwe
    kuru-kuru . . . kuru-kuru

then one night
the trees whispered
the winds took up the message
savannah grasslands
made secret pacts with the
sinqu, ligwa, limpopo, zambezi
mouths opened wide
the mountains swallowed you

i woke up cuddling shadows

there were times
lodged between your loins
you told me you loved peace
more than you feared war
you said:
'fly doves from my last resting place'
but they sent us minstrels of death
who said:
'we are the harbingers of death

look upon our mighty work and despair
we wage war on peace prosperity progress
we wield superior fire-power'

we made bed together that last time
when in your sleep you tossed and turned
muttering unprintable imprecations in latin
lying beside you in the after-glow of love
i watched the clouds disappear
serenity spread over your brow
we had a solution
as all-embracing as the land
while they continued along the path of
immolation and mutilation

you left me the weapon of memory

remembrance refurbishes recreates
like the spring rain
love purges nourishes sustains
love has the taste of grapefruit
and the melody of john coltrane

love dispels the stench of death

Empowerment

LEON DE KOCK

Rondborstig, cool, bruingebrand
full, meaty throat, flesh pouring out
the low-cut, on-the-spot erotica:
Ja, ek check hierdie Pretoria girls uit
ek smaak hulle hip-hop heupe
ek like hulle smul-lekker kurwes
ek lek aan my cappucino
hierdie girls het rondtes
soos die binnekant van my bek.

Ek slurp, ek sis, dis fokken warm
hier, in die nuwe Pretoria
in die Hatfield coffee bar
waar die klonkies buite krepeer
en die karre blink & tokkel
en ouens soos ek ons swaelbekke
slaak met koffie & bier
met boepe wat krink
binnekant wit hemde
vasgeknewel in suit-broeke
waar ons piele onrustig slap hang
wagtend, wetend-wagtend
op nuwe horings-horisonne
die fokken ingee
as daai vrou sug en ja sê.

Ek sit maar so rond
here, there, everywhere
met die reuk van seks
in my Hustler-brein
besig om connections op to shine
want business is kakpraat
en kakpraat is groot geld, hierdie dae

ons praat mos van eddercation
the golden panacea, soos ons sê
ons verkoop solutions vir illiteracy
packages with CD-ROM en quick-fix
redressal of disadvantaged heritage
ja, ons verkoop application met technology
dis mos onse motto daai
dis die kakpraat Nuwe RSA hierdie
and money makes the world go round
so what's new, ek sê?

Vandag sit ek maar so
ek check hierdie girls uit
netnou maak ek 'n oproep of twee
grease some palms, ek en my broertjies
in die empowerment game
ons dans mos deesdae saam
cha-cha-cha in black & white
ek en my swart broertjies, smooth, smooth
ons vaar uit in silwer BMWs
together we can make it happen
almal weet die rainbow is vol kak
maar die pot geld, my vriend
ai, daai pot geld, ou broer
hy lat wit en swart
sommer saam die toekoms invaar!

Two Poems

TATAMKHULU AFRIKA

I Heard A Land Cry

I heard a land cry
out in a far
realm of the night.
The thin moon lit
it; its lamentation was the wave's
rearing even as it died,
a stricken beast's
rising from its prints of blood,
pawing at the passing of the stars.

I heard a land cry
in the voice of a troglodyte,
heard it stumble with a tired step
over the cold stones,
heard its back crack
like a snapping tree as it crashed
to the pleading of its knees;
I heard a land cry
in a tonguelessness that was pain's.

A chirruping bird stopped,
a stone wept, a bat,
scissoring, swept
into a far realm of my sight
dwindled into the heart
of darkness of my own
heart's deepening night;
I heard a land cry,
felt the threshing of its flesh.

Like a face, that
flesh, a flower still
turning for its cradling by a love,
but the petals trodden, the sweet
heart's centre transgressed.
I heard a land cry –
or was it I –
testicled hamadryad left
to its withering in a wood?

Outpost

I pause at the gate:
crush a sprig
of mint,
smell
my old-world fingertips;
raucous late afternoon grows
suddenly quiet.

The room is dark;
figures stand around in it,
heavily as drapes.
I hear the clink
of glass,
catch the glint
of eyeballs' slewing whites.

Glass in hand, I stand
sidelined and inept.
Someone sidles up to me,
smiles uncertainly;
moves on again,
trailing
petulance and scent.

Slowly my eyes adjust
to the twilight, dredge
details from its depths.
A cigarette
traces flaming arabesques,
breadsticks flail a gaudy sauce,
mouths open to olives' succulence.

Nameless breasts and buttocks mesh
in an anonymous new beast.
Even the eyes that turn to me
are blank.
Man without a face,
I tinker with my drink,
nibble a breadstick.

Feigning diffidence,
he comes
forward,
raps a glass,
speaks of London,
New York;
there's a hunger in his voice.

They swarm in on him,
touching cheeks to his
in a mystic
sacrament of flesh.
The room resounds
with the soft
lamentations of the lost.

He looks at me,
sovereign and benign;
comes to me,
takes my hand in his,
hopes,
with his very heart, he says,
that I am enjoying myself.

I praise his speech
with the statutory warmth;
he makes the little moue
he knows he must;
moves on, then,
with nothing said.
My corner's chafing at my sides.

Far beyond its cleft I hear
the sirens wail:
an accident, perhaps,
the ultimate revolt?
The laughter swells:
a little drunken now,
they drink a toast.

I think of the black
backs bent
on the road to here:
muscled torsos rank
with sweat;
my own
back bent.

She turns her head,
stares,
questioning, intent.
Does she sense
how alien is the shape
that clots this corner with its bleak
denial of her hopes?

She turns away again;
I make my quiet way out
to where the garden sleeps,
thread my way between
its flower-beds,
carefully, as though they held
these dead.

Mid-winter concert

DON MACLENNAN

The sun gives up without a fight,
dragging his orange chariot
behind the leafless trees.
Inside the chapel the temperature
hovers around three degrees.
For my crumpled note I get
a wisp of steam for change.

The light goes fast,
abandoning that place deconsecrated
now the Jesuits have left.
The choristers who have survived
the Asian flu
sing out Guerrero with unbated breath,
vapours of ancient sound
that once wove filigree
around the Saviour's death.

As they sing their fragments of the mass,
through a door they left ajar
I see in the bleak grey sacristy
where priests once robed
high on the wall a showerhead.
In the dying light a horror seizes me:
the showers of Dachau bloom again,
the apertures where deadly
pale blue crystals fell
on naked, wet humanity.

The listeners, mummified
in overcoats, gloves and scarves,
await transcendence
for which this world starves.
But darkness clings
beneath the singers' exaltation,
death and horror vainly swept away
in five-part harmony.

Life Sentence

GUS FERGUSON

Jonathan Plaatjies
Who was born in the remote Cape hamlet
Omdraaispad which is known for a statue
Of one of its postmasters Jan de Klerk
Representing him holding a limp fish
In an outstretched palm which was erected
In Nineteen-nineteen in his memory
By his eccentric wife Tamara who
Later scandalised Genadendal by
Living in sin with the Persian painter
Omar Barry (there were some who said he
was not Persian) who invented Karoo
Cubism by meditating on the
Rock formations in the Bamboesbergen
Died today.

Two Poems

ESSOP PATEL

On a Sunday in February

on a Sunday
in february
cornelia arabus
resting, quietly
on an abyssinian mat
manicuring
her broken fingernails
chipped
from picking grapes
from dawn to dusk
from dawn to dusk

sunshine
dancing on her forehead
waving
at an old man, smilingly
shrugging off
twenty seven winters
of incarceration
on a hot summer's
day in February

in the valley of hope
he heard a slave
girl singing:

rolihlahla
in the cup
of your wrinkled hands
are the seeds
of a new nation
o madiba
sprouting
from your fingertips
is a budding blossom of peace

chuchaliza mandela!
proclaim
to the world
your colourful vision
of freedom for all
in the sun

Stained Glass Images

from the floral crown
of etosha
to the shuffling soles
of agulhas
along the skeleton
coast
fragmented shadows

d n i g
a c n

d n i g
a c n
on
shards
of stained

g
(*string*)
lass

(*braless*
jeanless)

nagali

supple & superb
long
spindlegs
pirouetting
whirlwünd
round-&-round
the
klolo
lolo

o

158

the rain
dr
(*w*)
ench
wind
stroking her
tingling
tan
gerine   plum
thighs

arrie ousie
kan jy dans?

dans

dans

dancing

cutting
ochre pathways
in the amphitheatre
of cactus and desert rose
beyond the palimpsest of im/
ages
mis
(*t*)
cege
nation
(*s*)
of sand-&-seas
lime
slit
her
(*r*)ing

and the rapacious sun
ravishing
the misty maid
an
head
of native hills
in
the wind

arrie ousie

dans

dans

her anklet flickering
shimmering in the sun
and with inviting arms
she vanishes
behind stain
glass im/
ages

Two Poems

JEREMY GORDIN

After the Fall
176 Blackwood Street

Here, near the Union Buildings, is the sinkdakhuis,
with its garden of indigenous plants,
its swimming pool and the message
branded on a cellar rafter, allegedly
by Eugene Marais. Here is father,

tall, thin, a little unsure perhaps
in plus fours, while mother is beautiful, trim,
probably wiser than he in the world's
ways. Here, too, are their handsome,
bright friends; together they bought

bargains at local auctions and spent
hilarious evenings on the stoep,
discussing Darwin, Marx and Trotsky
but speaking quite fluent Yiddish
with pleasure. More about those years,

when their world was Eden, I'm unable
to relate; they're a foreign country,
my only guides these photographs.
                        But as for the days
after the fall, the days of Hitler,
Stalin, and Afrikaner nationalism; days

of the creatures from the camps and mom's
dead babies; when dad's rages
with an indifferent world
and himself burgeoned and mother's
stoicism harshened; as for those days,

I was not there either, yet about them
am deft and certain. For they are my birthright,
they laced the seed that grew me:
                    jaundice-yellow,
squalling, I began my breathing
in the cold air of Cain's country.

from **Pomegranates for My Son**

1. Note to My Son

While many of his peers, sizzling with gumption,
were firing up financial empires, my grandfather

progressed commercially from pushing his barrow
himself, to hiring a black man to do it for him.

Then died, leaving behind perhaps 200 pounds,
a quaint spice box and a silver kiddush cup.

My father bequeathed approximately the same,
plus a hip flask; I'm likely to do no better.

What was it that sidled into our blood line
to ensure we are wholly inept at making money?

I could smugly pin the blame on there having been
far too many scholars among us. But we are told

that devout and learned men, especially them,
shall be blessed with 14 000 sheep, 6 000 camels,

and the rest. Personally, I suspect the fault lies
with an ancestor who deep into the nights dabbled

secretly in alchemy. *Life can be transformed,*
he claimed, *into both gold and a modicum of happiness,*

as follows: Aim to achieve scepticism, stoicism,
and wit. Practise plain speaking, precise

writing, and understand the virtue of being able
to remain quietly by yourself in your room. Piss

often on patriotism, cant and money. Trouble is
he was wrong; about the gold part, I mean.

Two Poems

FRANCIS FALLER

Katỳn Monument

In memory of 14 500 Polish prisoners of war murdered by Stalin's assassins. Remains of 4 254 of these prisoners were identified in massacres at Katỳn, USSR. The world conscience calls for justice. – *Plaque at the base of the monument, Melrose, Johannesburg.*

Here – near the artificial brook
in a tranquil, well-trimmed park –
stand the neat blocks of concrete that hold,
within, a crucifix of Highveld air.
The structure doesn't dwell on panic. Serene,
eschewing nastiness, approximating the dead,
it stands: grandly damning a massive shame.

(Instantly, you slouch before a corpse-
littered pit: peering down the muzzles,
the prison number on your smock your sole
identity.) Then on you go: you stroll
among the couples lazing over lunch,
twittering upon the trimmed tranquil lawns
(lush foil to this silent symmetry),

this tidy, obstinate epilogue whose bulk
and line betray the chaos of cruelty,
the shattered moment of each singular act.
In Katỳn: a callous lust for carnage;
here: memory's exquisite technique.
Shapely stone mauls the suffering
into elegance – erotic, discreet.

Revival of the Fittest

Sunday surburban scene: the road
outside the old-age home.
In stained tuxedo, stubbled tie,
black buckle-brimmed homburg,
a curled, decrepit man shuffles
up the gentle hill. His centimetre steps
accordion his spine caterpillar-like.
He pauses after every few
to bolster up a tilting garden wall.
He coughs; trembles; spits, sniffs –
then on again the ancient aims
to clear his calisthenic cliff.

Petermango, out on his rejuvenating
jog, glazed in sweat and grit,
goose-gangles down the slope;
passes the geriatric; pauses.
Hopping on the spot, he ponders
the predicament of this patriarch.
His ego anxious to show solicitude,
he canters across to the guard
sitting at the tusk-topped gate:
'Is he one of yours? Shouldn't
that derelict be accompanied?'

The old man hears. Like a clockwork toy
he twitches around to face the threat.
Instantly all over-bullied boy,
he totters forward, spumy, rheumy-eyed.
He grabs his homburg. He hunches; snarls;
and flings it like a frisbee
at this interloping youth –
who ups his hands as if to breast the tape
and goggles, like an ape pelted
by a little brat buggering around the zoo.

Summer Poems for the Beloveds

ANTJIE KROG

1

husband
man with rampant tongue

hold me
and hear my heart howl with lust
flaying my skirt to the thigh
as I ride out on your voice

man
who holds me as if embracing womb

I am with young by you
my abdomen lowers its fertility
in the festive midsummer light

our pelvic bones snap like horns
your buttocks knuckle white
you smear me out
man massive man
around whom I cave in
who groans for god and beast in my throat

When I come to my senses
from your cheek I see
I bit blood

2

the earth is unfinished
and when the wind starts
the child stands in Kloof Street with his schoolbag

Child of mine I call to his back
there where my heart is tightest

as always I am elsewhere
I think him into almonds
and arms full of pulled up tight
I trace his whisper in my matrix of blood

shyly the child shoots across the street
the wind takes his orthodontic drool

it's me
your mother
but his eyes are on the brink of leaving me
the earth lies unfinished
the wind splinters from him the last that is child
and I tighten about him
past a gull past all neglect

I love him
way
way beyond heart

3

the bay shines milk
sailboats sown like duwweltjies
behind waxpaper the mountain gnashes December blue

4

come day! come mountain
bloused in blue
come make me yours
gather me against yourself
lightsoft bundles
of bluebreast sky
fathoms and fathoms thereof

5

(christmas 1993)
after the rains
the veld gives herself like a slut to the green

of bare plains there is suddenly nothing of

everything sprees everything revels green
among the thorn trees the braggart tassels
the karee heaves a vastrap in wild olive steams
and for christmas the katbos tiptoes small red berries

wait, oh wait
every afternoon the gingergreen kuil is filled out
by a boon of clouds in – is it hailwhite?

the excess of the veld so unimpaired
so sudden
so drenched with cicada sound
so lavishly festive
and fraught with green
it attests to a gross insensitivity about us
us to whom the veld belongs
belied and belittled we feel
we to whom the veld belongs
eroded bewildered assaulted we feel;
we to whom the veld belongs

this is perhaps our last together
like this.

Translated from the Afrikaans by the poet

Heron's Place
(for Nadine Gordimer)

JEREMY CRONIN

Here the winter Tongati trickles from miles of cane-field,
Through the indentured smell of molasses,
Under the M4, to come to sea.

A sand-flat under an inch of water.
A place that might be lifted
On a fringe of incoming wave-surge
That flips and spins up
Minnows the size of small coins.

Which is why   she is here
All afternoon, holding fast to place,
Pinning down the specific,
Unregarding of the heavy-duty mill trucks
That grind upon the highway behind.

Further along, a curve of beach, here, there,
Solitary rods mark fishermen, hoping for shad.
Most of them the unemployed-retrenched
Some still wearing frayed mill overalls.
For them, this is not hobby
But the pursuit of proteins
For the squatter camp hidden
In a patch of vestigial forest behind
As they cast   lines
Weighted with old spark plugs.

'*In the past, the tourism industry*
Presented South Africa merely as an exotic landscape',
It's my friend, on TV, the minister,
'*Now communities must learn*
To package themselves and their cultures'.

I think of poetry – when
There's a sudden, flouncing, knock-kneed
Holding up of skirts that's neither
Exotic nor packaged
As the heron bolts off in pursuit of minnow

A digestive shaking of her neck tells the outcome.
And then she returns   composed
Back to place, her neck a supple rod,
Her beak a poised cast.

I think, as I was saying, of poetry
The least commodified of arts,
Solitary, a bit, given to outburst
Suspicious of shine, wakeful to slipperiness
Each line weighted   just so,
Insisting upon the actual, unpackaged, this-sidedness of things.
Tenacious to place,
Standing its ground,

Whatever the highway behind.

Two Poems

MARLENE VAN NIEKERK

small ballad for the last days of the SAR&H

from the fullness, from the original
idea of completeness stated in impasto
of aloed ridges, karooveld scented
with mimosa and studded thickly
with clumps of grass, with the casual clicking
of rams horns
locking and pushing
to find triumph in small measure
sated with blood when blood was just a message
of the world unto itself –
from this fullness buck
you have been abstracted by the depictors
of mere emblems
traced banally on compartment windows
mascot of the TRANSKAROO
your body elsewhere stretched and slender
with white switch flashing
now fulfils the final paces
of your maledicted death
and the works of God in Africa
are rearranged within the empty claim of your now stiffened head
like for example the exceptional blue
of our heavens above ikageng
where the dungfires unremittingly multiply
to the sound of melancholy responsory song
and on makwassies empty plains
where once elephant shrouded in light
went by with holy rocking tread
now platoons of silos rise, excessively
estranged from the indigenous hunger

and further south where the crags would ring with echoes
they instead pronounce death on the blue headed lizard
with every load of dynamite –
but the mountains around Touwsrivier are still
in the early morning hour
showing no sign of wanting to oblige
they just sniff lightly
like giant chameleons at the morning wind
and on their trembling flanks softly overgrown with heather
I can see that they are holding in
their breath preserving it
for the day when they will balk and smash
the stacked up stone
spelling out the town in white upon their withers
from this fullness buck of the resurrection
of everything that got tamed in this land
from this completeness you are totally excluded
you fulfil with tight snapped snout
the prescription of the narrow rails
and shrouded in steam and scraping sounds
your destiny is fixed
at arrival and departure
by station masters
wax figures staring across the twilight wilderness
with the signal lights flickering
as they slowly drop their fists

Translated from the Afrikaans by the poet

photographer at the agricultural show

today I find this edenville
so desolate and wild
beyond context and imagination
the paunches bulge beneath khaki shirts
like provisionally thornless cacti
and the shadows of hat rims fall too low
over the eyes to recognise family
just a moment ago I witnessed
corsetted ranks saluting each other
and battalions of sweet koeksisters
carrying out wide ranging manoeuvres

I fear for my safety

from the left advances an overgrown cabbage
with a flapping of ears
and to the right like a many headed cyclone
three dahlias, red hot, rage upon a single stem
the free state will not focus
my shutter is jammed it is stuck
until thank god blooming betsie slabber
just cupping into maiden form
bearing still the smell of biesmelk
between her thighs
poses coyly
with her father's champ merino
granting me the chosen moment
to gather in a single frame
the rampant fatherland:
a portrait for the morning news
of farmer maiden and master ram!

Translated from the Afrikaans by the poet

The Fragile Library
for Nadine Gordimer

ANDRIES WALTER OLIPHANT

In the guinea fowls' speckled egg
A life the size of the earth
Beats, beating as cool and fragile
As paper pulsing with
Inscriptions and transcriptions
Of this writing life you live.

What artifices are the twins
Of truth and being
Held in lower case
Between the fingers
Or falling from the lips of one
Who hears the stones singing?
These meagre letters
Of the alphabet
In which the living like the dead
Must strangely become stranger
Than the strangeness of estrangement
Only to live as fiction
So familiar, it startles the mind
Out of its old reasoning
And jolts the body
Out of its sedentary seasons?

The red dust, wounded, bleeds again.
Unblinking the eye flies out over
A storm not forecast
Nor prophesied but seen
Blowing in from the future over the plateau
Where time hunches close
To the earth's dark fires.
A portent with wings bent
Strained, and further straining
To breaking point
Falling, falls upwards
Towards the sun
Raging in its blue settlement.

Time smiles, flashing its teeth
Glittering with spittle
In the degraded light
Where truth goes bare
At once revealed and still concealed.
The sky is a burning mirror
Above the fragile library of memories
Where shelves stacked
With stories
Hold us to the words
Won and woven with patient craft
Into sly sentences
which change with every reading.

Oh, prose of people and this place
in which poetry ticks
Like the heart
Of a jeweller
Its steel springs coiling and uncoiling
In the soft casing of a Zobo
Like some painter-prankster's plasma clock.

FICTION FOR A WRITING LIFE

From Untitled Fiction

J M COETZEE

The sign outside the clinic reads ANIMAL WELFARE LEAGUE W.O. 1529. Below is a line stating the daily hours, but this has been taped over. At the door is a line of waiting people, some with animals. As soon as he gets out of his car there are children all around him, begging for money or just staring. He makes his way through the crush, and through a sudden cacophony as two dogs, held back by their owners, snarl and snap at each other.

The small, bare waiting-room is packed. He has to step over someone's legs to get in.

'Mrs Shaw?' he enquires.

An old woman nods towards a doorway closed off with a plastic curtain. The woman holds a goat on a short rope; it glares nervously, eyeing the dogs, its hooves clicking on the hard floor.

In the inner room, which smells pungently of urine, Bev Shaw is working at a low steel-topped table. With a pencil-light she is peering down the throat of a young dog that looks like a cross between a ridgeback and a jackal. Kneeling on the table a barefoot child, evidently the owner, has the dog's head clamped under his arm and is trying to hold its jaws open. A low, gurgling snarl comes from its throat; its powerful hindquarters strain. Awkwardly he joins in the tussle, pressing the dog's hind legs together, forcing it to sit on its haunches.

'Thank you,' says Bev Shaw. Her face is flushed. 'There's an abscess here from an impacted tooth. We have no antibiotics, so – hold him still, boytjie! – so we'll just have to lance it and hope for the best.'

She probes inside the mouth with a lancet. The dog gives a

tremendous jerk, breaks free of him, almost breaks free of the boy. He grasps it as it scrabbles to get off the table; for a moment its eyes, full of rage and fear, glare into his.

'On his side – so,' says Bev Shaw. Making crooning noises, she expertly trips up the dog and turns it on its side. 'The belt,' she says. He passes a belt around its body and she buckles it. 'So,' says Bev Shaw. 'Think comforting thoughts, think strong thoughts. They can smell what you are thinking.'

He leans his full weight on the dog. Gingerly, one hand wrapped in an old rag, the child pries open the jaws again. The dog's eyes roll in terror. They can smell what you are thinking: what nonsense! 'There, there!' he murmurs. Bev Shaw probes again with the lancet. The dog gags, goes rigid, then relaxes.

'So,' she says, 'now we must let nature take her course.' She unbuckles the belt, speaks to the child in what sounds like very halting Xhosa. The dog, on its feet, cowers under the table. There is a spattering of blood and saliva on the surface; Bev wipes it off. The child coaxes the dog out.

'Thank you, Mr Lurie. You have a good presence. I sense that you like animals.'

'Do I like animals? I eat them, so I suppose I must like them, some parts of them.'

Her hair is a mass of little curls. Does she make the curls herself, with tongs? Unlikely: it would take hours every day. They must grow that way. He has never seen such a tessitura from close by. The veins on her ears are visible as a filigree of red and purple. The veins of her nose too. And then a chin that comes straight out of her chest, like a pouter pigeon's. As an ensemble, remarkably unattractive.

She is pondering his words, whose tone she appears to have missed.

'Yes, we eat up a lot of animals in this country,' she says. 'It doesn't seem to do us much good. I'm not sure how we will justify it to them.' Then: 'Shall we start on the next one?'

Justify it? When? At the Great Reckoning? He would be curious to hear more, but this is not the time.

The goat, a fullgrown buck, can barely walk. One half of his scrotum, yellow and purple, is swollen like a balloon; the other half is a mass of caked blood and dirt. He has been savaged by dogs, the old woman says. But he seems bright enough, cheery, combative. While Bev Shaw is examining him, he passes a short burst of pellets on to the floor. Standing at his head, gripping his horns, the woman pretends to reprove him.

Bev Shaw touches the scrotum with a swab. The goat kicks. 'Can you fasten his legs?' she asks, and indicates how. He straps the right hind leg to the right foreleg. The goat tries to kick again, teeters. She swabs the wound gently. The goat trembles, gives a bleat: an ugly sound, low and hoarse.

As the dirt comes away, he sees that the wound is alive with white grubs waving their blind heads in the air. He shudders. 'Blowfly,' says Bev Shaw. 'At least a week old.' She purses her lips. 'You should have brought him in long ago,' she says to the woman. 'Yes,' says the woman. 'Every night the dogs come. It is too, too bad. Five hundred rand you pay for a man like him.'

Bev Shaw straightens up. 'I don't know what we can do. I don't have the experience to try a removal. She can wait for Dr Oosthuizen on Thursday, but the old fellow will come out sterile anyway, and does she want that? And then there is the question of antibiotics. Is she prepared to spend money on antibiotics?'

She kneels down again beside the goat, nuzzles his throat, stroking the throat upward with her own hair. The goat trembles but is still. She motions to the woman to let go of the horns. The woman obeys. The goat does not stir.

She is whispering. 'What do you say, my friend?' he hears her say. 'What do you say? Is it enough?'

The goat stands stock still as if hypnotised. Bev Shaw continues to stroke him with her head. She seems to have lapsed into a trance of her own.

She collects herself and gets to her feet. 'I'm afraid it's too late,' she says to the woman. 'I can't make him better. You can wait for the doctor on Thursday, or you can leave him with me. I can give him a quiet end. He will let me do that for him. Shall I? Shall I keep him here?'

The woman wavers, then shakes her head. She begins to tug the goat towards the door.

'You can have him back afterwards,' says Bev Shaw. 'I will help him through, that's all.' Though she tries to control her voice, he can hear the accents of defeat. The goat hears them too: he kicks against the strap, bucking and plunging, the obscene bulge quivering

181

behind him. The woman drags the strap loose, casts it aside. Then they are gone.

'What was that all about?' he asks.

Bev Shaw hides her face, blows her nose. 'It's nothing. I keep enough lethal for bad cases, but we can't force the owners. It's their animal, they like to slaughter in their own way. What a pity! Such a good old fellow, so brave and straight and confident!'

Lethal: the name of a drug? He would not put it beyond the drug companies. Sudden darkness, from the waters of Lethe.

'Perhaps he understands more than you guess,' he says. To his own surprise, he is trying to comfort her. 'Perhaps he has already been through it. Born with foreknowledge, so to speak. This is Africa, after all. There have been goats here since the beginning of time. They don't have to be told what steel is for, and fire. They know how death comes to a goat. They are born prepared.'

'Do you think so?' she says. 'I'm not sure. I don't think we are ready to die, any of us, not without being escorted.'

Things are beginning to fall into place. He has a first inkling of the task this ugly little woman has set herself. This bleak building is a place not of healing – her doctoring is too amateurish for that – but of last resort. He recalls the story of – who was it? St Hubert? – who gave refuge to a deer that clattered into his chapel, panting and distraught, fleeing the huntsmen's dogs. Bev Shaw, not a veterinarian but a priestess, full of New Age mumbo jumbo, trying, absurdly, to lighten the load of Africa's suffering beasts. Lucy thought he would find her interesting. But Lucy is wrong. Interesting is not the word.

He spends all afternoon in the surgery, helping as far as he is able. When the last of the day's cases has been dealt with, Bev Shaw shows him around the yard. In the avian cage there is only one bird, a young fish-eagle with a splinted wing. For the rest there are dogs: not Lucy's well-groomed thoroughbreds but a mob of scrawny mongrels filling two pens to bursting point, barking, yapping, whining, leaping with excitement.

He helps her pour out dry food and fill the water-troughs. They empty two ten-kilogram bags.

'How do you pay for this stuff?' he asks.

'We get it wholesale. We hold public collections. We get donations. We offer a free neutering service, and get a grant for that.'

'Who does the neutering?

'Dr Oosthuizen, our vet. But he comes in only one afternoon a week.'

He is watching the dogs eat. It surprises him how little fighting there is. The small, the weak hold back, accepting their lot, waiting their turn.

'The trouble is, there are just too many of them,' says Bev Shaw. 'They don't understand it, of course, and we have no way of telling them. Too many by our standards, not by theirs. They would just multiply and multiply if they had their way, until they filled the earth. They don't think it's a bad thing to have lots of offspring. The more the jollier. Cats the same.'

'And rats.'

'And rats. Which reminds me: check yourself for fleas when you get home.'

One of the dogs, replete, his eyes shining with well-being, sniffs his fingers through the mesh, licks them.

'They are very egalitarian, aren't they,' he remarks. 'No classes. No one too high and mighty to smell another's backside.' He squats, allows the dog to smell his face, his breath. It has what he thinks of as an intelligent look, though it is probably nothing of the kind. 'Are they all going to die?'

'Those that no one wants. We'll put them down.'

'And you are the one who does the job.'

'Yes.'

'You don't mind?'

'I do mind. I mind deeply. I wouldn't want someone doing it for me who didn't mind. Would you?'

He is silent. Then: 'Do you know why my daughter sent me to you?'

'She told me you were in trouble.'

'Not just in trouble. In what I suppose one would call disgrace.'

He watches her closely. She seems uncomfortable; but perhaps he is imagining it.

'Knowing that, do you still have a use for me?' he says.

'If you are prepared . . .' She opens her hands, presses them together, opens them again. She does not know what to say, and he does not help her.

The Old Man and his Cats

JAMES MATTHEWS

The kittens, like creatures lured from the wilds and domesticated, displayed pink tongues as they purred their pleasure. They circled his ankles, tails swinging like pendulums, fawning around his feet. A kitten prestigious in smoky-grey attire, its larger growth indicative of aggressiveness at feeding time, meowed for attention. Two kittens dressed in formal black-and-white jabbed at his trousers, claws momentarily digging into the material. The pride of the litter, its face a black mask with glittering emerald eyes, was splendiferously draped in orange with brown shadings, Cleo their mother, a matron begowned in glossy black with a white half-circle traced across her brow, reposing in the background favoured him with sly, almost amorous glances, looking for approval of what she had produced with her second litter. He leaned forward on the chair and pursed his lips. 'Pist! Pist!' Their ears stiffened to attention like sentries alerted. Cleo responded and glided forward to his outstretched hand. His hand caressed her chest, his fingers reaching up to gently press behind her ears.

He got up and reached to the top of the chest of drawers for the litre of milk he ordered with the Home's daily delivery. The bowl he used for feeding the cats was at the base of the chest of drawers. He placed the bowl in the centre of the cats, filled it and poured the remainder in a glass. Sipping from the glass, he watched their joggling for position, droplets of milk spilling from the bowl on to the floor. His gaze lovingly embraced them and the delight he found in their gathering. Their presence made his stay in the Home more bearable.

His aversion to form a closer relationship with some of the

inmates of the Home made it difficult for him to be altogether at ease in their company. He refused to join the groups attending denominational church services away from the Home and neither would he be party to the Sunday morning service arranged by a missionary group. He found satisfaction in solitary worship in front of his portable television set, enjoying the fervent spirituality displayed by a Negro Baptist congregation. Cindy, despite the invisible barrier he had erected to avoid intimacy, made a point of seating herself opposite him at the dining-room table. Withdrawing behind lowered eyelids, he replied monosyllabically to her conversation. Her hand would reach out to cover his and his flesh cringed beneath hers as he shifted his eyes to avoid reading the message hers held. His reaction was like Cleo's when he, at first, tried to make her respond to his overtures with the placing of a bowl of milk within reach. Cleo would sip warily from the bowl but moved away at his approach. Cleo had gradually consented to his presence and purred her acceptance as he rubbed behind her ears as she sipped from the bowl. At times he was lulled by Cindy's words that wove a net skilfully drawing him into her orbit. Eyes cleared of protective cover he would look into hers and respond with words that had more meaning than those used for minimal communication. He wondered whether he, at the end, would also emulate Cleo and surrender himself to Cindy's ministrations that would make him as dependent on her as he had been in the past on Martha for her solicitude.

Schooldays, for him, were a torturous period. His haplessness as a youth in the company of his peers was one of torment physically and emotionally, the pain transferred to adulthood albeit to a far lesser extent on the physical side. The choice of watchmaker as occupation relieved him of the constant company of those around him.

A woman, a score of years younger than himself, dressed in the garb of the cleaning staff, was framed in the doorway. Arms on hips, supporting aggressively huge breasts, eyes unblinking behind the thick lenses of her spectacles, she glared at him before speaking. 'Matron wants you,' voice truculent and eyes sparkling malignancy. She turned and stomped her way down the passage, muttering angrily under her breath, 'Damn cats!' Her damnation of the cats was beyond his comprehension. His eyes embraced the cats around his feet to shield them from the aura of malevolence emanating from the woman.

Filled with foreboding, he recalled the conversation between the matron and himself after a nursing aid had come to his room two days before and informed him that the matron requested his presence.

'Sit down, Mr Saunders,' the matron said as he entered her office. He eased himself on to the office chair, his back supported by the half-circular steel stand.

His eyes switched beyond her features, shifting to the framed certificates on the wall recording her achievements at a university and as a social worker, and her appointment as matron of Erica Home for Senior Citizens. His eyes rested on a photograph on the desk depicting the matron seated on a garden chair fronting a flowering rose bush. On each side of the chair was a child – a boy and a girl, hair blonde like the matron, about the same height with almost identical features. The photograph must have been taken years earlier as displayed by the youthfulness of the matron's face compared with the face that faced him.

Her eyes were honey-brown, warm and sweet, not unlike those of Martha who had passed away almost on her sixty-fourth birth-day. The expression on the matron's features was also very similar to that of Martha's, bringing on a stab of pain as his mind transported him back to their first meeting, leading to a cautious courtship on his part, filled with diffidence, ending in a coupling that brought satisfaction soothing his shyness.

Martha and he were from households that had had only one child. Her warm strength quieted his apprehension, and he was secured in her presence, their years together bolstering his sense of security.

For three years after her death, he had remained on his own in the cottage they shared in Sondousteeg, a block and a half from the old age home, trying with difficulty to adjust to a time bereft of her being. His relationship with the married couples of the other three houses in the close lacked the responding conviviality of Martha whose feelings went beyond the boundaries he had erected for himself. His feeling was one of reserve towards them, although reacting favourably towards the visiting grandchildren who addressed him with distanced respect.

He consoled himself during the day with things that had given her enjoyment; tending the small patch of garden, arranging and rearranging flowers in the scattered pots and polishing the brass ornaments he had bought her when he discovered the delight it gave her when he presented her with the first one – a brass elephant.

At night he would lie abed holding framed photographs resting on his chest, lighting up the loneliness of hours after midnight waiting for dawn. There were no letters exchanged between them that could act as a lifeline binding him close to her departed image. Each Sunday, he made a solitary visit to the graveyard, deposing the faded flowers with fresh blossoms in the pots positioned on the cement-bordered, pebble-covered grave. At its head was a modest marble slab inscribed with her name and date of birth and death. He had felt tempted to add a line stating how much he missed her but it would have meant an intrusion to his sorrow by each and every passer-by.

Loneliness was the deciding factor in selling the cottage and seeking admittance to a company, although peripheral, consisting of those in his age circle. Mementoes of the cottage were framed photographs and the brass elephant evoking memories of Martha.

'It's about the cats, Mr Saunders.' His feet shuffled imperceptibly on the carpet at the mention of the word 'cats'. He shifted his position so that he did not have to take in the face of the woman on the other side of the desk, his eyes sought assurance in her framed photograph. 'They have become a problem to most of the residents who constantly complain of the noise during the night that keeps them awake. You must do something about them.' The few words said, despite the gentleness of tone on the part of the matron, depressed him at its conclusion.

Back in his room, thoughts filled him with dread at a possible expulsion of what he held dear. What was he to do if the cats were taken away from him? He could not settle himself at a table with the rest. To be taken in by their conversation, the words links binding him to them. He shuddered as he envisaged himself being smothered in an embrace. Not even Cindy could assist him in easing the tensions arising when he was in their midst. He could present his thoughts to Cleo and her brood in words, words expressing his pain at the loss of Martha, who with her presence had at no time hinted that her strength was cover for a fragility that would be destroyed with the first attack of illness. He had never thought that he would pace out the years left on his own. And if a thought of impending death had come, it would have been him laid to rest in a coffin and Martha, faced filled with love, brushing his hair from his brow. What he revealed to the cats, he could not relate to Cindy despite a comforting willingness she displayed to ease his pain. The cats were privy to his anguish.

He clung to the protective image of Martha as he closed the door behind him so that the kittens would not prowl the passage in his absence. The distance from his room to the matron's office was a short one but the reluctance on his part to face her weighed his footsteps. He rubbed his hands on the edges of the cardigan Martha had knitted.

The matron indicated the chair fronting her desk.

'Mr Saunders, we will have to do away with your cats!' Each word held a cutting edge. The flesh on his face lost the support of structured bone that left him numb, unable to respond. The matron read the panic signals evident in his eyes. 'I don't exactly mean it that way. I've made arrangements with the SPCA to come and collect the cats. I'll get John to take them from your room and place them in the shed in the yard until the arrival of the SPCA.'

Hands raised in supplication and a voice as faltering as his subdued spirit he beseeched her, almost inaudible, her image transformed to that of Martha. 'What am I going to do, matron?'

She lowered her gaze to avoid his pleading eyes, giving herself time to formulate an answer that would soften the blow of the ultimatum.

'I'm sorry, David,' sympathy evident in the three words was not balm enough to ease the anguish reflected in his eyes as he raised his head.

He eased himself off the chair and left the office, his plea unanswered, leaving the matron with her head downcast.

Cindy was seated in his chair, the kittens sprawled around Cleo. Cindy looked at his tear-streaked face and opened her arms. He sank on to his knees and rested his head upon her bosom. Cleo sensed his despondency and responded with a consolatory meow, arched her back and caressed his scarf.

Mr Cypher's Collection

PETER WILHELM

When Gregory Simons reflected on what events, what chain of circumstance, had brought him to his present happiness – even fulfilment – his mind's eye swept far into the past and he saw himself, one shoe on and the other one off, a bedraggled, unformed creature.

The precise image was that of a tiny boy labouring beneath the pressing weight of a satchel, followed by dogs. The dogs were stunned by his scent, his presence, and loped towards him to be loved. The day might be frosty – the underside of the West Rand sky vast and slaty – or broadly struck by summer sun, but the dogs would always be there: the mongrels and loping reddish breeds, all kinds, all jumbled in memory to a following chorus of barking, ranting, wanting beasts. How absolutely forlorn they had come to him, full of the fear of rejection, as he shuffled past the domesticated houseyards where they were kept. Their woe when they could not get out! His heart broke; he would have taken them all in.

His astonished parents demanded that he take them back. This initiated a lifelong sense of injustice in the world.

Nor could he ever pass the circus allure of a pet shop without pausing and studying the puppies and kittens whose enormous eyes filled him with purest love and such responsibility, such a need to gather them in his arms and cuddle them.

As a cat will smell the hostility of one who is allergic to fur, and insinuate herself upon your wriggling lap, cats and dogs would unerringly find his home and his compassion.

His mother scolded in her limp way; his father inspected him for defects of character; his sister laughed. With bitter horror he gave up those animals whose homes could not be found again to be 'put to sleep' when their numbers grew ungovernably. It was a genocide of small, inoffensive creatures. He day-dreamed of a world of pets. He was their only lordling, fondly feeding them a manna that fell from trees. Being grown-up would be to be free to make his world their kennel.

Yet beyond a certain age – somewhere in the torrid midst of adolescence – he could not be said to be insatiable any more, not for cats and dogs or languid marmosets; for people found him out and followed him.

It was the luckless who befriended him. While he sat in class and thought of ways to dazzle the girl with the golden hair who had all the popularity of Miss Universe, his fawn-like glance might fall upon the raw, boiled face of the ugliest boy in the school, the one who never washed, and he would involuntarily smile at him with warmth and invitation. Nothing sexual: but still – afterwards it would be the raw boy who accosted him and stuttered praise and affection, while the golden girl would be part of another, more glorious parade.

When he was at university he fell in with losers who wished him to save them. These were people rejected even by revolutionary groups and the secret police. One of this company – a spectral youth with a hideous face rash – followed him so persistently that they were laughed at, out loud and openly. This was not a time of gay pride, and they were tormented. It was dreadful to have to take evasive action, sliding down corridors and around granite pillars, thinking himself alone – only to find the stricken youth shivering with joy at the end-point of even the most intricate escape route.

Each afternoon he took the train home, clattering across suburban sprawls in a swaying, smoky carriage, this being a time when everyone smoked; and the youth would follow him into the carriage, carrying his bicycle with him, tucked under his arm, and stand there in his full absurdity while commuting secretaries and clerks moved their eyes from one to the other as if following the arc of a tennis ball at Wimbledon. And they choked on mirth.

Years later he saw a photograph in the *Rand Daily Mail* which showed the youth – no longer a youth, a mad, middle-aged being, bald now – pedalling his bicycle out of a burning township, immune in his innocent lunacy from riot and insurrection, having been placed there by the slow, cruel processes of time and the soft evil of the education department.

Tears welled from Gregory's eyes at this sight; and guilt racked him because if he had been kinder, more considerate of the yearnings of the doomed youth, he might have saved him. The wrongdoing of the world appalled. By then he had become a foremost liberal and philanthropist, although his private life was disaster and carnage. He was so kind that he slept with anyone, marrying them freely, fathering many children, ever unfaithful out of the purity and goodness of his heart.

Some forty years passed since the childhood episodes of longing dogs and cats: he was again married, recently divorced, and it seemed to him that everything that had happened to him had come and gone in an incandescent flash. He could make no particular sense of it. His desire to be a saviour was insidiously being taken from him by the grit and obsidian accumulation of tedium; and there was nothing more disquieting in his consciousness than that – until he began to dream horribly.

Night after night the same dream recurred: and he would scream. At least, violently shaken into wakefulness, he thought he had screamed. The force of his own cry was like the taste of dirty snow in his mouth, in his head, a sound forced out of him; but it seemed it was a dream cry, not uttered, since his wife never woke when he did, upright and strained, slick with fear.

The pounding of his head and heart – swift painful beats together – was sickening. Truly so: often he would have to lurch through darkness to the bathroom and spew. Then he would sit on the edge of the bath, feeling the cold ceramic touch of it from his balls to his lungs.

And he could never remember what the dream had been about. In the moment of awakening, slimy, turbulent images scuttled like a billion silvery fishmoths. He felt stupendous dread. He was on the edge of a terrible discovery, of seeing the shape of mortality; but the very process of awakening, the violence of his abrupt-self-awareness, dispersed the dream.

Seeking not to wake his wife when he returned to bed, sedated by a midnight swig of Scotch, he would equally seek to move closer to her: to insinuate his cold fever upon her, curve upon curve, and often he did wake her and she responded. Or she became aware of him remotely, shifting and murmuring and he felt love spring from him in a solid rainbow to enclose her. 'I love you,' he would whisper, and forlornly await her drowsy puzzlement, for this was not something he told her in the light of day. It was an affirmation he had relinquished, having spoken it so often in the past he was fully aware of its potential for debasement.

But then often he could not return to sleep; he hovered in an unending time of anxiety. Sometimes he would go to his study and read a book, Barbara Tuchman's *A Distant Mirror* or *The House Gun* by Nadine Gordimer. He was humbled by the century. Once he walked in the expanses of his garden, the autumn air gliding in chill smooth planes over his rugged body under its tissue of pyjamas, aware of a certain arrogant strength for all the softness of his life, which had, as it were, overlapped so much of the modern history of his own blighted land. He was cautious not to confuse interior turmoil with external upheavals, however colossal, however revolutionary. He had an immense will and attacked age with exercise, and melancholy with a mute, hopeless deism. That was why the unregulated imagery of nightmare filled him with loathing: the unexamined life was not worth living.

It seemed to him there was someone in the garden. Shock! This was his fortress, behind his high walls with electric fencing entwined in razor-wire. There could be no one here in the azaleas or green immaculate lawns with outcrops of ornamental rocks and trickling artificial streams. Any sensed presence – and a female one, at that – lay in the realm of the irrational, of Elvis in a flying saucer, telepathy, ghosts, voodoo. So he grew angry and contemptuous of himself, infiltrating shadows and peering around trees in search of the source of this formless intuition. And of course there was nothing: the inevitable cats and dogs of the household, the guardians of his CD player and drinks cabinet, sniffed his familiarity and gave him soft signs of happiness.

Baffled by the content of his recurrent dream, he considered his life. He was fifty-six years old; an age he had never thought he would be. The children from the earlier marriages had grown up and gone away; and there were as yet no children from this marriage, his latest.

He was a broker's analyst, specialising in commodities futures.

He possessed a large house in Rivonia, a long way from the flatness of the West Rand and its railway rigidity and decaying mines. The property imbued his self-possession with amplitude, for the encroachment of walled suburban fortresses left him untouched behind his own high walls and wire. He made contributions to the correct political parties and was an affable host, tolerant, worldly. In almost any sense he could give the word, he was blameless and had always – prompted by the wreckages of marriage – demonstrated blamelessness by taking blame upon himself. His best marriage had been the one in which his wife, rather hopelessly, had fallen in love with someone else and he had let her go rationally, with insufferable generosity. He was profoundly grateful that she had strayed before him.

But that was all gone. Now the dreams affected his smooth functioning. Abstracted in his cool office near the stock exchange – essentially a devolved patchwork of computer workstations far from the inner collapse of his city – he found himself making mistakes, making the wrong calls. There was a general deterioration in the quality of his research; he skirted work and read cheap novels behind a closed door. He forgot to bring his secretary flowers on Secretaries' Day. Open spaces caused a terrible nameless fear, a new thing.

For example: it was necessary one day to walk a few blocks to a club where he was having lunch; he often did so. For no reason whatsoever, he suddenly halted and heard blood in his head and looking around saw with unusual clarity absurd structures of steel and glass suspended on a whirling planet set in disturbing and illimitable spaces. The void, the void! His physical form, his breathing, his existence itself had a malignant and heavy quality. Yet who or what perceived this vastation was not answerable since his self-awareness became hallucinated and resonant with dread. There arose in his mind the silent scream that woke him at night; but from this deeply intimate fear, nested in his dislocated self, there could be no awakening. The brute stuff of matter pushed against him.

Exposed on shimmering deserts of concrete, he saw a figure approaching him: a woman of no age, in dirty blouse and trousers one leg of which was pinned up at her waist, for she had lost a leg, was on crutches and held out a hand in entreaty, begging. She was close now: he saw her face livid and ugly behind twin waves of dirty, streaky hair, a cracked egg in a foul nest. Her mouth open, he could see the gaps in her teeth, and their shark-like raggedness, and before him opened a blue abyss of desolation. She breathed upon him methylated spirits and old dead sweat and in return seemed to breathe him in.

He closed his eyes and walked blindly, rapidly, stricken, to the club. The gin-soaked men in suits thought he was ill, sweating as he did. He had to drink quite a lot to make the fear go away.

Gauging that all this might be the symptoms of mental breakdown, he sought the services of a psychiatrist. The man had an abrupt, diffident manner, and prescribed tranquillisers. He took these as directed but found that the benzodiazepine made him feel as if he was surrounded by coarse, abrasive sacking; and that his sleep was so heavy and submerged that the nightmare's florid impact, while reduced, was extended so that when he was finally able to claw his way choking back to consciousness, his muscles were corded and cramped. The fear did not go away, nor was he able to work any better: in fact, his thoughts came like bubbles in depressive mud.

He said to the psychiatrist: 'Shouldn't we try to find out why I feel the way I do?'

'I'm not a witchdoctor. If you want "therapy" you'll have to go to someone else. I don't deal in that sort of thing.'

'I was under the impression that you did.'

'What we're dealing with,' said the psychiatrist primly, 'is a medical problem. The limbic area of your brain is in an agitated state; the result is anxiety manifested in sudden panic attacks. The drugs I have prescribed for you reduce the excitation of the cranial neuroreceptors through an enhancement of the gamma-amino-butyric acid which infuses the brain and spinal cord.'

'But isn't there a cause? A reason?'

'That lies in the realm of speculation. Your symptoms are common in old age. If you want some sort of unscientific "explanation" you might as well consult an astrologer.'

His attention drifted. The timbre of the psychiatrist's voice had a quacking, mechanical element. Until now, the simple idea that he could, whenever he wished, see a psychiatrist, had furnished its own reassurances; if his problem was that he was losing integrity of identity, there would be a healer, an accredited shaman, to whom he could turn just as one relinquished control in a jetliner to the pilot and did not seek to fly the great machine through one's own will. But now, listening to gabble, he felt intensified fear.

And when he left, the psychiatrist said, 'And please continue to take the tranquillisers, Mr Cypher,' and the fear grew huge.

'What? What did you call me?'

'I didn't call you anything. What do you mean?'

'Just now: you called me . . . by a word.'

The psychiatrist looked at him. 'Perhaps you should take a tranquilliser now, Mr Simons.'

He sat on a stone bench beside a lake in a park. The water's surface was coated with thick green slime and dust so that it had a hard, jelly-like appearance. On a small island in the middle of this substance geese and ducks clattered. He assumed the things were breeding, though there was little else in the park to suggest it was spring. The trees had a lifeless, deserted aspect, and the grass was scanty and windblown. He had thought he could have a cup of coffee but the restaurant was closed up and shuttered behind a vast infestation of papery bougainvillaea.

It occurred to him that nothing would ever happen to him again. All those marriages dissolved with swift glances of adulterous entreaty; the pain of succumbing; the flickering scenes of different homes and gardens – that had been his life. Now he might have to endure the nullity of living on and on in mental entrapment. After all, he did not smoke and hardly ever drank and but for the worm in his mind he had perfect health: there was no reason why he should not go on living for some decades. He had the physique of a much younger man.

When someone settled on the bench beside him – a shivering, grey impression – he was so enwrapped in the elaboration of his small misery that he did not at first take in who she was. He was leaning disconsolately forward, his gaze somewhere between the lake of green slime and his shoes. Only when the woman sighed, or groaned, did he become aware of her pungency and, raising his eyes, recognised the figure which had approached him on crutches in the concrete desolation between his office and the club. The most positive feeling he had was happiness.

Her eyes on his, she reached into a pocket – her legless side was towards him and it was into those pinned-up folds that she reached with a bitten claw – and took out a packet of cigarettes and a red plastic butane lighter. She put a cigarette between her teeth, clenching it, and scraped the lighter into flame: a gushing aurora into which she dipped the tip of her cigarette. She blew smoke through the gaps in her teeth. She offered the packet to him and he accepted and his hand touched hers and he had a sensation of coldness and scale, at once disgusting and intimate.

'Did you follow me here?' he asked abruptly, knowing immediately that such a thing was not possible.

She shuddered, shifted away; her hands trembled greatly. Now her eyes could not meet his and she spoke in a tiny, pathetic voice: 'No mister, I been here all day, excuse me.'

'I'm sorry,' he babbled. 'I thought – but it doesn't matter what I thought. I've seen you before, but that was somewhere else.' He stared at the cigarette in his hand, not knowing what to do with it. 'Where do you . . . stay?' To ask where she lived might have seemed hopelessly patronising, but the conversation had to be continued.

'Wherever I can, mister. My friends take care of me. I was with them yesterday but they went too fast for me. I think maybe they've gone to Durban. It's nice down there by the sea.'

Now she did lift her eyes to meet his: they were shrewd but otherwise vacant. 'I just need a warm place. It's nice and warm today.'

He felt socially inept. Yet there had been a time when he knew how to talk to people like this, and quite unconsciously he shifted his body so that it had a nurturing or sympathetic aspect. 'Yes,' he said, 'it is. I've taken the afternoon off – I wanted to come somewhere quiet so that I could think.'

'I can go away if you like. If you want to be by yourself.'

'No, please don't. I hate being alone. And I feel cold.' As he said this there came with great force a memory of the past winter, of how he had fallen asleep one Sunday afternoon and while he slept the sun had set so that when he woke it was dark and cold, and he had lain there bewildered and infused with bleakness: terribly, terribly alone with the certitude of death close and hideous. So what he told the woman was absolutely true. But the coldness was in his soul. It was difficult to determine her age; perhaps she was thirty. What he had taken for ugliness in her face was dirt and pain; and he felt the awfulness of her life, the spiritual vagrancy and unfulfilled longings it encompassed, as he saw it. The circumstance of her mutilation provoked in his mind the imagery of blood-stained rooms and distant, time-shadowed screams, the thin baying of ambulances.

'Mister,' she said at last, 'I'm asking if you could maybe let me have a bit of money? I don't like to beg, but you know how it is. I just need something to get me started.'

'Look,' he said, 'I don't have any cash on me; but why don't you come home with me now? You can have some food there. And some drink. If that's what you want.' He would also offer her a bath, he considered, but not now. 'It's a nice house,' he enticed her.

'I'm not a prozzie, if that's what you think.' She was shaking very badly but none the less began to assemble her crutches as if to lurch up and away. The effort made her mouth foam and he thought of all the diseases she might have; but at the same time, shame flushed him at the misinterpretation. 'No, no,' he said, 'I don't think that. Of course I don't. Just let me give you something to eat and drink. I'll get you started.'

'Mister, if you've got any money please give it to me here. I don't mind giving you a blow-job, but we can do that here, we don't have to go anywhere, I'm not like that.'

She extended one arm towards him with gruesome coquettishness.

'No,' he said, 'no, no – come on. That's my car over there. The silver BMW.'

She looked at him. 'OK.'

Her name was Mopp. That was what it sounded like. By the time Gregory had negotiated the hi-tech entryway to his castle, a form of living signal had been passed about her arrival – for the dogs ceased stripping open black plastic garbage bags and came running in infantile joy to greet them; the cats were sinister and clawed trees possessively; a pocket of servants gathered at a distance in silent animosity. Gregory knew his wife was shopping and took Mopp directly to a bathroom where he locked her in with soaps, towels and scents, though first giving her several glasses of white wine which she drank with implacable greed.

He drank a glass of wine himself, listening to opera on his CD player. His situation, or the music, or the wine uplifted him. The opera – Verdi's 'La Forza del Destino' – was an over-complex tale of flight and revenge, misunderstood events and military passion. As the arias and duets flowed, Gregory saw before his mind's eye a curiously dramatic, one might almost say operatic procession of images from his past. They did not constitute direct recall, nor even loops of memory; but rather a narrative concerning his fate.

His entire early life – it came to him – had been in harmony with his fate and his fate was his character: every moment pre-determined by immense, world-spanning compassion for others. And that deep, aching fellow-feeling for suffering creatures was not a quality learned in his family or school; it flowed from his essence as the music flowed from the CD player. It had made him different then; he was different now, awakening again.

It followed that most of his life – his marriages, his career – had been false to his fate. The political turbulence of his society, through which he had been churned, might have been averted had he grasped the power of his compassion and entered public life, rather than merely quivering charity's web.

Perhaps it was not too late?

He had sufficient awareness of his limits to know that much of this reverie was fantasy; yet it seemed to hold an unalterable truth which so late in life he should not evade. His late mental turmoil, he understood, arose directly from lifelong evasion of his destiny. What the psychiatrist had termed an excitation of the limbic region of his brain was a warning that he had for too long betrayed his authenticity of compassion.

Towards the end of the second act of the opera, as Leonora was calling upon God not to desert her – 'Deh, non m'aabandonar!' – Gregory's wife entered, her arms full of boxes of shoes, and brushed past him with a fleeting smile, going on to the interior of the house, a dark-haired woman of forty. He rose and stopped the music, then sat again, bending his face down in his glass of wine and breathing deeply.

His wife screamed.

Gregory put down the wine and went to her. She was in the bathroom doorway, staring, horrified.

'What's that? Gregory – what is that?'

The legless Mopp was naked in the bath, half submerged and half unconscious. Through dirty water her tattoos swam in luminescence. Laid upon a pool of her filthy clothing was a crutch. The air was full of steam.

'That's Mopp,' he said. 'She followed me home. Can I keep her?'

His wife looked from him to Mopp, went a little way into the bathroom to see more clearly. The figure in the bath heaved and Gregory's wife went pale and stepped back, sick. 'Oh God! Christ!' She was spitting, shuddering, pushing him away. 'You sick horrible bastard!'

Gregory followed her to their bedroom and, quietly, serenely, attempted to explain. His wife had a Gucci suitcase open on the bed and was putting clothing into it. Her face was wet with tears: rage and humiliation drove her. Gregory's omniscience endured. He would have wished to sit beside his wife and explain his vision, embracing her, convincing her of the logic of Mopp's presence. But when he said, 'Lorraine –' she threw a hairbrush and it struck his chest.

'I don't want to hear it. I don't want to hear anything. How could you –'

'She was in the park. She needed help.'

'I don't care about anything you say. When I came in the servants were whispering and laughing. I'm leaving and I want a divorce. I should have known you were a pervert. She doesn't need help, you need help, you should be locked up.'

Within moments Gregory stood alone in the portal staring at the door that had been closed on him. Briefly, his soul was ashen; briefly, the certitudes of reverie faded and there was a salt tang of doubt. Then came the moment that brought his fulfilment, for down the corridor came Mopp, her crutches squeaking. She wore no clothes. She stopped before him, swaying, drunk, balancing, reaching out a tender hand to his face with gentle understanding. He faced her.

'Oh my poor darling,' said Mopp. 'Don't worry. You and me will be together forever. Don't worry about what she said. She doesn't understand. You're the kindest man I've ever met; I'll never leave you.'

Gregory spoke with sombre authority: 'My name is Cypher. I am the Resurrection and the Life. She that believes in me shall never die.'

The Fugu-Eaters

IVAN VLADISLAVIĆ

'Hey, Klopper, what's a gonad?'

Klopper did not answer.

Tetrodotoxin. Bate turned the word over carefully in his wounded mouth. It was found in the *gonads* of the fugu fish and a grain of it was enough to kill you. It paralysed the nervous system, shutting down your organs one by one, until you died a horrible death.

'Listen here,' he said. *'The fugu fish is twenty-seven times more deadly than the green mamba.* Incredible.'

The back of Klopper's head bristled. Bate could imagine the morose expression on his face.

Bate was sitting on the bed reading a copy of the *Reader's Digest*, which he had carried away from his dentist's waiting-room the day before. He'd been half-way through the article on fugu fish when the nurse summoned him to the chair and so he'd slipped the magazine into his jacket pocket. This morning, when he put the jacket on again, there it was. A label stuck to the dog-eared cover read: Please do not remove from the waiting-room.

Klopper was at the window of the hotel room, looking out into the street. He was sitting the wrong way round on a chair, with his folded arms leaning on the backrest and his chin propped on one wrist. Glancing down through the gap between the frame of his glasses and his cheek he saw the digits on his watch steadily flashing. Eleven hundred hours, eleven hundred hours.

Bate shifted on the mattress so that he could rest his shoulders against the headboard.

Farmer's son with his nursemaid, Marico Bushveld, 1964

On an old Transvaal farm near Fochville: the farmer's wife, 1965

Ballroom dancing teacher Ted van Rensburg watches two of his pupils
swinging to the music of Victor Sylvester and his orchestra
in the Old Court House, Boksburg, 1980

Margaret Mcingana at home on a Sunday afternoon, Zola, Soweto, 1970

J J Oosthuizen, Senior Township Superintendent Senoane, Soweto, 1972

A peasant woman at home, Coffee Bay, Transkei, 1975

The peasant woman's oil lamp, Coffee Bay, Transkei, 1975

Sunset over the playing fields of Tladi, Soweto, 1972

'Don't put your shoes on the bedspread,' Klopper said, without looking round.

'Get off my case.' And Bate thought: He's got eyes in the back of his head – but how do they see through that stuff? In the nape of Klopper's neck was a sludge of bristly grey hair, like iron filings in grease. Maybe his glasses had little mirrors in the corners, like those spymaster specs they used to advertise in the comics.

'Is he coming?'

'I told you already, he won't pitch until this afternoon.'

'What's the point of watching all day then?'

Klopper's neck bulged. 'Did you go to school or what?'

Bate stuck the tip of his tongue in the hole at the back of his mouth where his wisdom tooth had been. It was no longer bleeding, but it tasted of blood.

'Mr Bate,' Dr Borkholder had said, 'it doesn't look good. These wisdoms will have to go. But a clever chap like you won't even miss them. Some of the others are also too far gone . . .'

'It's sergeant, if you don't mind.'

'You haven't been flossing, sergeant. This molar is holding on by a thread.'

'Do I need a filling?'

'I'm afraid it's too late for that. You should have come to me ten years ago. There's not a lot I can do now. I might be able to save a couple at the side here and these two' – tapping on them with a silver rod – 'but most of them will have to go. To give you a better idea . . .'

He opened a drawer in a cabinet and took out a plastic model of the human jaw. It was a gory-looking thing, with glaring white fangs jutting from inflamed gums.

'Forget it!' Bate said, trying to sit up in the chair. Bloody sadist. Any excuse to use the pliers. The whole profession was a racket. He jerked the armrest up and a tray of instruments clattered to the floor. The dentist gaped behind his plastic visor. Bate would have punched his lights out, but the nurse came running.

'Sergeant Bate' – bitch had been eavesdropping – 'Please, you must get a grip on yourself. Or we'll . . .'

Or we'll what? . . . Call the police?

He calmed down. Even made an apology of sorts.

'How would *you* feel if he told you your gums were shot?'

'You're putting words in my mouth,' Borkholder protested.

Then the nurse prepared the syringe and they gave him an injection and pulled out a wisdom tooth, bottom, left. He felt no pain. It should rather have hurt, he thought afterwards, then the sound might have been less sickening, the splintering in his head, like a door being battered down, as the dentist worked the pliers backwards and forwards, twisting the roots out of the bone.

'So what's this crap about fish?'

'Page 76.'

It was Bate's turn at the window. He was sitting back to front in the same pose as Klopper, sitting that way to feel what it felt like to be Klopper. He heard Klopper leafing behind him. All ears, that was the secret.

A little yellow card, with the proposed date of Bate's next extraction scribbled on the back of it, fell out of the magazine. Klopper put it in his pocket and began to read aloud:

The flesh of the fugu fish contains one of the deadliest toxins found in nature, and yet it is eaten everywhere in Japan. Some gourmets regard it as the ultimate gastronomic experience. Trust the bloody Japs. *In 1986, two hundred and sixty people died from eating fugu, but many cases go unreported, and the actual number of fatalities is much higher. What is the appeal of this deadly delicacy?*

'The appeal,' said Bate, who had already read the next paragraph, 'is (a) it tastes amazing, and (b) it makes you irresistible to chicks.'

The bedsprings creaked. Bate pricked up his ears and tried to picture what Klopper was up to. A soft thud. Klopper dropping the magazine on the floor. More creaking. Klopper making himself comfortable.

'Take your shoes off the bed,' Bate said without looking round.

'Piss off.'

He glanced over his shoulder and saw Klopper's shoes at attention on the carpet, his toes squirming in his socks.

The fire had been the Captain's idea. When Klopper thought about it afterwards, that was always the first thing that came into his mind. The two of them had brought the evidence to the farm on the back of the bakkie, wrapped in plastic and covered with a groundsheet and a load of firewood, just to be safe. The plan was to bury it in the veld behind the windbreak, but the wood gave the Captain the idea for the fire. 'What's buried can always be dug up again,' he said. 'But what goes up in smoke is gone for good.'

One of the constables was waiting for them at the house. It was Voetjie, the one with the limp. The Captain told him to off-load half the wood at the end of the stoep, where they usually made the braai, and call them when he was finished. Then they took the cooler bag out of the cab and went to wait inside.

They were drinking beer at the kitchen table when Voetjie came to the door to say it was done. You'd think he was a bloody servant, Klopper thought, you'd never say he was one of us.

Voetjie climbed on the back of the bakkie and they drove out towards the bluegums. Then it occurred to the Captain that a fire might look suspicious out there and so they circled back to the dam. From down in the dip they could see the roof of the farmhouse on the ridge in the distance, glaring like a shard of mirror in the dusk.

When they untied the groundsheet Voetjie didn't bat an eyelid, and Klopper guessed that he'd already sniffed out what was concealed underneath it. The two of them dragged the bundle off the tailgate, stretched it out on the ground, next to an overgrown irrigation ditch, and piled logs over it. It was like building a campfire, Klopper thought.

The Captain himself sloshed diesel over the pyre. At the last minute, he bent down, jabbed a stiff forefinger through the plastic and tore it open. He gazed through the gash as if he was trying to read something in the dark. Then he stepped back and struck a match.

Klopper kept watch while Bate ate his lunch at the dressing-table on a sheet of newspaper. 'When we leave,' Klopper said, 'I don't want a crumb left behind to show that we were here.' All Bate could manage was ice cream. The Sputnik Café downstairs was out of tubs, which would have been more convenient, so he had to settle for a Neapolitan slab. He ate it from left to right, which happened to be the order of his preference – chocolate, strawberry, vanilla. He spooned it into the right-hand side of his mouth, away from the tender hole, but it made his teeth ache.

The *Reader's Digest* lay open beside him, pinned flat with an ashtray, and he read as he ate, glancing up at himself from time to time in the dressing-table mirror.

'This fugu stuff is so dangerous you have to get a licence to cook it.'

'Come off it.'

'It says here: *Only qualified chefs are allowed to prepare fugu dishes. The training is long and arduous, and at the end of it the candidates have to pass a stringent examination. Identifying and excising the poisonous parts of the fish is an exact science. But mistakes still happen, even in the best establishments.*'

When the ice cream was finished they changed places and Klopper ate his Russians and chips. In the cooking oil the sausages had burst open into gnarled shapes. Deep-fried fungus, he thought, something a Jap might eat. Organ meat. He wiped them in the smear of tomato sauce congealing on the wax-paper. He looked at Bate in the mirror while he chewed.

'I suppose you still hungry?'

'I could do with a steak.'

'I should of got you some of that fish.'

'Fugu.'

'And chips, no salt and vinegar.'

The burning had taken longer than they anticipated. Klopper and the Captain sat on a ruined wall, drinking beer and watching the light fade on the water, or squatted in the flickering shadows, tending the fire. Klopper had imagined it would be over in half an hour, that they would be back at the house in time to watch *Due South* on the television. But at seven o'clock it was still burning fiercely. When they ran out of logs the blaze died down at last, and then a jumble of angular shapes became visible in the cinders. Folders and files. Dockets and statements. The covers of the duty books, with their leather-bound corners, the thick boards of the minute-books and logbooks, the tightly bound spindles of invoices and receipts. The knuckle-bones of rubber stamps. The Captain poked around with the end of a stick and layers of blackened leaves came away from the spines. Inexplicably, in the heart of the fire, new white pages unfolded. They should have torn the covers off the books first and shredded the paper. Stirred up by the stick, a black-edged sheet spiralled up on the smoke and then fluttered down again next to the Captain's boot. The words were still legible, the handwriting recognisably his own.

The Captain tossed the keys to Voetjie. 'Looks like we're going to need the rest of that wood. And bring the cooler bag, and the grille from the stoep. We'll eat here.'

As soon as they were alone, the Captain began to speak. He told Klopper that his wife had left him. He thought she was having an affair with some Sandton desk jockey, something to do with computers, software. What was he supposed to do now? He was lonely, he was living on take-aways, he had to get a girl in to wash his shirts. His voice thickened and Klopper thought he was going to cry, but he just went on speaking, and he didn't shut up until they saw the headlights coming back down the track.

While Voetjie and Klopper built the bonfire up again, carefully laying the logs on the smouldering papers, the Captain made a smaller fire at the edge of the water. Then they braaied the chops and the wors. When the meat was done the Captain cut the wors into pieces with his pocket knife and speared some of it on to a polystyrene tray for Voetjie, who went to sit on the tailgate of the bakkie to eat. The other two ate their share straight from the grille.

All this time the bonfire went on burning, with the pages wavering in it like ashen palms, burning and burning, as if the evidence would never be consumed.

Sixteen hundred hours, Klopper thought, and wiggled his toes.

'Tell me something Bate: if these fugu fishes are so poisonous, how come they don't poison themselves? Hey?'

Bate looked at the street. It seemed cold and grey, but that was because the glass was tinted. A scrap of his training floated into his mind: Surveillance. In certain circumstances, you see better out of the corner of your eye. Something to do with the rods and cones. There was some story about listening too . . . you heard better . . . with your mouth open. The cavity of your mouth created a sort of echo chamber. The best attitude to adopt when you thought the enemy was near: turn your face away from him, look at him out of the corner of your eye, keep your mouth open. Bate opened his mouth tentatively. It hurt. He opened wider, and wider, driving the pain from the empty socket up into his ear, into his temple, into the top of his skull. He turned his head slowly until he could see Klopper from the corner of his eye on the bed.

'What the hell are you doing now?'

Once during the meal the wind shifted and blew the smoke over them. It was bitter-sweet, compounded of leather and ink and sealing wax. For some reason it made Klopper aware of the meat in his mouth, of its texture, the fibres parting between his teeth, the taste of blood on his tongue, but he took a mouthful of beer and swallowed, and it went down. Soon the wind shifted again and carried the smoke out over the water.

'This is the bit I really don't understand. They call it the philosophy of the fugu-eaters . . .'

'Hang on,' said Klopper, 'here he comes.'

'Listen to this: *He who eats fugu fish is stupid . . . but he who does not eat fugu fish is also stupid.* What's that supposed to mean?'

'Beats me.'

Bate went to stand behind the chair and they both looked at the man in the street, a man they knew from photographs, coming towards them in the flesh.

Two Excerpts from Untitled Fiction

CHRIS VAN WYK

Ouma and Oupa Adams

Uncle Ben was no relation of ours, neither a brother nor a brother-in-law, nor a distant cousin. But any neighbour or close family friend was called Uncle or Aunty or Ouma or Oupa So-and-so. Hence Uncle Ben.

If Uncle Ben could ever stand out in a crowd, it was because of his broad shoulders, for nothing else. He had short, curly hair. He had a set of decent white teeth. He was about five feet ten.

Uncle Ben did not laugh easily, but he did have a sense of humour. He was friendly to everyone, black, white, old, young, male . . . he was shy in the company of females but this did not mean he was unfriendly to them.

Uncle Ben taught at a primary school in Newclare, a coloured township near Noordgesig. He got home in the afternoon, marked books and went to sit at Uncle Foxy's. Home was a room at the home of an old, childless couple, Oupa and Ouma Adams. They were pleased to have Uncle Ben living with them. They called him their 'built-in security'.

Actually, the stories about Uncle Ben roughing up misbehaving customers at Uncle Foxy's were a little exaggerated. He did bash the face of a fractious youth who tried to throw his weight around once, and physically dragged two men out from under the shade of Foxy's backyard awning, around to the front of the yard and out of the gate and on to the dusty street.

What gave the spectacle more attention than it deserved was

that the two men, remorseful at being thrown out of their favourite shebeen where their two almost full bottles of beer stood open absorbing the hot sun, began to howl and cry, pleading to be accepted back in.

'Ben, Ben, ag please, ou Benny!' wailed the fat one.

'Ben!' the fatter one called, trying to stand up. Turning to his friend, the fat one, he said, 'Say sorry for Ben.'

'Sorry, Mr Ben!' the two chorused.

On and on it went all afternoon. And while the gate remained wide open, swinging wider still every time patrons marched in and swaggered out, the two stayed right where they were, not daring to put one foot back in, and eventually passing out.

An even better spectacle took place one Saturday afternoon, drawing a much bigger audience.

Oupa and Ouma Adams were probably in their early seventies. They had both retired decades ago. She had worked in a food canning factory and he in a furniture factory, both in Industria, about four or five miles from Noordgesig.

Both retired with very meagre pensions (apartheid saw to it that white pensioners got the lion's share of state pension) and they began living frugally and eking out a living by their own designs.

Oupa Adams, as we called him, seemed to have less going for him than Ouma Adams. Six or seven years into his retirement he landed a job with the Department of Coloured Affairs. This was a job designed especially for elderly men. Ma had a hand in this appointment as she worked at the Department and one evening I recall us going down to the Adamses' home in Findout Street to give him the news. The only reformatory for coloured boys in the country was in Ottery in Cape Town. From time to time the courts in Johannesburg sentenced delinquent boys to spend their school years at the reformatory. The courts – or maybe the welfare department – provided the train fare for this 800-mile journey down to Cape Town as well as for an adult 'supervisor' to accompany the youth.

Oupa Adams enjoyed a dozen or so of these trips to the fairest Cape over two years. He felt especially lucky because he had a sister in Bo Kaap whom he went to visit. She plied him with wonderful gifts and on his return he would send us some of these in appreciation of my mother's role in his good fortune. And so every time a youth got caught breaking into a shop, stabbing another boy, raping a girl, it would result in the Petersen family being treated to a pound or two of snoek, bottles of delicious sourfig jam and other konfyt or a bunch of Proteas.

But one day, as all things, this came to a sudden and dramatic end.

One cold July evening Oupa Adams took his place in the second-class coupé of the trans-Karoo with a fifteen-year-old felon called Denzil Baaitjes. Denzil sported a tattoo on his forehead which declared in clumsily etched small caps: When times are hard friends are few.

The policeman who handed him over to Oupa Adams said: 'Don't worry, he's handcuffed.'

Ouma Adams stared at him in the light of the coupé, huddled in the corner under the night light.

'Nou die goed op sy kop?' (Now what's this on his forehead?) she asked the cop. She was illiterate.

Oupa Adams had not yet seen it, even though he had been sitting opposite the youth, staring at him. Oupa Adams leaned forward, squinting through his thick spectacles. Still finding it hard to read, the old man fumbled in his pockets – of which there were many, he being dressed for winter – and found his reading glasses. He put these on and read out the 'headlines' to his anxious wife, shivering on the station platform.

On hearing the sentence Ouma Adams pulled her thick cardigan more tightly around her shoulders as if the temperature had suddenly dropped two more degrees.

'En nou?' (What do we do now?) she asked the cop.

'Don't worry, Ouma, he's handcuffed,' the cop said again, 'and I've informed the ticket examiner to make a call in here every now and then, just in case.'

The train pulled out of the station leaving behind a very apprehensive old lady.

Well, it turns out that Ouma Adams had good reason to be worried. Oupa Adams had a supper of vetkoeks and curried mince, koeksisters and sweet tea from a flask, all of which he shared with the youth – except the tea which he spat out contemptuously.

'En nou?' asked Oupa Adams, uttering the same expression of surprise as his wife had done an hour ago.

'Too fucking sweet!' Denzil spat out the words.

'Young man,' Oupa waved a fat finger at him, 'where you're going they don't even have sugar.'

Denzil shook his head, arching his eyebrows so that the words on his forehead squashed up.

Oupa stared quizzically.

'Where am I going?' the youth asked with a sneer.

'To the reformatory . . .'

'That's what you think,' Denzil laughed.

Maybe it was his age, the monotonous rattle of the train, the hearty meal of home cooking or a combination of all of these, but an hour later the old man was slumped back on the stiff green SAR seat, snoring loudly.

And sleeping so soundly that Denzil managed to take the handcuffs keys out of his waistcoat pocket. (The police had omitted to tell the old timer that Denzil was a pickpocket and cat burglar of incredible skill.)

Oupa Adams woke up to find himself handcuffed to the bar that stretches across the luggage shelf. He was alone in a tiny coupé. For almost a full minute he tried to work out where, what, how. Indeed he was on the verge of tenderly calling out his wife's little name which he had last used on his return from active service in Tobruk, when he remembered: When times are hard friends are few. He suffered a mild stroke and when the train pulled into Kimberley he was sawed loose and rushed to hospital.

Denzil Baaitjies was recaptured on the banks of the Vaal River in Standerton after having broken into a white school principal's house and made off with eighty rands.

The people of Noordgesig did not forget this little misadventure too easily. When they did eventually stop poking fun at the septuagenarian, Ma said it was Ouma's delicious koeksisters that tempted them into silence.

On Sunday mornings all roads, shortcuts and alleys led to the Adams household. The Sabbath began with church bells, the *Sunday Times* and *Post*, chicken curry, roast chicken and beetroot salad for lunch, football on the 'grounds' – Arsenal and Blackpool – and more church in the evenings. But the koeksisters were an essential, sticky start to the day.

Women in curlers and holey slippers, men with Saturday evening hangovers, barefoot boys and girls still in their pyjamas, all made their way to Oupa and Ouma Adams with their enamel bakkies and their soup dishes.

There they sat crowded into the Adamses' steaming kitchen, huddled around the stove in winter and choosing the back stoep in summer, in the shade of the overhanging grapevine, waiting to be served, breathing in the aroma of viscous, sweet syrup, cinnamon sticks, mixed spice – aah, and the tangy redolence of naartjie peel.

On a kitchen cupboard under the kitchen window were three huge plastic dishes piled high with the plaited confectionery.

Ouma and Oupa took up their positions in the kitchen and went to work. He stirred, she dunked; she dunked, he fished them out; he counted them – six or twelve – into the bowls or bakkies; she rained coconut on them; he slipped in an extra bonsela, she complained good-naturedly; he stirred, she dunked; 'Thank you, dankie . . .'

Koeksisters and instant coffee on Sunday mornings . . . aah! Many bought on the book, forgot to pay, and there seemed to emerge a tacit agreement that you don't pay, you don't tease.

Uncle Ben

Then, one day, a month or so before their new border, Ben, arrived, Oupa Adams did it again.

His pre-war bedroom suite was in a poor state of disrepair. Which is a nice way of saying it was falling apart. The mattress sagged in like the face of an old man who had lost all his teeth. The mirror no longer copied exactly what the old people did before it. It blurred them out, it had warts and moles and cracks. One drawer refused to open, another stubbornly remained shut. Don't talk about the wardrobes: each of the two had lost a leg and balanced precariously on bricks. Ouma was convinced that these wardrobes would come crashing down on them in their sleep and crush them dead.

Noordgesig teemed with skilled cabinet makers. Many had been approached to restore and refurbish the Adamses' ancient furniture, many promises were made, but the Chez Gaye on Saturday nights, the shebeens on Friday evenings and the football fields on Sundays kept these young men away from honouring these promises.

'All I ever hear from these boys is next week, next week, next week,' Ouma Adams told my mother.

'I might as well ask them to build me a coffin,' said Oupa.

Matters came to a head one day when a family of mice moved into one of the wardrobes. They could not be caught because the back panel against the wall had come loose, providing the rodents with the perfect emergency exit.

The mice seemed to know that their unhappy landlords were not as fleet of foot as other Noordgesig residents: they spent all night carousing, nibbling on slippers, shitting, squeaking and making sorties into the kitchen for the remnants of last Sunday's koeksisters.

'I shouldn't have handed in my rifle,' Oupa wheezed in the wee hours of the morning.

Matters came to a further head the following night. Oupa and Ouma went to bed as usual at a quarter to ten, after listening to a comedy half hour, *George and Rita*, on Springbok Radio. They fell asleep almost at the same time, back-to-back. The alarm clock was on a stool on Oupa's side of the bed. It was set for 5.45, although they both usually rose before that.

It was just one tiny squeak that woke Oupa up. He opened one eye and it fell on the top of the wardrobe. The light of the full moon showed him where the squeak had come from: Papa Rat had his furry torso spread over the rump of Mama Rat and he was humping away – whether it was happily or as a matter of course was hard to tell from Oupa's worm's-eye view.

Oupa was about to wake Ouma when Papa Rat dismounted and they both scurried into the wardrobe, there to relax in the afterglow in the pocket of a moth-eaten double-breasted corduroy jacket.

Oupa Adams resolved to take all the coins and dirty rand notes in the koeksister jar, to head for Lubners in town and to buy a new bedroom suite.

He put a small deposit on a white and mauve suite with gilded handles on the doors and drawers.

When the furniture arrived Ouma Adams lay on the mattress rubbing her wrinkled and calloused hands over its smooth rayon and its sunken buttons.

It was two years to pay or twenty-four easy instalments.

Sleeping had never been such an enjoyable experience. Ouma

Adams's backache disappeared, the mice vanished, the room smelled new. 'Just like bananas,' Ouma said. Oupa didn't quite agree but he nodded magnanimously. Sleeping was a truly wonderful affair.

But maybe the Adamses were sleeping too much. Somehow Oupa Adams forgot all about the instalments, the 24 months to pay. And even three months later, when Uncle Ben moved into the spare room with his new single bed and wardrobe, this triggered nothing about instalments.

One Tuesday morning found Oupa Adams alone at home. Ben had gone to work at Newclare First Primary, Ouma Adams had gone over to the other end of the township where she had been called to help with an old woman who had bronchitis.

Oupa Adams was listening to the pleasant hum of the fire in the coal stove. He had just filled the kettle up with water and put it on the stove for coffee, when he heard a van stopping outside his house. Well, the houses were packed so solidly together that no one ever knew for sure if it was themselves who were having visitors. Oupa Adams assumed it was the Pintos next door.

He heard the sound of his own gate being loosened from the makeshift wire clasp, the thud-thud-thud of footsteps, the knock on the door. He wobbled to the bedroom window from where he would have a clear view of his visitors.

His old heart which, as you know by now, had had its fair share of near stoppages, skipped yet another beat: he recognised the men who had come to deliver his furniture three, four months ago as they stood in the dappled shade cast by the grapevine.

In a flash it dawned on him what was about to happen. He realised that he had not paid his instalments. His thoughts became a muddle. He let them in.

'Sorry, Baba,' their leader said, 'If you want to argue go to the office in town or go to the magistrate.'

In ten minutes the room was empty. The truck was idling in the street, ready to depart with its repossessed mauve and white cargo.

'Goodbye, Baba!' the men said, their voices echoing in the house. Baba did not reply, but this was not unusual: these men seldom left people in a cheerful mood. The driver and a companion got in the front, the other two men settled down on a sofa repossessed earlier that day in Newclare.

They drove up Findout Street and were passing the shops when the two men on the sofa got the fright of their lives. The mauve and white wardrobe swung open and out popped Oupa Adams like an ancient jack-in-the-box. The men screamed as Oupa landed in their laps, dead.

The van screeched to a halt.

Entertainment in the townships was in short supply. Indeed apartheid had made sure that it was a famine. There were no parks, swings, movie houses. These were to be found in white suburbs only. And even the Rand Easter Show which came round annually with its popcorn and lollipop and big dippers and carousels, all these came marked 'FOR EUROPEANS ONLY'.

The youth of the township – especially the unemployed and those who refused to work, hung out at the shops. Why? It was the place most frequented by the community. You could watch a fellow play pinball, be a lucky ringside spectator when a knife fight or a fistfight broke out, ogle the legs of the girls who came to buy bread or milk. In a lull you could simply join in or listen to a debate on whether the Florsheim or the Nunn Bush was the better shoe, the Pringle or the Pierre Cardin the superior jersey. The conversations were inane and spiced with a shallow slang the purpose of which, apart from communicating, was to ensure that a conversation did not go deeper than its desired inanity and vacuousness. Afrikaans was the base of this slang, spiced with words from English, Zulu, SeTswana and SeSotho.

And so it was that, when Oupa Adams fell out of the wardrobe and on to the laps of the two furniture removal men, the youths at the shop decided that this was the moment they had been waiting for. This was not for EUROPEANS ONLY but for all those who had spent years in the dusty streets of the township, waiting.

But nobody was to know just then that we were in for a double feature.

The schools in the area were coming out and the kids in their frayed schoolbags, sagging socks and crooked striped ties gathered round.

The layabout youths at the shop had come over, swaggering, hands in pockets, laughing. Two of them, Taks and Japie, decided to take centre stage.

'Aw, what have you done to the timer?' Taks asked the men.

'We went to fetch the furniture. He was not paying. He hide in the hodrobe.'

'You people, I know you,' said Japie, waving a finger, 'you want to steal this old man and cut off his balls and make muti.'

We swayed about in the street with laughter.

Andrew van Ross arrived, his bell ringing so that the crowd could make way for him. But before he could make another abortive attempt to assert himself in any way, a woman shooed him on with, 'But Andrew, don't you then know your duty? Go and call Sister Anastasia.'

Of course he knew his duties, and to prove it, off he went with a tring-tring-tring.

In the mean time the two men on the lorry were dancing about as if it was getting hotter and hotter up there.

'Is the Oupa dead?' Japie wanted to know.

They shrugged in the coarse collars of their blue overalls.

'Take his pulse,' shouted Japie.

'If we don't get koeksisters on Sunday, I'm coming personally to your house with my okapi.'

This was a Noordgesig joke which the men shrugged off.

'Put the old man on the couch,' Taks said. 'And give him some artificial recitation.'

'What?' one of the men said.

'I think you better take his furniture back home,' Japie said, 'then maybe he'll live.'

And on and on it went: taunts, jokes, good-natured threats, laughter.

Before long Sister Anastasia came, riding side-saddle on Andrew's bicycle, looking anxious in her Bata Toughies and her maroon and white uniform. My friend Neville of all people ran behind carrying her big black bag. He told me later that he had been commissared as he came out of the toilet with a girlie magazine.

'I was so relieved when they asked me to carry the bag, I could carry it every day,' he said, taking up a position next to me. 'What happened here?'

'Oupa Adams,' I pointed with my eyes just as Sister Anastasia was being hoisted up by two youths who stared under her dress to loud cheers from everyone.

'Order, order,' Andrew van Ross called with a tring-tring. 'Are you up, Sister?' he asked unnecessarily.

'What's he doing up there?'

I explained quickly what I knew, not wanting to miss anything more.

Before we knew it, Sister Anastasia had revived Oupa Adams. He sat up looking very confused. His wisps of grey hair stood on end like a startled bird's – an African Grey I suppose. One band of his maroon braces was off. He was drooling. He looked down on us, and even though we were all applauding his having regained consciousness, he looked like a baby who had been woken up far too early.

Sister Anastasia asked him how he felt. He spoke with a squeak, as if he was learning to speak.

'His batteries,' Neville said to me, 'they're still a bit flat from the whole thing.'

This was not meant to be funny even though I thought it was. I nodded and looked away from Neville and smiled.

The men on the lorry were a superstitious bunch of guys. Sister Anastasia wagged her finger at them and told them, in Zulu, to take the furniture right back if they didn't want to be the cause of the old man's death.

They obliged happily. And to make sure it was done, a few boys ran behind the lorry as it made its way back, chanting, 'Happy, happy, happy.'

Neville and I would happily have joined the entourage, but I wanted him to show me the picture of the girl who had made him go into the toilet.

It really was a double-feature, but there was a bit of a long intermission – twenty-four hours to be exact – before the second episode played itself out.

If you picked up a five bob or a rand, your natural instinct was to quickly comb the general area where you struck it lucky in the hope of getting more of the same.

It was the same with the Oupa Adams incident. At the same time the next day, school kids (myself included), Japie, Taks and their cronies (although they were always there), maids and other general passers-by gathered in Findout Road opposite the shops for more of the same.

One obvious newcomer on the scene was Pedro. He was known

and feared by all in Noordgesig. Everyone called him the local fahfee runner's oupa, an insult inspired by his 'China eyes' and his immensely ugly features. This insult was flung at Pedro when his detractors were safe on the other side of a fence. Pedro had four legs and belonged to a breed called pitbull. His owner was none other than Taks who had brought him to the shops to prove some point about his teeth or his enormous paws, or maybe just for some diversion. There was certainly a lot of diversion at the shops that day as people took a detour past the drooling, barking Pedro as he strained at his leash, barking and growling and slipping and sniffing.

All day the shopkeepers, a butcher and two cafés, had asked Taks to take Pedro home to his hok where he belonged.

Taks, drawing on a cigarette or chewing bubblegum, had a string of witty answers for these men. But Pedro and his master stayed, one at each end of a four yard long chain.

One of the people who needed to buy her daily provisions from the shops was Ouma Adams. She ambled up to the shops and past the boys and, spotting the dog, cautiously gave it a wide berth, rather than stumbling smack into it as her husband might've done. He had been ordered to stay indoors and only to venture as far as the toilet – which he had done three times that morning as the traumatic events of the day before had given him the runs.

Ouma Adams had come to buy some Chamberlains together with bread and some mince. Even she knew that she could not have made this trip to the shop without being lampooned in some way or other. But she was not prepared for the rude tongues of those boys who had nothing to do but play pinball and 'go on' with the girls.

She heard the giggles and saw the nudging of ribs through the corner of her eye. But she ignored it all as she disappeared into the café. When she emerged the boys formed a semicircle around her. They were not threatening her in any way. All they wanted to do was have some fun – squeeze some more juice out of that wardrobe incident.

Ouma Adams stood and surveyed the 'shopstanders' with a baleful glare. The only other way to go was to take a slight detour past the butcher, but that route was blocked by that ugly Pedro whom she knew very well.

'Out of my way!' she said irritably, adjusting her white scarf.

'First tell us, how's the old man?' Japie asked.

She sighed.

Taks expounded a theory he had. 'So you have a new man living at your house,' he said, pointing an accusing finger. 'And you stuffed the old faithful in the wardrobe, hoping to get rid of him . . .'

'Rude, unmannerly children!' Ouma Adams cried and broke through the semicircle – which had broken up anyway, as the boys spilled all over the place with loud laughter.

'Skollies!' cried the ouma – which caused more laughter as this word was confined to those coloureds in the Cape who extracted their front teeth and spoke with those sing-song voices.

One, two hundred yards up the road Uncle Ben was sitting quietly in his room marking a pile of Afrikaans exercise books, clicking his tongue and his red Bic ballpoint pen in annoyance at the putrid spelling and punctuation of adolescent coloureds. The front door burst open, but he did not hear it close. This was unusual but he continued making his Xs and the occasional tick with his pen.

Was that a sniffle he heard in the kitchen? What should he do about it? He was a border in this house, confined to the space of one tiny room. Was the old couple having an argument? Was it about him? He decided to do some cautious investigating, on the pretext of going to fetch a drink of water in the kitchen.

And there he found Ouma Adams having a cry, her scarf now at half mast around her neck, her head in the crook of her arm on the table, an old woman crying like a little girl.

He feigned a cough. Her tear-stained face swept up from the old panelyte table to look at him. And then she jumped out of her chair and set to feigning work, opening two cupboards and a drawer.

(By the way, Oupa was fast asleep in his room dreaming: he and Ouma are on top of a lorry, sitting in a sofa made for two. They are waving to the people of Noordgesig who are waving and throwing kisses. They wave back, they are on their way to Cape Town . . .)

'What's the matter, Ouma?'

She had only told him half the story when he was already out the door with the names of two of the hoodlums on his mind: Japie and Taks . . .

'Be careful of Pedro!' Ouma called through an anxious sob.

Now he had three names.

Uncle Ben stood in his vest and his PT tracksuit pants (he took the standard threes and fours through their paces on Wednesdays) and his green slippers. From the gate he had a full view of the shops, which were a mere four houses away.

The derisive laughter coming from the shop confirmed the humiliation that his dear landlady had just been through.

'He-e-ey!' he shouted, using his playground voice.

'Joh!' said Neville in wonderment, 'iets soos Tarzan!'

'Ja-ja-ja,' I agreed, shaking his hand off my shoulder, not wanting to miss even a flicker of what was to follow.

The laughter at the shops turned to silence, except for a vicious sounding dog.

Uncle Ben put his hands on his hips. The pavements along the street began to fill up with people. Doors opened and housewives, maids and children holding on to their grannies' dresses appeared in them. Neville and I stood half-way between them and him.

The silence was momentary though. Japie and Taks swaggered about in their tackies sneering and grunting and flinging gobs of spit on the cobbled floor (which Pedro immediately licked up).

'Who does this teacher think he is?' Taks said.

'A teacher from the bundu coming to play big in our town.'

'I'll show him his mother if he doesn't go in and mark some books.'

At that very point a little girl emerged from the shop. Taks spotted a wad of steel wool under her arm which she had just bought and this inspired his next witticism.

'Hey, girl,' he said, 'go and give that steel wool to that teacher there and tell him to knit himself a bicycle and ride out of town.'

I didn't mean to laugh. Uncle Ben was a regular visitor to our house. I hoped he hadn't heard me.

When Uncle Ben lifted up his hand to speak, the laughter stopped. He said: 'Taks, Japie and Pedro. Come here!'

The last name brought murmurs of confusion rippling through the elongated crowd of spectators.

Oh, Uncle Ben, Uncle Ben! If only I had one of those megaphones that the police use. I could call, above the noise of the crowd, 'Uncle Ben, Pedro is the dog. He's vicious! He once bit . . .'

Taks, as they say, took the gap. He loosened the chain around Pedro's neck, pointed at his tormentor eighty metres away in vest and slippers, and said the two words which the hound loved to hear: 'Vat hom!'

The story goes that all Taks wanted to do was scare Uncle Ben into fleeing back whence he came. There was enough time and distance between him and the dog to do so.

But Uncle Ben stood his ground. The dog ran through the gauntlet of gasping and screaming onlookers. But Uncle Ben stood his ground. The dog passed me, a flash of sharp yellow incisors and dirty thick paws. Uncle Ben stood his ground. The dog gave a metre-long growl, opened its mouth, and jumped. Uncle Ben's right foot lashed out and met the dog in the air.

Pedro, still in the air, flipped back, crashed on to the ground with a howl, shook spasmodically three or four times, and breathed no more.

Noordgesig was more silent than we had been in assembly when Verwoerd had been killed and the principal called for a minute's silence. (But that came later.)

'A Fosbury flop!' Neville said with a triumphant shout and a slap on my back. Most people in the crowd just said: 'Jo-jo!'

Now it was Taks's turn to show a set of yellow fangs.

'Taks, Pedro and Japie . . .' Uncle Ben commanded again.

Bobby Crutch hobbled up to him and pointed a crutch at the dead dog. 'You already have Pedro,' he said. 'It's only Taks and Japie left.'

Uncle Ben frowned and whispered: 'Are they dogs too?'

Taks! Taks did a strange thing. He started jumping around the place shouting: 'My dog! My dog!' and doing a kind of mad dance in a semicircle, almost as if he himself was now tied to the pillar that the late Pedro had been tethered to all this livelong day.

Someone in the crowd near me suggested 'artificial recitation' but not too loudly because Taks was in no mood for jokes now, especially ones that backfired.

'Where's my knife?' Taks called to somebody, his friends, anybody who would listen.

Somebody in his circle of shopstanders stretched out a hand

and handed him an okapi. This was the most popular of murder weapons. They were used to take money off people, to stab members of rival gangs and to threaten anyone who wandered too close to your stash at the gambling 'schools' – yes that's what they called gambling dens in the townships.

A woman standing behind me and abbaing a baby, slapped her hands together. 'Hoe!' she wailed despairingly, 'vandag spat die bloed weer in die Noordgesig.' The next thing she said made me turn around and study her face a little more closely: 'Ask for a piece of bread and nobody will give you a crumb, but ask for an okapi and one falls into your hands just like that.' She patted the child's bottom through a dirty yellow blanket even though the bundle inside it was contentedly sucking its thumb.

In the mean time Japie had also acquired a weapon: a Coke bottle was smashed against a pillar and its serrated edges were ready to draw blood.

(Actually, in far more peaceful times this Coke bottle became a dagga pipe. But I'm sure there would be time for a skyf later.)

I had the ability to listen to conversations between my mother and I which take place in the future. These exchanges came to me at the oddest places and times. One of these, a brief one, entered my brain right now. It went like this:

'But how many times did I tell you to come home when you see knives?'

'I was on my way from school, Ma.'

'But you stopped to watch.'

My response is a quick shrug of the shoulders.

'You watched.'

'I didn't want Uncle Ben to get hurt, Ma.'

Ma stops ironing and gazes at me across the steamy surface of the ironing board that mists up her glasses. When she speaks again she is just as querulous as before, but this time her tone is softer, as if she has ironed her words out too.

But let's get back to the action.

Taks is still jumping and dancing about as if fleas are living it up in his pants, his tackies, everywhere. He is obviously finding it hard to accept the death of Pedro.

'Let's take this mother's arse!'

Uncle Ben is still standing. Pedro, of course, is still lying there as if a car has bumped him. Taks and Japie walk the walk, that I'm-rowing-a-boat walk of theirs, knife and Coke bottleneck glinting in their search for human flesh.

'Pig!' Taks spits.

'Ma se gat!' Japie refrains.

Uncle Ben is still standing, hands on hips, giving them a look reserved for pupils with vetkoek stains and ink on the pages of dog-eared schoolbooks.

The two layabouts sway about the sand road as if they're in a heavy current, still waving knife and bottleneck about, still cursing Uncle Ben and his mother's private parts. They come within a metre of Uncle Ben – which means they're abreast of the dead Pedro.

Suddenly Taks drops to his knees and sobs: 'Sorry, Ben! Please, Ben!'

Japie flings his bottleneck down on the ground and approaches Uncle Ben with his open palm. He says: 'I come in peace, bra Ben.'

Uncle Ben slaps his face with a crack that resonates and Japie also drops to his knees, his hands on the ground, looking as if he is saying all five of the prayers demanded by his religion. Taks got a slap too.

Ouma Adams in the mean time had come out of the house and the youths were told to remain on their knees and to apologise to her.

'And you used to be such nice boys,' she said. 'But look at you now, saying ugly things in the street about me.'

'And after you made them fat on your koeksisters,' the woman with the baby on her back added.

Highveld Hibiscus Garden

ELLEKE BOEHMER

Though shy about most things Ada Dunlop was fiercely proud of her hibiscus. She had five grandchildren growing up big-boned and sturdy in far-flung places like Sydney and Toronto. But as anyone could see, Ada's pride talking about her hibiscus plants was almost as strong as the pleasure she took showing off the glossy photograph album to which her daughters-in-law contributed family pictures. Her pride in the flowers might even have been ever so slightly stronger than her pleasure in the photos. When talking about hibiscus Ada leaned forward in her chair and her cheeks glowed. She forgot to tidy the back of her perm with a cupped hand, as she usually did in conversation.

Ada's garden was by common consent handsome. It had won municipal prizes. But while she treated the roses, the azaleas, the thriving syringa and poinsettia bushes and the huge beds of brilliant dahlias with quick efficiency, the hibiscus plants she tended pains-takingly, as if they were children.

She began by rearing them on the kitchen window sill. On frosty mornings she held the earthenware pots between her palms to coax warmth into them. The mature plants in the neat round beds cut out of the lawn she swaddled in special coats of her own devising, layers of sacking and felt and a central core of cotton wool lightly soaked in linseed oil. There were other concoctions too, some of them secret. Dish water, a drop of golden syrup and Johnson's baby lotion basted on to the hibiscus leaves was good during a drying wind. In the matter of her hibiscus plants Ada seemed to herself something of a witch. A good witch with green fingers.

If ever she had an audience – though this wasn't very often – Ada went so far as to boast of her hibiscus.

'I'm glad you like that red,' she would say to the interested neighbour carrying a basin of windfall apples, to the window-cleaner, to the garden help she occasionally hired for big jobs. 'The reds can be especially difficult to persuade to grow that large. Yes, I'm fond of the white too. That glow of the petals in the sunlight. But have you seen the orange? Let me show you my lovely orange hibiscus. Do you have a minute? Orange hibiscus usually refuse to grow at all in this climate. At this altitude.'

And she would walk the guest to the sheltered corner round the side of the house where, bright against the silver razor wire and the concrete blocks of the security wall, the sheeny orange hibiscus drooped its thick red pistils.

This morning Laura, the wife of Ada's middle son, stood at the guest room window and watched her mother-in-law watering the orange hibiscus. Laura, Charles and their two small sons were visiting for three weeks from Toronto. Laura picked up Frankie her youngest so he could also watch his grandmother. She jigged him on her hip. He patted the glass with a sticky hand.

'You know, I really do think she cares more about her flowers than her grandchildren,' Laura said. 'No Frankie.' She rubbed at the boy's hand smudge with a tissue. 'I mean, Charles, here we are, just arrived, off to the game park in a few days, and all she's done this morning is fiddle in the garden.'

Charles was counting out their traveller's cheques at the bedside table.

'Give her time, Laura,' he said. 'Remember this is her routine. This is what she does on the hundreds of Monday mornings that we're not here.'

'But don't you think it's a bit weird, you know, kind of obsessive? I had the garden tour for more than an hour yesterday afternoon. We'd hardly unpacked. Doesn't she care about anything else? Your father had the papers spread around him in the living-room. Stories about armed raids and state corruption and God knows what here on her doorstep. But when I began to talk about that stuff she changed the subject.'

'But wouldn't you, if you lived this close? If it was your daily fare? Look, give her time, love. She'll come round. Like I've said

224

before, she always made a garden wherever we lived, wherever the mining company sent Dad. In the Kalahari, in Zambia, no matter the conditions, Mum's made a garden. Roses, sweet peas, the whole thing. She once constructed a honeysuckle trellis across a dried-out stream bed. The hibiscus are a new thing. Maybe that's why she's so hooked. For her they're unusual, not English. She's usually liked Englishy plants. English oases in the savannah. Hibiscus is exotic for her.'

Ada heard the rhythms of Charles's voice drifting down the stairs to the kitchen. She began making tea and smiled to herself. It was lovely to have their company again. They came so rarely, too rarely, though of course it was a long way to fly. Expensive. 'In terms of time and money,' Laura once said. Each time Ada had to get used to having children around again, the spiky toys underfoot, the noise. And then she was used to it, and they were gone, and she'd think she could still hear shrieking and laughter out in the garden.

Laura's voice rose above the churning sound the kettle made before it boiled. Yes, that force of Laura's, Ada thought, her *push*. How was it that she forgot about that side of Laura until she saw her again? Laura's push and success. The smart shoes and ironed shirts she wore even for Sundays with the kids, even for air travel. Laura worked on the same corridor at Coopers and Lybrand in Toronto as Charles, she did the same auditing job. It had been an office romance. Lucky for Charles. An economic exile they called him, in a strange country, bitterly cold, and him an asthmatic. He hadn't been there a month before Laura had taken him in. It was a good thing. A local girl. Make him feel at home.

Ada arranged rock cakes on a plate for the little boys. The eldest liked them the last time they visited. Two and a half years ago. Maybe the little one would be at the stage to like them now. She wished she hadn't slightly overdone them. Stupid of her. The raisins on top had smelted into shiny black knobs. Being out of practice did it. Losing her touch.

She thought about teatime, about maybe putting the tea things out on the veranda. She thought about how they'd all be together. It made her feel nervous. Each time, each meal time, it was like beginning from scratch. There was so much to ask, she didn't know what first to say. They got so little news. Charles sometimes sent faxes from work to Peter's head office here. 'All well', the faxes said, or 'All's well'. And Laura wrote once, maybe twice a year, usually at Christmas time. 'Happy Xmas', she'd scrawl under the greeting printed on the card. To fill up the space, Ada thought.

Of course the two of them had no time, of course Ada understood that. Charles took after Peter, all of her three sons did. They drove themselves hard. He wanted, he and Laura wanted the best for their children. That's why he left this country. The insecurity. He wanted stability, safe gardens, plenty of vitamin-enriched milk for his children to drink. In each generation the need acrose, like sap. For safety. It was natural. She and Peter had had it too, they had wanted to do the best for their children. They had always insisted the company give them a spread-out bungalow with big bathrooms and lots of bedrooms. But she did crave more news, she couldn't help that. At tea on the veranda it would be nice to know how to begin.

The rock cakes looked dry and inhospitable on their plate. Ada went out to pick a hibiscus flower, one of the special orange ones. She slupped her feet into the old leather gardening shoes, she let them drop off again on to the mat when she came in. The familiar double thud. She put the glossy flower in the middle of the plate.

'A touch of paradise,' the thought came to her. She stroked a satiny petal with one finger. It was a pity though that hibiscus didn't have a scent. The pollen was so sticky and golden you'd imagine they'd smell rich and lovely, of honey, heat and ginger, and something fruity, plum pudding, birthday cake.

She went upstairs in her stockinged feet to call the children down to tea. 'Dah-do-dah,' she heard the little boy chant as he toddled round the room. Charles said yesterday he'd taken his first steps four months ago. A late walker but for all that steady on his feet, steady and confident. He smiled like his father, a happy, open smile, nice full lips. She'd like to take him out into the garden with her, show him round, tell him about rose children and flower fairies, other stories she remembered, that green fairy-folk story book the boys thumbed until it fell apart, but she hadn't yet liked to ask Laura if she could. Seeing the grandchildren so rarely, you didn't want to make them grow too attached to you.

And maybe Laura and Charles didn't believe in fairy stories. You never knew. Times changed. Fairy stories had warped hidden meanings, people said. It was especially difficult with the children of sons. You didn't want to rile the mother. She mentioned it again to Peter the other night. You didn't want to be clinging and interfering. Dreadful if Laura began to see her as possessive. A clinging mother-in-law.

Ada stood at the guest room door. Laura suddenly spoke on the other side of it, loudly. Ada froze.

'Look Charles, I'm sorry to go on about it but, really, you have to be honest here. You've got to admit it's strange.'

'What is, Laura?'

'Well, a lot of things about her are strange. But mainly it's that everything in her life is so covered up, so closed in. I'm reminded of it each time. All this cover and protection is a sign of something for me, Charles, and I'm not comfortable with whatever it is. I'm not thinking of the hibiscus garden only. It's more than that.'

Ada turned but couldn't pull herself away. Laura was talking about her, almost to her face, there on the other side of the door, except she wouldn't say all that to her face. Not in that harsh biting tone. Laura was pushy and startling and abrupt, but not this sharp. Ada could never have believed she was this sharp.

'I know it's a dangerous society. You need the alarm system on the house, the security wall, the razor wire, all of it, I realise that, though I do worry the whole time that one of the boys will get his hands stuck in the wire or something. But it's like the security system has taken over her personality. She holds people at arm's length. I think of how she was yesterday when we arrived. She just stood at the door, waiting for us to come and greet her. OK, your father said it was going to be a cold night, the hibiscus needed to be covered, and the job took time, that's why she didn't come to meet us at the airport. But then to wait at the door. After almost three years. It's as though she herself is coated with some layer. Like her plants. Something that prevents her from bringing the boys close.'

The top step crackled under Ada's weight but Laura wouldn't have heard it. Her excitement had infected the little boy who was now crying. 'Ma-ma-ma,' his voice beat out, growing louder.

Ada shut the kitchen door behind her and went to stand at the breakfast bar. 'Ma-ma-ma,' the boy's crying warbled through the ceiling.

She was blushing, she could feel it, but her body was very cold and her arms and hands were trembling. She cupped her hands round the teapot. Still warm. Comforting. She pressed the pot tightly to her.

She thought of the baby hibiscus plants, warming the frost out of them. She held the teapot tight. She could never have imagined it. Forceful, beautiful Laura. So sharp. So sharp, so cross. It was dreadfully sad. She was so very sorry. Now she'd never be able to explain, after what she'd heard, how it felt. How it was missing them, missing them and missing them, month after month, and eventually half getting used to it, learning to fill up the day, gardening, caring for the hibiscus. How it was tending them, spending the days caring for them, fearing for them. It was a colder climate up here on the high African shield than they were used to. If only she could mention this to Laura one day over tea. One day soon, but casually. That this was why she liked hibiscus so much. They were tropical weather flowers and they reminded her of all the hot places where she'd brought up the boys. In Namaqualand and the Richtersveld, far north beyond the Makgadikgadi salt pans, in the middle of Broken Hill in Zambia. Hibiscus signified making gardens out of mine dumps, rocky fields, desert, bits of stone. The pride in it. In the Kalahari she used to put her boys to sleep under a mimosa tree she had planted. She wheeled them in their Silverstream pram along the rows of snapdragons, tiger lilies, and they reached out their hands to touch the flowers.

She might even explain more, if she got Laura on her own. One evening maybe, when the children were asleep. Except she never could catch Laura alone, she remembered from before. Whenever Ada was in the room Laura made sure she was holding a child, or just off to fold some clothes, find a travel brochure. 'Charles, please help me, where's that pack of recent photos got to? I seem to keep misplacing them. I wanted to show them to Peter and Ada.'

But say, say one day this visit, she was lucky to get Laura alone, lucky enough to feel the courage to go up to her, then pull her down beside her on the settee, and say, Laura.

'Laura, there's something you might find interesting.' That's how she will begin. 'There's something interesting and funny I've been meaning to tell you. It's about the hibiscus, but it also says something about what an odd sort of person I am. Do you have a minute?'

And Laura will take her hand, of her own accord, and nod for her to go on.

'It's when a frosty night is predicted, the frosty nights at the cold season. It's the combination of sudden frost and the cakey earth you get out here on the highveld that the hibiscus especially don't like. It can kill them. Overnight they flop and die. And there's just this one remedy I know. It works for children's chilblains, I remembered this from the past, so one day I thought I'd try it on my hibiscus. And it works, it really does. It's wee. As simple as that. You know, soaking them with pee. In this case women's pee especially, especially an old woman's pee. It must be the sourness in it.'

This with a laugh. And maybe she will catch Laura's eye at this point, a little embarrassed, wanting to see her reaction, and they will giggle together. Laura's dark showy eyes will light up, still watchful but waiting to be surprised, and they will laugh.

'Yes, I don't know why but it works. Old woman's pee.'

And she will speak more slowly now, savouring the words.

'I tried it again only the other day. I did it while Peter was picking you up at the airport. This was why I didn't come to meet you. I wanted to though, but I was worried about the frost. Dad, I mean Peter, doesn't know about this of course. I do it privately. He'd think it silly, I'm sure. So keep it secret, between you and me. The old enamel chamber pot the little boys use holds the warmth nicely. And then I go down to the kitchen and add warm water from the kettle. I pour the stuff on the feet of the hibiscus, just a little, just to chafe them a little and dry out any frost that might be edging its way down. And you can see how it works. A good homely recipe. The frost came but the flowers are still lovely.'

Then she will feel Laura's hand squeeze hers, Laura's face still smiling.

'I always knew it, mother,' she will say. 'You're an old wise woman. I always suspected you knew a thing or two about magical powers and growing spells.'

Ada put down the teapot. It had chilled. In the room overhead the little boy had stopped crying. The flower decorating the plate of rock cakes looked the worse for wear. The petals had blackened and curled. She picked it off and put it in the refuse pail. Hibiscus

229

didn't decorate well. They were really such perishable flowers though they looked so vivid.

She switched the kettle on again. There were footsteps on the stairs. Charles came in pushing the two little ones ahead of him. The youngest's eyelashes were still dark with tears.

'Laura's resting, mum,' said Charles. 'I think she must be completely exhausted after the flight.'

'Time for tea,' Ada said.

She held out the plate of rock cakes. She noticed there was a thick pollen dusting on one of them. It was too late to fix it.

The elder boy jammed his fingers in his mouth. The little one clawed on to his father's legs.

'Frankie doesn't like rock cakes, grandma,' the elder boy said.

He backed towards the door. He was grimacing. The little boy pulled away from his father and dodged around Ada. He tugged his brother along with him into the garden.

Wild Flowers for Poppie

JOAN BAKER

The two male children, separated by their fathers' ranks of employment on the olive farm, which was sunk in a green basin of farmlands on one of Paarl's most picturesque wine routes, spent their childhood demonstrating their incompatibility.

Years later their lives were coupled together by fate, which loves to turn our ordered existence upside down.

Pieter van der Berg's arrival in the world was noisy and without privacy. His first act of defiance was the breaking of birth-giving norms: he made his appearance not in the usual small hours, under the dignified cloak of darkness, but on a bright Saturday morning when all the farmworkers were boisterously enjoying the first day of the weekend.

The men sat in the narrow spaces between the farm cottages, taking turns to barber and be barbered. In the shade below the window of the labour room, a game of dominoes proceeded by way of arguments and ear-shattering bangs. Loud cries of 'Milo! double blank! vark vir julle!' competed with the sound of labour pains.

Women on their way home from the supermarkets in Paarl popped in to ask, 'Nog niks daar nie?' Progress reports and concern for the mother, who was trying to bring forth a broad-shouldered infant, were passed along through the cluster of cottages.

The newborn boy broadcast his entry into the world with loud wails from unquestionably healthy lungs, relieving the nurse of the task of slapping his bottom.

'Magtig, maar jy's 'n kwaai kêrel, nè! Jy wys sommer van die intrap slag jy wil nie geslaan wees nie,' the nurse scolded affectionately. She slipped his legs through the holes of the canvas-sling scale, and watched as the needle registered his weight. 'Maar kyk nou soe 'n groot meneer, moeder! 'n Visterman kan maklik eerste prys wen op 'n snoek derby met soe 'n vangs.'

The domino game was cancelled out of consideration for the exhausted mother, and the players were compensated with jugs of wine to celebrate the birth of a future olive-grove worker. They all slapped Fred van der Berg on the back, congratulating him on the son who would one day secure his parents' future on the farm. In accordance with farm custom, the son who fills his father's shoes earns the right to house his pensioned parents.

'Daardie mannetjie met sy breë skouers gaan sorg dat Fred en Anna ou bene maak op hierdie plaas,' the well-wishers predicted.

The baby, whom they named Pieter, was two months old when a loud knock in the early hours summoned his mother to the farm manager's house.

'Kom gou, Anna!' the messenger explained. 'Mevrou Cloete se baba is aan die kom.'

'Maar dit is nog nie haar tyd nie.'

'Ja, dis juis waarom nursie jou help nodig het. Die dokter is langsaan op die buchuplaas. Hy kom nog.'

Three hours later, in the large house near the entrance to the farm – in the privacy of the dark hours, and without spectators or bulletins from the orange-grove media – Douglas Cloete jnr showed signs of survival with a weak bleat, after several stinging flicks of the nurse's fingernail on the soles of his doll-sized feet.

Auntie Stienie, an olive-picker's wife and domestic help in the manager's house, brought home reports on the touch-and-go condition of the premature and jaundiced baby. 'Die arme skepseltjie is goudgeel,' she said.

The workers, who had little reason to harbour loyalty or affection for their surly farm manager, blamed him for bringing the wrath of God down on his wife. Some elaborated by claiming that his semen was as sour as his disposition, that he had sowed a lemon seed in his wife's womb.

In time, the 'lemon' outgrew his yellow complexion, but colic often reduced him to a screaming bundle, wriggling with fretfulness. Auntie Stienie's day-by-day description of the skepseltjie's irritability convinced the gossips that the child had indeed inherited his father's unpleasant nature.

Two years passed, and Anna van der Berg gave birth to another child, this time a daughter.

'Dié, is die blom van die plaas,' the visitors proclaimed, oohing and aahing over the fair-skinned, light-eyed baby with the silky beginnings of what was definitely going to be a crop of blonde tresses. Even mothers with baby daughters of their own admitted, somewhat reluctantly, that the child was exceptionally beautiful.

Sarah van der Berg was named for her late paternal grandmother. As she grew and was passed around from house to house, many other names were bestowed on her by the farm community, flattering little pet names like Prinsesie and Poppie. It was Poppie that stuck with her throughout her childhood.

Her parents were teased endlessly about her appearance. 'Is dié, nie miskien 'n witman se kind nie?' people joked.

Auntie Meisie, the oldest person on the farm, had her own theory, based on her knowledge of South African history: 'Die kind het vir Jan van Riebeeck uit die grond uitgegrawe.'

When he was six years old, Douglas jnr was enrolled in the primary school in Paarl. He was driven to and from school by his mother, and seldom saw Pieter and his devoted band of followers, who attended the farm school, a large barn which the farm owner had converted into two classrooms. Douglas jnr acquired two or three friends at school, and he paraded these smartly dressed visitors past the shabby farm children at weekends. He himself kept his distance from the farm children, especially the tall, broad-shouldered one called Pieter.

Then the poorly qualified farm-school teacher gave fate a hand and meddled in the course of Douglas jnr's life.

When this teacher discovered the reason for Pieter's restless fidgeting in the makeshift benches, and his bored disregard for the lessons she taught, she approached his parents, and then the farm owner. 'This child is streets ahead of the rest of the class,' she said. 'He needs the challenge of a proper schooling.'

The farm owner, who had noticed the boy's alertness, and his ability to supervise the younger boys in the gathering of fallen olives after the picking, agreed to pay for his school uniform and fees, so that he could attend the primary school in Paarl. The priming of a future farm manager was well disguised as an act of benevolence. Only the wise old Auntie Meisie saw through the scheme, and predicted that Pieter's own hand would push him out of reach.

Douglas jnr was unpleasantly surprised to see the boy called Pieter at his school the following year. He made plans of his own, campaigning among his friends to ostracise the farm boy. But Pieter's charisma and talent for mischief gained him a following that brought about the collapse of his opponent's campaign.

Mrs Cloete, in her usual friendly way, had offered Pieter a lift to school, but was politely turned down. She did not force the issue. When she and her son passed Pieter on the farm road, Douglas jnr would stick his head out of the window to sneer at the boy left behind in a red fog of dust. His smug smile stimulated the flow of bad blood between the boys.

Pieter's consideration for his father and his job on the farm, menial though it might be, was all that stood between his extra-large fist and Douglas jnr's sharp, pinched nose; it was like a leash on his fist, which tingled with the urge to beat that puny face until it resembled an olive, twice pressed.

Douglas jnr's main afternoon entertainment was to sit half-hidden in the low chair on the front stoep, with the farm dog panting in the shade beside him, until one of the labourers' children passed. Then he would open the gate and egg the mongrel on with a whispered, 'Sa! Hitler . . . Sa!' It gave him pleasure to watch the children run for cover, with the slobbering dog at their heels.

Usually reports of these attacks reached Pieter. The next day – the day of reckoning – he would stroll with an inflated chest past the manager's house, a protective arm slung around the victim's shoulders. He kept close to the gate. A wordless challenge invited Douglas jnr and his dog to give a repeat performance.

When it became obvious that all the farm children were protected by the Don of the olive groves, Douglas jnr abandoned his sport.

Pieter underlined his message by practising his stone-throwing skills whenever he and his gang passed the manager's house on their way to the mountains to pick wild flowers. Most of the stones aimed at Hitler found their mark. When the boys came back with the pocket money they earned by selling the flowers next to the highway, the chair on the stoep was empty, and Hitler was lying in the shade licking his wounds.

Pieter would be the only one still bearing flowers. His harvest was for his sister. He made the climb to spare his genteel Poppie the rough and tumble of the excursion, and exposure to the bad language that followed scraped knees and encounters with sharp thorns.

Sarah loved wild flowers more than roses and other hothouse blooms. She knew the name of every flower. Her growing stacks of exercise books filled with drawings of wild flowers were regularly examined and admired by the people of the farm.

Years passed, and the farm children grew up.

Pieter became a teacher and went to live in Cape Town (most of his boyhood friends inherited their fathers' jobs on the farm). When Sarah graduated from college she would also be leaving, as she had applied to do her BA at the University of Cape Town.

Fred and Anna planned to join their children in the city, where they had resigned themselves to spending their old age. But before that could happen, they both died – as if by some pact – within months of each other. Sarah therefore made the move to Cape Town on her own.

Unbeknown to her, Douglas Cloete – he had lost the 'jnr' that had once kept him in the shadow of his father – was also in the city, and teaching at the university. His swagger had become more pronounced now that his degrees had elevated him to heights far above his late father's managerial status, and he applied himself with overbearing zest to his role as a political science lecturer.

Douglas was unlocking his car door one afternoon, when a female student crossing the parking area caused him to fumble and drop his keys. When he straightened up again she was gone. That briefest of encounters had an unfamiliar effect on him. She was the most beautiful girl he had seen on campus. Never had he felt so sexually attracted to a woman before. Just thinking about her, as he drove home, gave him an erection.

Although he had merely glimpsed her, she had sneaked inside his head with distracting effect, and he found his tongue tripping for lack of concentration in the middle of his lectures. He looked for her on campus, hopefully scanning the faces in lecture halls and corridors. But she eluded him.

Then one afternoon, as he was leaving the parking area in his car, he saw her walking, and drew up next to her.

'Going my way?'

Identifying him as a lecturer, she climbed in beside him.

His face burned with embarrassment. He wished he could rephrase his offer. 'Going my way . . .' Had he really said that? Surely a student would expect something more original from a lecturer. He sounded like a cruiser, he scolded himself silently.

He wanted to tell her he had seen her before, but that would sound juvenile. In the end, he chose silence. It was more dignified. They drove along the main road, not speaking at all, until she showed him where to pull over.

'Thank you very much.' Blushing with appreciation. He liked the cultured tone of her voice – soft, but not timid.

'We could make this a permanent arrangement if you like,' he suggested, reluctant to see her go. 'I drive this way every day.'

'Thank you, that's very kind, but my brother fetches me most afternoons. He teaches not too far from here.'

She opened the door.

'I'm Douglas, by the way,' he said quickly. 'Douglas Cloete.'

'Sandra van der Berg.'

For a moment, he was tempted to ask if she had relatives in Paarl, just to keep her talking, but he let it pass. Questions could lead to more questions and cross-questions, until his farm up-bringing was revealed.

She slid gracefully from the passenger seat, and he drove away. The scent of her, lingering in the car, excited him, and he tugged at the crotch of his pants, where his erection was pressing uncomfort-ably against the zip.

'I'm in love – I'm in love – I'm in love – with a beautiful girl!' he sang. He was not one for breaking into song. Even the privacy of his car did not stop him from feeling foolish.

'I'm in love – I'm in love –' Composers of love songs had yet to provide the world with the words to describe adequately the phenomenon that made his temples, his heart, and his penis throb simultaneously.

He pursued her with contrived, accidental collisions on campus.

Through his inexperience with the opposite sex, several opportunities to make a breakthrough in their courtship went wasted. There was also the taboo on fraternising between staff and students to contend with. Deciding between a stainless career record and his uncontrollable desire left him with dark-ringed eyes and nails bitten to the quick.

The afternoon lifts slipped into a permanent arrangement. Soon he was taking her to restaurants in out-of-the-way places like Constantia and Hout Bay. Places students could not afford to patronise.

'My brother would like to meet you,' Sandra announced one afternoon.

'Did you tell him about us?'

'Well, he wanted to know who the gallant gentleman is who gives me a lift every day.'

'What's he like . . . this brother of yours who always manages to creep into our conversations?'

'He's not at all like me. He's very charming, outgoing. And loads of fun – he has legions of friends. He bullies me sometimes . . .'

'In other words, he's not at all like me either.'

She neither confirmed nor contested the observation.

Two evenings later, the manager's son and the Don of the olive groves stared into each other's open mouths from opposite sides of the threshold.

'Poppie, do you know who this is?' Pieter asked.

'Don't be silly – it's Douglas. I told you I was bringing him.'

'Yes, but it's Douglas Cloete jnr . . . the farm manager's son.'

'So?' Sandra challenged, swallowing her surprise.

Pieter stuck his head through the doorway and made a show of searching for something. It flashed through Douglas's mind that he was looking for his newspaper.

Then Pieter asked, 'Where is Hitler?'

'Died years ago,' Douglas said weakly. The mocking reminder had stung.

'Come inside, Mr Manager jnr. Have a drink.'

'I don't drink.'

'Poppie, make Mr Manager jnr some tea. What's your poison? Rooibos? . . . Ceylon? . . . Earl Grey?'

'I'll have an Appletiser, if you've got.'

Sandra fetched the juice. In a way she was delighted by the coincidental twist that had put her and her admirer on more or less the same footing.

'I remember my mother always spoke about Van der Berg's pretty daughter,' Douglas was saying when she returned. 'But I thought her name was Sarah?'

'Same girl . . . different setting,' Pieter replied with an outstretched hand, like a compère introducing an artiste.

'I changed my name from Sarah to Sandra when I came to Cape Town,' she explained. 'I hated the name, and it sounded out of place in the city. It sounds so . . .'

'Rural?' her brother suggested. 'You see, Mr Manager jnr, like many other snobs I would rather not name, Sandra the city girl is a little ashamed of Sarah the farm girl.'

'It's not that, Pete.'

'Don't you Pete me, Miss La-di-da,' Pieter teased. He encircled her neck with his thick bare arm to show there were no hard feelings. 'I love this pretty little miss. I'll do anything, but die, for her. She's the only family I have. The jerk who hurts her will have acquired a taste for hospital food by the time he's well enough to be discharged.'

Douglas understood the message, delivered with a smile. All those years ago, when he had sneered at Pieter from the safety of his mother's car on the way home from school, he had provoked nothing but a cold stare. Now Pieter was articulating the threat that stare had always concealed.

'Why do you call her Poppie?' Douglas changed the subject.

But the explanation was cancelled out by the noisy arrival of Eunice, Pieter's gregarious live-in lover. She let a scuffed leather bag slip from her shoulder, flopped into a huge beanbag, and stuck out her hand. Pieter fitted the stem of a wine glass into the curve of her fingers.

Douglas envied this comfortable familiarity that required no language to communicate a need.

'Oh Eunice, this is Douglas Cloete.'

'Hi.'

'Pleased to –'

But she cut him off with, 'Don't ask how my day was.'

Douglas peered over the rim of his half-empty glass at this woman who looked as if she had twirled herself into her garments. She was wrapped in a skirt that was stitched down one side only. A confusion of long scarves over a tank top brought to mind a maypole waiting for dancers to put all the loose ends into some kind of order. An Afro hairstyle completed the picture. There were dozens of women like Eunice on campus, and Douglas found them slightly scary.

As he drove home later, Douglas cursed fate's sick sense of humour. This romance had taken so long to develop, but now it had to be reassessed. Were they really compatible? He had noticed the ANC posters on Pieter's walls. Douglas himself had political ambitions, but they were leading him towards the Labour Party, whose ideology could not have been more different. He had to weigh the emptiness of a future without Sandra against his reservations about a prospective brother-in-law who was not only a boor, but a social thorn in the side. 'Never mind a thorn,' Douglas warned himself, 'if he marries that unrefined scarf rack, I may as well prepare myself for an ice-pick.'

In the end, Douglas submitted to the pull of his heartstrings.

The wedding was quiet. The bride and groom spent just an hour at the modest reception before leaving for the honeymoon.

At the open door of the waiting taxi, Sandra gave her brother the last of a series of hugs. His qualms about her choice of husband upset her. For his part, Douglas was surprised by the tears zigzagging unchecked down the cheeks of the Don.

While they drove through the empty streets, Douglas looked at his wife's hands. Sandra, who had so carelessly tossed her expensive bouquet into the groping hands of the spinsters, was gently stroking the stiff petals of the wild flowers her brother had passed through the window of the taxi.

Time flapped its wings, scattering events in its wake: the marriage of Pieter and Eunice – the birth of their two daughters – a son to continue the Cloete blood line – Douglas Cloete's rise through the ranks in the Labour Party – his seat in the House of Representatives.

Despite his efforts over the years, Douglas failed hopelessly to disentangle the bonds between brother and sister, or between their offspring. He himself grew no closer to Pieter. In the end, he no longer needed to excuse himself from family gatherings, because no invitations were extended for him to honour or dishonour. Pieter's feet too felt out of place beneath his brother-in-law's dinner table.

But when an invitation arrived unexpectedly, Eunice hoodwinked Pieter into accepting by prodding his conscience. 'Ag, let's go for your sister's sake,' she wheedled.

Douglas went to the kitchen to fetch some ice. While he fiddled with the ice-trays, he observed his two guests, and complimented himself on the wisdom of keeping the dinner private. There was no telling what kind of atmosphere the ANC button on his brother-in-law's lapel would have created, had some of his colleagues been subjected to the defiant taunt.

And that rebellious feminist wife of his, Douglas sighed – all decked out like Mama Africa, in a tie-dye caftan with ethnic designs all over it. He was convinced she had her hair braided and beaded just to annoy him.

The three children clattered in from upstairs to seek a grown-up's opinion on a matter of debate between them.

'Uncle Pete! Uncle Pete! What is heavier . . .?'

It piqued Douglas that his son should prefer Pieter's opinion to his own. He followed the children into the dining-room. Sandra tagged along carrying two serving dishes. Douglas measured the robustness of his two nieces against the delicate figure of his son. A sly look at his brother-in-law's smug expression forced a backhanded compliment out of him.

'You've got two lovely girls, Pete. A pity you don't have a son to pass on the Van der Berg name. Why don't you have another try?'

'Are you advising my husband to have another child?' Eunice butted in.

'Yes! Why not?'

'Because he doesn't have a womb, that's why not.'

Sandra quickly snuffed the fuse of this conflict by calling them to the table.

They were hardly seated, when Douglas said, 'So, Pete, did your sister tell you about my portfolio?'

'No. I suspected there must be some reason for the invitation, but I have no idea what this culinary courtship is all about.'

'You are now dining with the Minister of Education.'

'Do you mean the House of Reps' overseer of coloured schooling?'

'The future looks bleak, Pieter,' Eunice lamented, 'better cancel that heir.'

This taunting discussion continued throughout the meal. Over coffee, Sandra tried to lighten the atmosphere by appealing to her sister-in-law. 'The Labour Party's wives have been invited to a garden tea at Westbrooke next month, and we are each allowed to take a guest. I'd like you to come with me.'

Eunice coughed a spray of Irish coffee over the scraps on her plate. Spluttering and choking, she grabbed a damask serviette to mop her mouth and the front of her caftan, and in the process toppled a glass of white wine. Pieter laughed out loud at his wife's reaction to the invitation.

'Go, Eunice, you may enjoy it,' Douglas coaxed her, with sincerity. He was sensitive to his wife's nervousness at these occasions. 'Sandra can lend you one of her outfits.'

Pieter's outrage was silenced by Eunice's calm response. 'That's very sweet of you, Douglas. I'll let you select the outfit. Why not go the whole hog? How about choosing my panties for me – what would you suggest? – a bikini – a G-string – or should I go bare bum? I'd love to moon those Stepford wives.'

'Don't be vulgar, Eunice, it's unnecessary. Douglas didn't mean to offend you.'

'What! The bastard offers me a cast-off from your wardrobe, and you say that's not offensive!'

'Pete, please say something,' Sandra begged.

'Well, I'm all for the G-string,' Pieter obliged, still flushed with laughter.

'Come, Pieter, get the girls. I'm out of here.'

'There's no need for you to spoil the children's evening too, Eunice. You are far too hasty.'

'Do you know what the pair of you need, Sandra – or should I say Sarah? – you need a bit of that wholesome farm humility.'

'And you need to climb off the back-to-my-roots bandwagon,' Sandra retorted.

'I'll never put my foot in this house again.'

'Suit yourself.'

The Van der Bergs left in a huff with their protesting daughters (they had been way ahead in the TV games).

At bedtime, Sandra's eyes were still swollen. She had not responded to any of Douglas's efforts to cheer her up by making small talk.

'What are all these flowers doing in the basin?' Douglas asked from the bathroom.

'Just leave them there. They were supposed to be for Eunice.'

'I don't know why you're so angry. Eunice would have embarrassed you anyway. That beaded curtain posing as a hairstyle would have raised quite a few eyebrows. Why does she have to dress up like a sangoma? You should ask one of the ladies you've met at the functions to go with you, or one of your old university friends.'

'I think I'll just stay home.'

'You have a book full of addresses and phone numbers. Why don't you nurture those links? You'll have a heavier social responsibility from now on. I sometimes wish you had some of your sister-in-law's feistiness. What about that woman who made you promise you'd visit her?'

'What woman?'

'The one you met at the art exhibition last week. The two of you had a long discussion on that still life with arum lilies, remember?'

'Oh yes! Doris Mayer. We were talking about flowers, not the painting. She makes picture frames and jewellery boxes with pressed wild flowers. I told her about my sketches.'

'Now there you are – you have the address – take your sketches along with you. You have to learn to use your initiative, especially now.'

'Perhaps I'll take her those flowers too.'

'Phone first. White people are funny about unexpected visits. And whatever you do, don't overdress. That's another thing white people judge you by. Why don't you wear that plain red silk dress we bought in London? It's casual, but tasteful.'

The next morning, Douglas left for his chambers with the sound of triumph on his puckered lips in the form of a tuneless whistle. The dinner party had been a success after all. It had allowed him to bring the curtain down on an unpleasant part of his life.

A domestic wearing green overalls and a matching doek opened Doris Mayer's front door. She looked familiar, although Sandra could not place her.

But Nomsa recognised Sandra at once – the face that had turned so many heads on that dreadful night.

It had happened a few months ago. Nomsa was working as a casual for Cut Glass Caterers, and that night they had catered a State function. She would never forget the moment her tray caught on the edge of the table and tipped a glass of water into the lap of one of the guests, a woman – this woman who was now standing on the doorstep. Her obnoxious husband had caused such a fuss that it had cost Nomsa her job and the badly needed extra income.

'Who is it, Nomsa?' a voice called from inside the house.

'Someone selling flowers, madam.'

'Say no thank you.'

'But I'm not –'

Nomsa shut the door.

'Won't you see who that is, Pieter,' Eunice called out.

Pieter opened the door. Poppie stood there weeping. He smiled at his sister sadly and reached out for her. He stroked away her tears with his thumb. Then he put his hand behind her head and drew her face to his chest.

'Who is it, Pieter?'

'It's someone with flowers.'

'Are they fresh?'

'They're wild flowers.'

'Buy a bunch, and I'll take them to Poppie.'

The Wheels of God

DAVID MEDALIE

The town in which Ina lived was uninspiringly new. Sue could only think of it as an instant town, created yesterday, even though it was probably more than twenty years old. It had been determined during the years of South Africa's isolation that it was necessary to convert more coal into fuel and a large town had come into existence as a result; a whole town, summoned with a click of the fingers out of the empty veld, as meek as if the mandarins of the old Nationalist government had been as omnipotent as God. And here it stood, all its history as new as a scab that has not yet been shed.

Sue thought she would remember where Ina's house was, but it was too long since her last visit and her vague memories proved inadequate. After a while, she accepted that she was lost. A petrol attendant set her in the right direction, and then she found Ina's home quite easily. She looked at the houses that lined the quiet Sunday-morning streets, wondering what it was like to live in them and why it was that the inhabitants did not get out while they still could. These soporific houses must have a secret power, some sort of drug which they administered to the people who lived in them so that they remained docile and compliant. 'There but for the grace of God go I,' she thought.

That was one of the sayings she had kept with her from her childhood, from her mother's stock of truisms. Her mother was a great believer in received wisdom: she found it in aphoristic hand-me-downs, which she offered solemnly as if uncorking bottles of vintage wine. Sue had misgivings about most of them and never sought them out deliberately, but they flitted none the less into her mind from time to time. Because she could not prevent them from coming, she made them mean what she wanted them to mean. In this case, for instance, she didn't believe in grace or in God, but she used the saying when she wanted to remind herself of a lucky escape. Looking about her at this town, she considered that, whatever misfortunes she had met with in life, this jaded newness she had at least escaped. But Glenda and her mother, Ina, had lived in a succession of platteland towns, each, Glenda had said, worse than the previous one. This town, to which Ina had moved after Glenda had left home, was undoubtedly the worst. The few times Sue and Glenda had come there together to visit Ina, towards the beginning of their relationship, Glenda had grown quiet and distant, as if seeing in the town the declension of her mother's life and of her own childhood.

Sello was growing restless. He hated long car journeys. 'We're nearly there,' Sue said to him. 'Just wait a few more moments.' She found Ina's house and parked in the street, but Ina appeared at the front door, calling to her to pull the car into the driveway. Ina kissed her on the cheek and then didn't seem to know how to respond to Sello. He, in turn, clung to Sue. 'Here's Ina,' she said to him. 'Granny Ina. Do you remember her?' There was no way he could, of course. He had probably only met her twice in his life and he had certainly not seen her since Glenda's death. He shook his head and was silent. 'He's shy,' she said apologetically.

'Come inside,' said Ina. 'I'm sure you want something to drink.'

They followed her inside, Sue carrying her overnight bag into which she had managed to squeeze a change of clothes for herself and Sello for the next day as well as some of his books and toys. The house inside was dark, very clean and austere. There was a framed copy of *Desiderata* on the wall in the sitting-room. Because it was there, phrases from it came unbidden to Sue, like a monotonous tune that one cannot get out of one's head: 'avoid loud and aggressive persons . . . the universe is unfolding as it should . . .' She found herself wondering if it was possible to sing 'the universe is unfolding as it should' to the tune of *London Bridge Is Falling Down* or *Here We Go Round the Mulberry Bush*?

Enough! She rebuked herself, but not sternly, and paid attention instead to what Ina was saying: 'I wasn't sure where to put him.

Will he sleep in a room on his own?'

'No. Put him in with me.'

She left the overnight bag in the bedroom that she and Sello would share and then they all sat down at the kitchen table. Sue and Ina drank tea, while Sello had a glass of orange squash. Ina put a plate of biscuits in front of him. 'Choose the one you want and eat it,' Sue said to him. 'Don't touch them all.'

After a while Ina said, 'Sue, I want to thank you for coming to see me.'

'Thank you for the invitation. We haven't seen you since the funeral.'

There was a silence. 'How have you been?' Sue asked.

'Not too bad. And you?'

'I have my days. And Sello can be difficult. He misses Glenda. Being a single parent was never one of my plans, I can tell you.' Ina made no reply. 'But I have no regrets. He is a lovable little boy. Glenda adored him. I cannot look at him without thinking how much she loved him.'

She considered her own words with mild astonishment. They seemed to have sidled out of her mouth while she wasn't looking. Without setting out to do so, she was marking her territory, claiming the dead Glenda for herself and for Sello, rebuking Glenda's mother by hinting – more than hinting – that her love had fallen short. The habit of fighting for Glenda was so strong that it seemed to have survived Glenda herself.

Ina said, 'Would you mind very much if I got straight to the point? I've invited some people for lunch and once they arrive, we won't be able to talk. I know it's not polite to bombard you as soon as you walk in.'

'Please go ahead.'

'I haven't been very well lately. I suppose old age is creeping up on me. I'm sure I'll be around for quite a while, but, in any case, I decided recently that I must get my will sorted out. After Glenda died, I changed it in favour of my sister, who lives in Durban. But now I want to change it again.'

Sello was growing restless once more. Sue asked if she could take him outside to play in the back garden. 'He's been cooped up in the car for hours. You can't blame him.'

Sello scurried ahead of her. He was content to be left to play by himself. 'Call me if you want me,' Sue said to him.

'OK.'

'See ya later, alligator.'

'In a while, crocodile,' roared Sello.

When they sat down again, Ina said, 'I've decided that I want to leave everything to this child. Also, I have a policy coming due this year which I want to make over to him now, while I'm still alive. I don't really need it for myself.'

Sue's mother would have said, 'Miracles will never cease.' Sue didn't believe in miracles, so for her the expression merely signified astonishment.

'You didn't need to *tell* me of this decision. You could simply have changed your will in his favour and put the money from the policy away for him.'

'No, I wanted to discuss it with you. Firstly, I don't even know what his proper name is. I'm sorry.'

'His first names are Sello Michael. It's spelt S-e-l-l-o. Those are the names he had when Glenda and I adopted him. His surname, of course, is Glenda's. In other words, it's the same as yours.'

All her efforts notwithstanding, some sarcasm was creeping in. She told herself to be more careful.

'The other thing,' said Ina, 'is what exactly to do with the money. I'm not a wealthy woman, but this house is paid off. He would get quite a lot. Should I leave it in trust, with yourself as the trustee, so that it can be used one day for his education?'

'If you really want to do something for him, you should leave it to me to use on his behalf. And you should make the policy over to me as soon as the money becomes available. I'm sorry to be so blunt, but you wanted to know what I think. So I'm telling you.'

Ina hesitated.

'You don't have to worry. I won't use a cent of it for myself. It will all be for him.'

'I don't doubt that. I just want to do what's best. That's why I asked you to come here.'

'What is best is what I have told you.'

Sello was calling her. 'Sue-Ma . . . Sue-Ma.' (He had always called them 'Sue-Ma' and 'Glenda-Ma'.) As Sue walked through the house, she noticed a framed photograph of Glenda, aged about eighteen, on a sideboard. There were also photographs of her when she was a baby or still at school. Predictably, there were no photo-graphs taken during the last ten years of her life, nothing from the period in which she and Sue were together, nothing from the years in which they lived with Sello as a family. It was as if the Glenda who had loved another woman and who had adopted a little black boy had been wiped out. Yet that woman and that child were all that Ina had left to her now. It was a cruel retribution, too cruel even for Ina. Sue had thought that there was no punishment severe enough for a woman who rejected her only child. Yet now she felt that there was no crime severe enough for this punishment.

More trespassing words crept up on her: 'the wheels of God grind slowly,' she thought. This was a corruption of another of her mother's maxims. Making her voice as stern and declamatory as possible, her mother used to say, 'The mills of God grind slowly, yet they grind exceeding small.' When she was a child, Sue thought her mother said 'the *wheels* of God'. Even when she learned what it was supposed to be, she thought 'the wheels of God' sounded better, so it stayed that way. She spent most of her childhood in awe of that saying, frightened of the wheels of God and the relentless monosyllables in which they thundered along; but she had no idea what it meant. Later, when the meaning came to her one day, unmasking the familiar words as if bringing a spy in the house to light, she found the expression disappointingly banal. It seemed to be about retribution and reward. Wait long enough, it seemed to say, and the retribution or the reward will come. Well, big deal.

She went out to the backyard. Sello had discovered that there were scuttling creatures that lived beneath the stones that lay scattered about the rockery. Glenda would have been able to tell him what they were. Sue tried her best. She showed him that some of the ants were red and others were black. The long, slow, black millipede, she told him, was a shongololo. Sello repeated the delicious word to himself – *shongololo* – and laughed with pleasure.

'We're going to have lunch,' she said. 'Let's go and wash.'

They went inside. Ina was setting the table. 'Can I help?' Sue asked.

'Thank you, but it's all done.'

Ina covered the table with a net. 'The flies are very bad here,' she explained. Sue took Sello to the bathroom. When they came back, Ina said, 'Did Glenda ever mention a girl called Veronica Johnson? They were at school together in Brakpan.'

'Yes.' Veronica had been Glenda's first great friend. Afterwards Glenda realised that it was her first great love, but she didn't think in those terms at the time. She had recounted anecdotes of their friendship and Sue, who had been jealous, had pretended to find them amusing.

'You won't believe it, but she's living here. She works in the library. She's Veronica Schutte now. Her husband, Pieter, is the town clerk. She recognised me immediately. Isn't life full of extraordinary coincidences?'

'Indeed.'

'I invited them for lunch today. They want to meet you.'

The guests arrived not long afterwards. 'I was always sorry that Glenda and I lost touch,' said Veronica, after they had been introduced. 'When her Mom walked into the library one day, I couldn't believe my eyes. I was so excited. I thought: here is the chance to get together with Glenda again. Then she told me about the accident. I was devastated.'

Sue sighed. 'Yes. The most careful driver, the one who didn't drink at the office party so that she could drive the others home. And someone shoots through a red traffic light. Everyone else survives and Glenda is killed.'

'So much for caution.' Veronica shook her head. After a pause, she continued, 'I'm so pleased to meet you. And your little boy. Ina has spoken of you both.'

Pieter, lowering his voice, said, 'Ina is a very special woman, is she not? So dignified, despite all her troubles.'

'Yes.' Ina's dignity was not something Sue could appreciate, for it seemed inseparable from her aloofness, and therefore from that which had wounded Glenda. But she did not begrudge Ina the admiration of these people.

During lunch, Pieter and Veronica assured Sue that the town was not as arid a place as it seemed. There were a number of educated, professional people like themselves who had seen the mushroom town as a place of opportunity. 'It's not often nowadays that people can feel like pioneers,' said Pieter. 'And we haven't neglected culture. There is a new, state-of-the-art theatre. We've been able to enjoy plays, ballet, musicals – even an opera or two.'

There was some perfunctory talk of Gilbert and Sullivan, Gershwin, Prokofiev, Wilde and Shaw.

When Ina went to the kitchen to see to the dessert, Veronica leaned over to Sue. 'Speaking of pioneers, I hope you won't mind if we say how much we admire you. The adoption of this little boy is such a wonderful thing. I thought it was amazing when Ina told me about it, but now that I see you together, I realise even more how incredible it is.'

'It was Glenda's idea. I wasn't keen at first, but I came round to it eventually.'

'Did you not consider having a child of your own?' asked Pieter. 'You know, through insemination?'

'I hope you don't feel we're prying.' Veronica patted her hand. 'We feel so relaxed with you. It's like being with an old friend.'

'Yes, we did think of that,' said Sue. 'But Glenda wanted to go for the adoption instead. She had specific reasons for wanting it that way.'

'And now you're bringing up a black child – all on your own! Are you going to cope?'

'I have no choice.'

Ina came back into the room. She had baked an apple tart, which they ate with cream. Sello didn't want any and was given a bowl of ice cream instead. 'Say thank you.' Sue tapped him on the arm. 'He loves ice cream.'

Veronica, she noticed, made no attempt to speak of her friendship with Glenda. Sue couldn't decide if she was relieved or disappointed. When the relationship with Glenda grew more secure, she had ceased to feel jealous of Glenda's past; but, now that Glenda was herself the past, she found herself feeling possessive once more.

Sello suddenly lost his shyness and went through his repertoire of rhymes and songs. *Pop Goes the Weasel* appeared unexpectedly in the middle of songs from *The Lion King*.

'Amazing how they still learn many of the same things that we learned as children,' said Veronica.

'Not in my case.' Sue was surprised by her own curtness. 'I wouldn't dream of teaching him some of the things I learned as a child.'

Veronica found a sucker in her handbag and gave it to Sello.

When the couple left, they both hugged Sue and urged her to visit again soon. 'You could stay with us,' said Veronica. 'But I don't imagine that Ina would be prepared to give you up.'

'No, certainly not.' Ina smiled at Sue.

After they had gone, Ina and Sue washed the dishes together. 'Such a delightful couple,' said Ina. 'Broad-minded, too.'

'Very nice.'

Then Ina said, 'I want to go back to the subject of the money. I still don't understand why you don't want me to put it in trust for Sello until he's older. You won't need large amounts of money while he's still small.'

'As I said before, you will have to accept that I know what is best for him. That is my advice. Of course, the decision is yours.'

Ina scrubbed at the bottom of a pot with a pot-scourer. 'Is this child sick?'

'No.'

'Please tell me the truth. Is that why you think you may need the money? Is he sick?'

'No.'

'Sue, don't play games with me. I'm not as stupid as you think.'

'I've never considered you stupid.'

'Then answer me. Has this child got Aids?'

'No.'

'HIV?'

'Yes.' There was a long silence. They did not look at each other.

'When did you find out?'

'We always knew. He was like that when we adopted him.'

'You adopted him, knowing that he had it? That he will die?'

'I don't believe that he will die. But yes, we knew.'

'But why? Why?'

'It was Glenda's decision. She wanted to adopt a child, not have one herself. And she was prepared to take an HIV child.'

'I don't understand.'

'No, I don't think you will. Glenda would have explained it better if you'd been around at the time. It's about – what's the right word, I wonder? – it's about intervention. It's about standing up to what I call the wheels of God.'

'Now I understand even less.'

'Is it *necessary* that you understand, Ina? Surely what matters is that it was Glenda's decision – what she wanted. And unless I am reading the situation wrongly, it seems to me that you are trying to make your peace with Glenda and her decisions. Isn't that why you invited me here? And isn't that why you are trying to do something for Sello?'

Ina nodded.

'Well then, don't balk now. Don't put the brakes on now.' Ina made no reply.

A quiet afternoon followed. Sue read to Sello and then they both lay down and dozed off. When she woke, she could hear that the radio was on in Ina's room. In the distance, there was the sound of children kicking a ball. The bedroom was full of languorous shadows. In her fuzzy state, it seemed to her that the tenor of the world was sloth, sloth and more sloth; that it was quite obviously so; that the shongololo had read the mood correctly all along. How had the tone ever come to be mistaken for frenzy? Who had announced a juggernaut when there was none? Sello lay curled up next to her; his innocence looked invincible. Sue had never imagined that there could be such serenity in this house of old pain, or in this town, stuck so hastily and with such gross expedience into the ground.

Ina appeared at the door of the bedroom. She spoke softly, so as not to wake Sello. 'Do you want something to eat?'

'I'm still full from that enormous lunch. It put me to sleep. I almost never sleep in the afternoons.'

'What about something small? Toasted sandwiches? Does Sello like that?'

'Yes. He does. Thank you.'

Ina walked to the kitchen and Sue could hear her switching on the light and opening the door of the fridge. She should get up, she thought; she should help her make the toasted sandwiches. But the effort was too great. Instead, she remained there, listening to Sello's even breathing, lying quite motionless in the room that had now grown dark.

Mister Donut

JENNY HOBBS

When the stock market fell again and the broking firms had to retrench, Philip Croeser accepted the package offered to him without regret. He had never enjoyed being a stockbroker.

Philip was a quiet meticulous sociable man with one driving ambition: to support his family in comfort by his own efforts. He wanted his children to be able to say with pride, 'My Dad is a self-made man.' His own father had deserted his mother when he was only two and her bitterness had corroded his childhood.

A one-man business with room for expansion would be the ideal way to start. He took his time looking around and two months later, after careful research, used his lump sum pension as down payment on a doughnut franchise in a new shopping centre nearby. The trading name was to be *Mr Donut*, and the three children were ecstatic.

His wife was not. 'A shop? But you'll loathe it, Phil. Standing behind a counter dishing out doughnuts, of all things. You'll die of boredom.'

'After fifteen years of handling other people's money, I want to make some of my own,' he said. 'You must understand, love. More franchises are available if we do well with this one, so there's room for expansion. It's a family sort of business too. The kids can lend a hand after school and you could help me in the mornings sometimes.'

'But doughnuts!'

'I never thought you were a snob, Selma?'

'I'm not.'

He saw by the look on her face that he was going about this the wrong way and said in a more placatory tone, 'Can't you see that I'd rather stand behind a counter – my own counter – selling doughnuts, than go on relying on other people's greed to make a living?'

'You've never talked like this before,' she accused.

'I've never stood on my own two feet before.' Unconsciously he moved one foot away from the other and planted it on the carpet.

Her breath seemed to drain away so that she was gasping as she said, 'I should have guessed. This must be what they call the male menopause.' The door slammed behind her.

Philip found refuge from her sour face in the many details to be seen to before the new shop could open. There was equipment to buy: apart from the doughnut machine, there were to be ice cream, cool-drink and coffee dispensers, fridges, washing equipment, a bar counter and stools, and a glass showcase for the doughnuts. Then there were the municipal by-laws to be studied and conformed with: so much space for washing up and utilities; so many lights, plugs, windows, ventilators, rubbish bins; such hours of closing, health regulations, bacteria counts. He wallpapered the front part of the shop himself in a yellow and orange daisy pattern, adding orange formica shelves to match the orange counter. He had *MR DONUT* painted in gold lettering on the plate glass window.

The children were thrilled with their father's new glamour. They broadcast the news at school and round the suburb: 'My Dad's opening a doughnut shop!' The day he opened (Selma came with a pinched smile to cut the orange ribbon stretched across the doorway) there was a long queue of customers as soon as school was over. It seemed as though every child in the neighbourhood had nagged for doughnut money. He did a roaring trade all afternoon and well into the evening with his opening offer of two for the price of one.

The automatic doughnut machine intrigued everyone. He had to tell and retell the story behind its invention during the First World War so that American troops in Europe would be able to have familiar food even at the battlefront, and how it had led to their being called doughboys.

The machine was a square stainless steel contraption with glass sides and could make 360 an hour. It stood to one side behind the counter, where you could watch it imperturbably squirting rings of doughnut mix from a swivelling arm into a bath of hot bubbling oil. A submerged conveyor belt carried them along in twos and at the half-way mark a steel gadget flipped them over. On reaching the other end they were scooped up by a strainer, sizzling and perfectly cooked. When cool, the doughnuts were decorated with different icings – cherry, vanilla, chocolate, mocha, caramel, pistachio, coconut, or jam and whipped cream. They sat in desirable sugary pyramids in the glass showcase near the window to tempt passers-by.

During the rush on that first day, Philip had the children helping with the icing while he took orders and gave change. By eight o'clock when the last customer walked out licking his fingers, the till drawer was crammed full. Philip was quick to point out that there would be no profit because of the special give-away offer. 'But we've certainly built up our goodwill,' he beamed. 'The whole district must know about *Mr Donut* by now.'

He drove them home elated and watched them hurtle into the house to tell their mother, laughing and talking in loud voices and crowing, 'Mister Donut! Mister Donut! Our Dad's Mister Donut!'

Selma said, looking at him over their heads, 'I don't suppose I'll mind being a rich doughnut-maker's wife, if it keeps up like this.'

The shopping centre was well sited next to a new townhouse development. It had grown from one row of shops on a gritty piece of open ground into a pleasant square with a supermarket and raised flower beds and fountains and a tarred parking area. Business was brisk and from the beginning *Mr Donut* made a small but growing profit.

After the first few weeks, Philip had to admit that the repetitive work was boring. The children's enthusiasm waned too. He said nothing to Selma, not wanting to give her the satisfaction of being right. The shop was making good money, he told himself, and that was all that mattered.

But the long days dragged. He was alone with the hissing coffee machine and the bubbling of the doughnut oil when batches were being fried. He tried to fill the void with modern history books which he enjoyed but had never had time for, but soon discovered that there were too many interruptions for serious reading. It was distracting to be asked for a fifty cent cone of Ee-Zee-Soft when he was engrossed in Hitler's last days in the bunker. He read only the newspapers after that.

And he began to watch his customers. As a stockbroker he had been trained to observe and analyse the movements of stocks and shares; it was an easy step to transfer his skills to the people who came into the shop.

There were a lot of regulars. Young mothers who came in for coffee after their shopping and who liked to call him Phil, kiddingly familiar, and flirt a bit over their parcels. Older women with stiffly set hair and flushed red necks from the dryers at Salon Jolene's down the pavement. Off-duty domestic workers who came sauntering past with their boyfriends in the quiet hot hour between washing the lunch dishes and taking the madam her tea. Home-going fathers picking up a treat. Grannies perspiring through their face powder as they dithered over flavours, determined to make contact with the grandchildren even if it was only a couple of minutes' worth of cupboard love.

Often people would linger to talk across the orange counter, playing with the sugar in the aluminium bowls as they let him into their secrets. So many of them seemed to be lonely. They talked and talked. He was amazed at the intimate things he was told, as though he were a robot confessor that could erase itself afterwards.

The families who lived in the new townhouses were not short of money either; many of the women worked. There were children who came in every afternoon clutching ten rand notes, to gorge themselves on ice creams and cool-drinks and several different flavours of doughnut.

'Mister Donut,' they called him, giggling and looking at him sideways at first, to see if he'd be angry. But he liked it. Being called Mister Donut made him feel like a community uncle.

One boy in particular stood out. He was a short plump sallow-faced youngster of thirteen or fourteen, with black curly hair and a full lower lip that gave him a petulant look. When not in school uniform he wore checked shirts ironed into sharp creases with expensive belted trousers and polished shoes, in dazzling contrast to the grubby T-shirts and shorts the other boys wore and their bare cracked feet.

What bothered Philip was that he seemed to have an unlimited amount of money to spend, and he used it to try and buy friends.

Quite early in the afternoon he would come grinning along the pavement surrounded by a noisy gaggle of children, who would stand outside scuffling with each other and squashing their noses against the window while he bought them sweets and ice creams and a box of assorted doughnuts. As the glass door hissed shut behind him, Philip would watch them fall silent and close in with intent faces. When the last crumb had disappeared they would melt away saying casually, 'So long, Fats,' leaving the boy forlorn on the pavement with the empty box in his hands. Wouldn't he ever learn? Philip wondered.

One day when he came in alone, Philip said to him, 'What's your name, son? Seeing as you're my best customer, I think I ought to know.'

The boy looked up at him with startled black eyes. 'Fats.'

'No, I mean your real name.' Philip picked up the metal tongs which health department regulations specified had to be used for handling the doughnuts.

'At home? Vasilios.' The name sounded very foreign in the daisy-bright shop.

Philip slid the two cream doughnuts the boy had asked for into their waxed paper bag. 'You prefer Fats?'

The boy nodded.

Philip thought, Now I'm getting somewhere. 'You must live around here?'

'Across the square.' The boy jerked his head at the row of smaller shops with flats above them.

His father ran one of the shops, then. An immigrant, Philip guessed, and doing well. The boy was proffering a battered ten rand note that had probably been peeled off a wad that morning.

After that Philip took a special interest in him. It was something to do. Something to keep his mind occupied. The boy seemed to have no brothers or sisters because he was always alone. His handouts of free doughnuts and ice creams were not entirely wasted, Philip was glad to see. Most of the kids who walked past him would mumble, 'Hi Fats' or, 'Howzit?' though they seldom stopped to talk. Often he'd spend an hour wandering up and down the pavements outside the shops flicking the cords of their canvas awnings. Or he'd lie on his stomach across the raised parapet of the fish pond in the middle of the square, watching the dim shapes of the goldfish slipping under the waterlilies.

And then at last he seemed to find friends, two older boys. They came into the shop together one afternoon and sat down on the stools at the far end of the counter. Vasilios called out, 'Three orange cool-drinks and six cream doughnuts, please!' His voice was loud, almost commanding.

Philip grinned as he slid the order on a metal tray down the counter. 'Coming up, son.'

There were no more free doughnuts for the crowd after that. It was just the three of them who came in, hustling each other through the door and going into a huddle over the food that Vasilios paid for, whispering together and laughing in raucous voices that would sometimes slide upwards out of control.

Philip watched them from behind his afternoon newspaper. The two older boys had fresh scabs on their chins where they'd cut the tops off their pimples trying to shave. One must have been seventeen or more; he wore dirty jeans and a black leather lumber jacket bristling with silver studs. His cheekbones were high and sharp and his thin shoulders hunched into the looseness of his jacket as though that was the only way to keep it on. The other boy was younger, thickset, slow speaking; only his eyes seemed to move in the broad stillness of his face, and they slid sideways whenever anyone looked directly at him.

Not ideal companions, Philip thought. I wouldn't like to see my kids with friends like that. Should I do something about it? Find out who the boy's father is and speak to him?

He went so far as to follow Vasilios across the quiet lamplit square one evening as he dawdled home alone. The boy stopped outside *Fun Foods* and stood looking in, his lower lip stuck out and his hands dangling at his sides.

It was a hot bright clattering place that sold cheap take-aways late into the night: fish and chips, wors or russians with steaming mounds of white pap, hot pies that were dried out inside from being kept warm all day, and nameless things swimming in little jars of reddish oil that labourers bought to eat with their half loaves of white bread washed down by Coke.

Philip followed the boy's eyes through a glass door trickling with condensed steam. A haggard man in an apron greyed with oily finger marks was shovelling chips out of a round wire basket, his movements angrily efficient. His head jerked up and down as he shouted at the black woman across the counter. 'You people all the same. First you want this, then you want that. Make up your mind, eh? I got plenty to do. I can't waste my time. So what you want then, chips? How much? Two rand? Three rand? Eh?'

The black woman put her hand over her mouth and looked across to the woman behind the till for moral support. The boy's mother, Philip thought. She sat with her huge backside overlapping a stool, trodden-down blue felt slippers hooked over the chrome rung to counterbalance the slumped curve of her back. She was flipping through a photo romance and did not notice the black woman's appeal. Twice she lowered her head to wipe the sweat off her dark upper lip with her forefinger.

Philip saw the boy's hands clench. Then he turned towards the steps that led to the flat above and ran up into the shadows. As he disappeared, the glass door swung open and the black woman came out giggling, followed by a blast of hot oil fumes. The man was shouting after her, 'Next time you think before you come in, nanny!'

Philip's half-formed resolution dissolved and he went home gratefully to Selma's crusty cottage pie and the children, damp-haired from their baths, in their dressing gowns.

Less than two weeks later the phone shrilled in the middle of the night and Philip, fumbling the receiver to his ear, heard, 'Is that Mr Croeser? Of the doughnut shop?'

'Speaking.'

'This is the police. I think you'd better come around to the shop. There's been a burglary.'

He knew at once who had done it. Groping for his clothes and stumbling out of the silent house and all the way to the shopping centre along the deserted streets, he dreaded what was coming.

Vasilios was crouched in the back of the police van, his full lower lip stuck out like a child who is about to cry. There were long smears of dust on his plump face and arms and down the front of his neat checked shirt.

'Know him?' the policeman gestured.

Philip nodded. His mouth felt dry and foul. 'But there must have been others?'

'Two. They got away on a motorbike. When the night watch-man saw them and started shouting, they ran off and left this piece of vuilgoed hanging half out of the high window at the back of your shop.'

'He's not . . .'

'Immigrant vuilgoed. Haven't we got enough troubles of our own?'

In the dead blue light of the street lamp, Philip saw the boy's eyes welling with shamed tears.

Selma couldn't understand his abrupt decision to sell the shop. 'But I thought you were doing to well! I've even got used to people calling me Mrs Donut.'

'I've been offered my old job back and I've decided to take it.' The stock market had begun to rally again.

'After all the fuss you made about being independent and standing on your own two feet and not relying on other people's greed to make a living?'

He turned away so she would not see his face. 'I was wrong. It's easier working for someone else. You don't have too much time to think.'

'Phil?' she said, alarmed, 'Phil? What is it?'

He shrugged. 'The community uncle fell off his pedestal. Must be the male menopause.'

The door slammed behind him as he went out.

Metamorphosis

MAUREEN ISAACSON

The buildings huddled together in conspiracy. A storm leaned on the roach-coloured sky. Sylvia dodged traffic. The rules of the road had long since been trashed. Pavements were for pissing and playing dead on. Murder screamed from eyes. Spinach reeked; the obdurate midday heat turned its greenness limp. Everyone was talking about the rain but no one knew when it would come.

Friday afternoon was ushering the weekend in and the blanket-sellers were shouting, 'Lions, leopards, madam, this blanket for only ninety rands, this one, two hundred. Madam, Madam!' Old attitudes were taking a long time dying.

Change had set in but not quickly enough. The old world squawked; like a decapitated chicken it made its last clumsy steps. But Sylvia had problems of her own; an infestation of cockroaches had moved in with an old fridge she had bought at the second-hand store in Rockey Street.

Earlier that Friday, she had heard a biologist say something on the radio about roaches having been around for four hundred million years, since the Silurian Age. He seemed impressed that they did not look as if they were going any place either.

She was still resisting the moral and physical smell of fumigation and the implications it could hold for her next life but she was close to giving in. It cost fifty bucks and those lousy roaches thought the Borax she kept laying on them was sugar.

Mr Salaminas, the landlord of the building where she lived in Bellevue East, Yeoville's better part, asked if Sylvia ate chocolates in bed. He accused Maria of bringing the roaches in from her room upstairs. Maria told him not to forget that she shared this room with her husband. And if you'd seen Vusi at that time, you would have understood that besides their paraffin heater, not even the world's tiniest creature would fit in when he was around. And that was all the time. No piece jobs, he told Maria. Maria did not believe him.

Maria charred for Sylvia on Fridays. The rest of the week she wiped Mr Salaminas's table, shone his cutlery and shoes and spat in the aluminum cup he had set aside for her tea. She tried to get him to die in his sleep by casting spells. Morning after morning, as sure as roaches slipped away into the warm backside of the cursed fridge, Mr Salaminas rose.

Sylvia was beginning to lose faith in Maria's abilities. Anyway, where does superstition end and where does magic begin? The day Maria brushed Sylvia's leg with a broom you would have thought the world had crashed. 'Now the worst thing that can happen has happened! You will never marry!'

If the broom had anything to do with foiled marriage plans, it was because of what Sylvia had done with it. The broom had belonged to Sandile, her erstwhile fiancé.

Sandile had promised to address his flaws but somehow he did not get around to doing this before she smelled her Wicked perfume on him and took that broom to his head. He said afterwards that the *klap* made him see stars, bars, then freedom. That was the last Sylvia had seen of him and she thought something inside her had been broken for ever.

But on that particular Friday afternoon, her nerves were no longer sewn on to the outside of her heart; she was on the mend. She celebrated her first anniversary under the melting Christmas lights of downtown Johannesburg. It was a month since Sandile's departure.

When she reached the city, Sylvia could feel her liberation coming. 'Piss off!' she told the beggars. She flapped her arms at the pigeons and crushed the fingers of men emerging from man-holes. You should have seen those muggers move.

'Viva Mandela!' shouted a vendor. 'Not today!' There was nothing to buy, except the president's fist, held close to his face on a tin plate. He stood out; handsome, among the plastic roses in glass domes, among the fake gems on a bilious orange gold for the ears; four-fifty a pair.

In a café down in President Street a woman dressed in black served Sylvia three almond biscuits and a cup of dark roast Brazilian coffee. A black cat jumped on to the table. Get down, Bianca, said the woman. The milk was creamy, the sugar connected with the caffeine and what was far became very, very close. A man at the table was reading that story by Franz Kafka, *The Metamorphosis*, about a man who turns into a cockroach.

Down to Kapitan's Restaurant in Kort Street, Sylvia sped. She grabbed a samoosa by the throat and bit some chilli bites back. She glared at the women who lugged ancient braziers and mielies across pavements, tripping over hawkers, competing with the men who cooked chops and mielie pap; seven rands a plate.

She ran past rows of Jarmain shoes. It looked as if they were longing to escape from the windows and stalk the mean streets, perhaps to dance next door at Kohinoor Records.

Inside Kohinoor, Brenda Fassie and Rebecca were raving, on two different stereo systems.

'Can I hear that number again?' Sylvia had to shout to be heard. 'The one by Brenda, I think it's called *Sgaxa Mabhanti*.'

'You mean *Sgaxa Mabhanti*.'

'That's what I said, didn't I?'

The last thing she felt like was being interrupted by a woman who said, 'Excuse me, I am trying to think where I know you from. Where've I seen your face? You look familiar. Aren't you Martha?'

'I'm Sylvia.'

'Sylvia who?' The woman's braids were tied at the ends with coloured beads that clacked like a sangoma's bones when she shook her head in time to the music. Her dress was tie-dyed with a vicious swirl of orange and yellow, as if it was trying to compensate for the sun that was hidden by the clouds.

'Sylvia Burns. I don't believe we've ever met.' Now Sylvia was by no means beautiful but she could be surprisingly polite.

'Oh yes,' the woman said, 'we have. I just can't think where it was . . . Where do you live? Could it be Sandton?'

'Bellevue East.'

What did she want with all these details?

'And what about your husband?' By now Sylvia had just about

had it up to there with the woman, who jumped up and down as if she'd just won the Viva draw when Sylvia divulged her date of birth. The woman held her right hand up and clapped it against Sylvia's. Her nail polish was cracked.

'You've got to be kidding! August three! Snap!' She grabbed her thumb and turned this clapping game into a three-point handshake, her Ray-Bans scouring Sylvia for details.

Sylvia had to admit that it was a coincidence. Maybe the woman wasn't so bad after all. Sylvia liked people who are born under the sign of Leo. They are all leaders, like Napoleon, but could she and this person be friends? The woman must have left when Sylvia turned around to flip through the selection of Rebecca's tapes. Why didn't she say goodbye?

Sylvia was trying to make up her mind – Brenda's *Umuntu Uyashintsha* or Rebecca's *Shwele Baba*? Brenda was wild and sexual and Rebecca was spiritual . . .

Then they played *Sgaxa Mabhanti* again and she forgot all about God. Sandile who? What roaches?

She turned Kohinoor into a nightclub for one. If only Brenda could have seen the way she was dancing in between the record racks and the counter. Everyone was watching. She was having a good time! At the end of the number, she paid twenty-five rands for the Fassie tape, lodged it into her bra and stashed the change from the fifty into her left shoe. She had another fifty in her right one.

Down Kort and into Commissioner street, she half-skipped, half-ran until she reached the Chinese Emporium. Sweat plastered her hair to her head as if the storm had already broken. The rain was still sending threats rumbling across town from the south west, where the mine dumps waited like slaves to offer up their yellow dust. At the taxi rank around the corner, gunshots drowned the thunder.

Snake soup, White Rabbit sweets, sex aids, Sylvia could never get enough of that emporium. When she held a white teapot to the light, delicate patterns breathed through the sensitive china. It cost thirty rands but did she really need it?

'You can't make up your mind, can you? What do you feel about it?' The voice had an American/Afrikaans twang and it belonged to a tall man with a skin as smooth as a lie and a long white beard. He wore a white shirt with a mandarin collar; his white cotton trousers were wide but short enough to reveal scrawny lower calves.

'I can see you are indecisive.'

He was quite attractive. He seemed very interested in Sylvia but not in a sexual way. He had the air of a psychologist on holiday; serious but casual.

'You are terribly unsure of yourself but that will not always be so.' His slate eyes locked her into a combination to which only he had the code.

'How do you know?'

'They don't call me The Prophet for nothing. I see future and past as they merge with the present.'

He bumped the pink glass bell chimes with his head, they started to sway violently and set up a raucous tinkling which he stopped with a large hand.

'They call me God's right hand man. I am never wrong. Look at me, Miss Leo.'

Leo! How did he know?

'You're wondering how I know, huh? I would say you're an early Leo, round about August two, no you're more like a three. But you must have a sun or moon in Gemini to make you so unsure . . .' She opened her mouth but he put a finger to her lips. It smelt of nicotine and body fluids. 'I am hearing from my friends in spirit that you are heartsore.' It was as if he was reading information off her pupils. Her left eye started to twitch.

'I can feel it. Wait . . . I am getting more details . . . You lose in love. You are carrying a wound but with the help of God, we can heal this gash in your soul. However, I have bad news and I hope you can take it . . . I can see trouble coming. Big trouble.'

Sylvia was concerned but flattered that she was inadvertently causing this man to tap into the secrets of the universe.

'May I take your hand?' he said. 'You are tired. You need to get out into the open more often. There is not enough greenery where you live. I see your home now, it is an apartment, no? It is not exactly in Yeoville but perhaps on its border, could it be Bellevue East?'

Maybe he could make the roaches leave.

'Yes, my dear, I see trouble. Would you like to come with me to my prayer room so I can make a little intervention to the Lord, on your behalf?'

His voice drowned out that of Sylvia's mother but she could still hear her, God rest her soul, saying something about 'the danger of strangers . . .'

'Leave me alone, ma,' Sylvia said. She did.

The climb was steep, but Sylvia felt fortunate to be in the company of such a gifted being. They finally reached a large, open balcony at the top of the stairs.

'I see that the prayer room is locked, somebody must be using it.' He gestured vaguely in the direction of a rusty door that looked as if it had not been opened in fifty years. Close up, he breathed liver and onions.

'We can pray here.' He pointed vaguely to the hot, fractured concrete. They were still standing. Lightning cracked the darkness with the swiftness of a snake's tongue. She shuddered.

'Close your eyes and relax, Sylvia.' She had not told him her name!

'I have great powers. I can help you but of course I must ask a little recompense in return.'

'How much?'

'That depends on how much it is worth to you . . .'

As Sylvia pulled off her left shoe to remove her money she saw a familiar figure. She was trying to balance on one foot before she put her shoe on again, when she recognised the woman with the clacking braids, whom she had met earlier in Kohinoor.

'Hi Sylvia, we meet again! Our destinies must be linked! Give the man your money, Sylvia, or you never know what the future may hold.'

Sylvia threw the twenty-five rands down and ran.

She was lucky to be alive!

For the second time that day, she celebrated. This time, she settled in the café where she had earlier enjoyed the Brazilian dark roast.

'Café au lait?" asked the woman in black. Sylvia nodded. She looked around for Bianca. The Metamorphosis man had left and in his place was – please believe this – a cockroach. That decided her. She would give in and call the fumigators.

Next to the roach was another young man who was circling a

section in *The Star* classifieds with a red pen. He looked up and offered her a cigarette. He said, 'Aren't you Sylvia?' Before you could wet your lips, Sylvia had jumped into the nearest taxi and the eye of the storm. She clung to the man seated next to her as the driver skidded through water. She prayed to any god who was unacquainted with the crook from the emporium.

Back at home, Maria was ironing Sylvia's jeans, the radio was on, full blast, playing Brenda's *Sgaxa Mabante* . . .

Maria had to sit down when she heard what had happened. 'You white people! Sylvie! When will you learn?' She laughed even louder when Sylvia fumbled through the yellow pages, saying, 'This is the second last Friday before Christmas!'

'Ha ha, hoo, ha, ahhh!'

'Stop it Maria, what's so funny?'

'Today, Mr Salaminas phoned Rent-a-Kill. Rent-a-Kill said, "Sorry, nobody to do the job." Mr Salaminas called Vusi and said, "If you don't go to Rent-a-kill, you don't have a home." Then Vusi came here with a big poison spray.'

'I can't smell a thing.'

'He used the no-smell poison.'

Where were the Hiroshima survivors?

'Vusi killed them all,' she said, 'there were hundreds.'

Superstition took its hold of Sylvia. She refrained from mentioning that the roaches could come out at any time. Who knew what would happen if she told Maria that she had heard that the heads of roaches sometimes live for twelve hours after decapitation? But she did cry out when she saw three little fridges speed across the room, white as milk, clean as Borax: 'Watch out, Maria, Maria!'

Portia's Porsche

GEOFFREY HARESNAPE

*T**he smart set in Shakespeare's* MERCHANT OF VENICE *were skilled at networking. Inherited wealth, sumptuous socialising, and the old school tie were part of their programme of privilege. This elite group had a marked patriarchal bias, even against their wives and daughters. Such people may be found in modern Johannesburg just as much as they were in the sixteenth century centre of trade and commerce. And – just as certainly – there is an intelligent woman to recount how she manipulates the system.*

*

Nerissa tells me – rather quaintly – that daddy was 'ever virtuous'. I don't quarrel with that, although I do think that he was more complicated than she gives him credit for.

He sometimes gave the impression of being coldly abstemious, but he liked his tot of Glenfiddich in the evenings. A medical warning about emphysema was enough to put him off regular cigarettes, but he wasn't going to retreat from the pleasures of nicotine completely. So he did smoke the occasional cigar.

Daddy could be like that – determined to have his own way, even when the dice seemed to be loaded against him. Ironically enough, when he eventually took ill, it wasn't the lungs – not directly the lungs, anyway.

He was out in the Kruger Park at the time, with his Merc parked under a mopane tree and near a large stream, hoping for a sighting of a fish eagle. Before help could be got from Lower Sabie, daddy had passed away.

'A massive heart attack,' the medics told me.

I was assured that if daddy had been in his home in Houghton, they might have saved him. A triple bypass at the Brenthurst Clinic would have been enough to do it.

I was left a small fortune in real estate and investments. The property is upmarket office blocks mostly, and the two houses. The investments, if you want to know, are shares in Mining Exploration and Tobacco and Match, not to mention a good spread in Eskom, Transnet and other gilts.

Our Rose Road home is rather fine, I suppose. It overlooks The Wilds and across to that high-rise Johannesburg skyline that gives my heart a flutter of excitement whenever I see it.

But it's the house at Plet that I really love. I must admit that daddy named it well, even if it does sound a bit Italian. 'Belmont'– bella monte – beautiful mountain. The place is actually on well-watered high ground overlooking the Indian Ocean.

∗

As the only surviving member of our family, I felt terribly lonely after daddy's remains had been consigned to the furnace at the Braamfontein Crematorium. (We'd brought the body all the way back from the Lowveld so that his considerable acquaintance at the JSE and in the multinationals could pay their last respects at a short but moving ceremony. It was gratifying to see that even some of the new black empowerment people were present.)

I went home to rattle around in the Houghton house. Its spacious rooms and plush furnishings had become oppressive to me. That's when I told Bill that I needed a break from my work with the partners. I also persuaded Nerissa to drop out of the city set for a while and to come and stay with me down at 'Belmont'.

Nerissa and I had our Roedean years in common and also the time at Wits when she was studying anthropology and I law. It was she who gave me moral support when I had to cope with some rather eccentric provisions of daddy's will.

He'd been anxious that my inheritance should be protected and had set up a trust for the employment of a financial manager at a most attractive salary. A test had also been devised to ensure that this should be just the right man. 'Man', notice – not 'person'! It hadn't occurred to daddy that a woman could handle the job.

The test went like this. Standing on the ornate stinkwood desk in daddy's 'Belmont' study were three small boxes. The first was overlaid with what looked like a scaley skin of 1/10 oz Krugerrands. The second had been crafted from hall-marked silver; the kind of box in which people kept cigarettes in the days when it was still socially acceptable to offer them to guests. The third was made from some dingy material – pewter, or most probably lead.

Daddy's idea – as expressed in his will – was that a would-be financial manager should enter the study, observe the boxes, and make a choice among them. In one of the boxes was the contract for the job. The challenge was to pick out the box which held the contract. Under no circumstances was I to tell an aspirant where it lay hidden.

*

My first thought was that this was a crazy plan. But I knew too much about legal practice to try to get the relevant provisions in daddy's will overturned. Many tyrannies and eccentricities far grosser than daddy's have been given authority when supported by the signatures of a testator and witnesses. No, the best thing to do was to go along with the situation and try to discover how I could work it to my advantage.

In the mean time applicants for the job kept turning up at my front door. They'd seen the ad for it in the *Sunday Times* and had motored down to Plet to try their luck.

If a financial adviser of the sort whom daddy envisaged was not exactly a husband, he was none the less a male with whom I would be stuck over a long period of time. I was quite fussy about males with whom I would be stuck, even on a purely professional level.

So you can imagine that I was on tenterhooks during each trial session, because I'd taken a peek and I knew where the contract was hidden. Whenever an unprepossessing hand wandered in the direction of the box, I had to suppress a shudder.

One man in a loose leather lumberjacket and tight-fitting Levis seemed very defensive; told me he'd studied at the University of Fez.

'Please don't be put off by my . . . er . . . complexion,' he said.

'Good heavens, do you think I'm a racist? This is the new South Africa,' I told him.

When he went directly to the wrong box, I was relieved; not on account of his pigmentation, even though it was distinctly Moroccan, but on account of his character. He thought much too much of himself.

Another man to give me a difficult moment had immigrated to this country from the Iberian Peninsula; an arrogant little Aragonese. His country's successful hosting of the 25th Olympiad had clearly gone to his head. I can't imagine why. It's no great shakes to host an Olympiad. As we all know, even little Cape Town thought that it could make a bid for the 2004 games.

Anyway, the Aragonese lisped and postured everywhere, looking down his aquiline nose and batting his eyelids.

'We who are of Thpain haf a thpethal apprethiation of life,' he told Nerissa while waiting to go into daddy's study.

Fortunately, he, too, chose amiss. I would have hated to have my estate managed by a blinking idiot.

I got all these men off the 'Belmont' property as soon as possible by recommending the accommodation on Beacon Island. I reckoned that there was nothing like the sting in a luxury hotel bill to pay them back for the inconvenience they'd given me.

✳

I was growing desperate thinking about how I was going to cope with this awful situation that daddy had laid on me, when relief arrived in the form of Big Bass driving a BMW 3 series. It looked like a new one straight out of the showroom, and I was impressed.

In the new South Africa the BMW is everybody's favourite when it comes to showing a slice of class. Everybody from deputy ministers down to special advisers to parliamentary committees drive them. Even the people's poet owns one.

As far as I knew, Big Bass had been running a crummy old Ford Cortina up until this time.

I'd first met him at Wits when he was freshly up from St John's College and the world was his oyster. Big Bass was a romantic, rather spendthrift character. He worked out at the gym, and looked great in tracksuit and running shoes.

Nerissa and I were already old friends in those university days. I was soon confessing to her that I had the hots for Big Bass. The temperature, it had seemed, was high on his side too. Big Bass had been on target for a BCom when his father's business had crashed. This meant that his allowance had run out and he'd been compelled to take a not-so-lucrative job in the city. End of our short but sharp affair.

Here he was coming into my life again, dressed by Hilton Weiner and dangling his car keys from a strong hand. Nerissa gave me a covert wink as we stood on the side lawn admiring the sparkling view over the bay towards Robberg.

'I'd like to apply for the position your late father set up,' he began. 'I hope it hasn't gone yet.'

'It's still vacant,' I said, and my heart leapt.

In daddy's study I carefully explained the exercise of the boxes. Like me, Big Bass thought the procedure was pretty crazy, but he was clearly in a mood to humour me if that's what was needed. I couldn't get over the elegance of his Rolex on its gold bracelet and the obviously new signet ring on his little finger.

All the old fascination which he'd held for me returned with force. Big Bass was looking just as always – a hunk with class. I knew that I wanted him to be the winner. As far as I was concerned, he could handle – I must be honest – all my assets, not only the financial ones.

'Can't you spend a few days down here?' I asked. 'The swimming's great at this time of the year.'

Big Bass replied that he needed to try his hand at daddy's eccentric game immediately. I had a shrewd estimate of how his mind worked, and there was just no ways that it would run to daddy's particular brand of hypocrisy. It would just not occur to Big Bass to pretend that dingy lead was worth more than gold. I knew that, left to himself, he'd go straight to the box encrusted with Krugerrands.

This was crisis time. Daddy's will required that I should not tell about the whereabouts of the contract; but 'tell' meant word of mouth. Where was the clause which ruled out the speaking power of the visual image?

Big Bass excused himself to prepare himself briefly before the test. While he was out of the room, I slid daddy's favourite photograph of me along the desk so that it stood directly behind the leaden box. It showed a young woman in her first low-cut gold lamé evening dress, a combination of cleavage and glittering thighs. It wasn't really the shot of his little daughter that one would expect a daddy to have.

When Big Bass returned, I could see that the photo's effect upon him was immediate. The Krugerrands and the silver caught his attention, but before I could take one puff on my Lexington Light he was in front of the portrait, smiling appreciatively.

'It's you, hey! This takes me back to my Wits years.'

In the mean time I started up some heavy metal on the cassette player.

'What's that?' Big Bass asked absent-mindedly.

'Led Zeppelin,' I said. 'A bit passé, as a group. They're pronounced the same as the metal, but spelled L-E-D.'

My hint was so heavy it was like one of those outsize sinkers that children tie on to their first fishing lines. I felt it couldn't be lost, even on Big Bass. He kept his eyes on my photograph and, almost without thinking, he began to toy with the leaden box which stood directly in front of it.

A short struggle with the cheap hinge of the lid, and he knew he'd succeeded. The folded contract was revealed. I was so thrilled and impressed by his acumen that I darted across the study and flung myself into his arms.

✳

I must dilate a little on the days which followed. The blonde beaches which matched our hair, the vigour of the surf, the quiet plit-plat of the lagoon – all contributed to our delight. Big Bass had brought a guy called Grat with him for company; and Nerissa made a move on Grat right from the start.

Our seafood braais were superb: Spiked Garlic Prawns, Perlemoen on the Grid, or sometimes Crayfish over the Coals. Big Bass introduced us to Cabernet Sauvignons, Gewürztraminers and Morio Muscats the likes of which I couldn't have imagined.

We were like a quartet playing all the instruments of pleasure. And like Paganini, each of us was a virtuoso of the G-string.

Some days we didn't go for outings, but rather stayed at 'Belmont' for a relaxing time in the pool. Shortly before his death, daddy had bought some inflatable lie-lows in the forms of African river animals. It was fun to jump on to the back of a pink hippo or to lie across a turquoise crocodile in order to bask on the surface of the sparkling water.

One morning I was astride a flame-coloured terrapin and idly watching Big Bass as he stood by the poolside bar. He looked scrumptious with his Piz Baun tan as he chatted to someone on his cellphone. I suddenly saw a stricken look come into his face, then he ended the conversation and put the instrument listlessly down.

I paddled over to the tiled pool edge to find out what was troubling him.

'Honey, I'm so sorry,' he said. 'The car, the clothes, the cases of wine – none of them are mine. All the payments have been coming from Tony.'

'Tony?'

'You remember him, don't you? I introduced you at Wits. We were best friends at St John's.'

A memory stirred in me. 'Oh! Tony. The gay!'

'The nicest gay I know,' Big Bass said loyally. 'He's been lending me the bucks for all this – and now he's in financial trouble.'

'We must do something,' I replied. 'You're running my affairs now – and we've got plenty of resources. Pay him back and be done with it.'

Big Bass leant forward and pulled me up out of the water. It was a filmic gesture that turned out to be a bit of a disaster. I giggled while Big Bass almost fell in and the flame-coloured terrapin bobbed away, its round eyes staring.

'You're a sweetheart!' Big Bass panted once he had me high but not so dry on the poolside pavings. 'I wish it was so easy. But I'm only part of Tony's problems. It's a threatened bankruptcy, and Ruben Shalakovitz wants to nail him for a large loan that he hasn't repaid.'

I tensed at the mention of the name. Daddy was no anti-Semite, and in fact some of our best friends went to Shul. But he'd often referred to this man as a very tough creditor indeed.

'Handle Shalakovitz with kid gloves,' daddy had recommended with a smile. 'If you fall foul of him, he won't let you off without his pound of flesh.'

And now my lover's friend was on the very hook that I'd been schooled to avoid.

'Shalakovitz's especially pissed off at the moment,' Big Bass added. 'His daughter Jess is shacking up with Lourens who's a member of Tony's circle.'

'I suppose he thinks Tony's to blame for that, too!' I said. 'I think Tony needs the best legal advice.'

'It's a pity you're not practising at the moment,' Big Bass told me.

I was charmed by this masculine vote of confidence in my expertise.

'I can always stage a comeback if necessary. But, in the mean time, we're off to Jo'burg and to Bill.'

'A bill for what?'

Big Bass could be distressingly thick sometimes. He's the sort of guy who thinks that The Full Monty means a guard dog whose overdone it on the dry biscuits. Were it not for his Chippendale shoulders and fluid thighs, I could sometimes think I was doing the wrong thing.

'I'm referring to Bill Bellario, my old boss,' I explained patiently. 'He and his partner, Mervyn Balthazar, are two of the best advocates on the Gauteng circuit. They're known as the big Bs.'

'You don't say,' Big Bass said.

*

Next morning we were up early and ready to depart from 'Belmont'. At that time – 5 a.m. – the ornamental electric lanterns were still lit along the stoeps. As a rule, I loved to see the little lights of my gracious home dwindle into insignificance as the sun came up over the Indian Ocean and filled the sky with its brightness. The experience always made me feel how small and insignificant I really was – and how shrewd daddy's Eskom investment had been!

But I would not be experiencing the sunrise this particular morning. Big Bass and I would be well into our journey before dawn broke. We were planning to travel via Graaff-Reinet, Colesberg and Bloemfontein – with 600 ks to drive that day. The toll roads on the final stretch would save a lot of time, because the company didn't dare to enforce the speed limit on paying travellers.

Nerissa and Grat had jumped at the chance of staying behind to caretake the property. My mind boggled at what they'd be up to in our absence. I reckon with them even the author of the *Kama Sutra* would've run out of ideas.

I'd pressed Big Bass for further details of Tony's predicament, and it looked as if Shalakovitz had got a good case against him. Bill and I would have to do a lot of homework to present a defence strong enough to stop the old skinflint in his tracks.

Within the hour we'd left the coast far behind and were heading inland comfortably and at speed. I felt good as I watched Big Bass. He was relaxed and happy in what was for him a new driving seat. It hadn't taken much persuading to get him to leave his – or should I say Tony's? – BMW out of the reach of car-thieves in the triple garage at 'Belmont'.

You see, there are more ways to the heart of an upwardly-mobile man than through his stomach or his balls. From the outset I had realised that, even more than getting his hands on me, Big Bass was dying to get them on the wheel of my metallic, shining, costly and golden Porsche 944 S2 Cabriolet.

The Goblin King

KEN BARRIS

To Phil Woolf

I was alone with my grandmother on the Saturday afternoon she died. She came down the passage calling my name in a strangling voice. I ran to her in alarm, and caught her just as she sagged. Her face was almost the colour of woad, but darker, and she struggled to breathe. 'My pills –' she said. Drowning in fear, I half dragged her back to her bed and found her little box of heart pills. I placed one under her tongue and raced to the phone. But it was no good. My mother hadn't paid the account and the phone was disconnected. It was also too late; when I returned, I could see that she had died. Her expression was tormented, recording the pain of her death, the struggle for breath. If she was at peace now, her body did little to show it. I was too shocked to know what I felt.

Shock compounded shock as her dead limbs convulsed and her mouth stretched into a rictus resembling laughter. Her soft once-loved flesh – the very meat of kindness – took on the flux of accelerated corruption: swelling, distending, darkening, blistering. I wonder if my own heart beat once during this panic moment. Then out of the inexplicable ruin of my grandmother's corpse, assembling itself from her suffering face, from her destroyed organs and skin, rose something I had never seen before.

How does one describe a goblin? Words are largely instruments of order. How can a goblin be imagined, reconstructed in memory? Consider that ugly, powerful name. The first part is like stone, impenetrable and blunt; the second syllable more akin to sapling wood, flexible yet very hard, strongly alive. The creature was far stronger than its name. If it had texture it might be called a buzzing harshness, an implacable density of purpose. As to its grin – the first thing, the very first – fiercely sarcastic. Then the eyes, doomed and malicious. Flesh of bronze blackened by the aeons. But when it raised its limbs clear of the corpse and stretched, how exquisite were its proportions! Here was male beauty taken to staggering, ridiculous extremes. My grandmother began smoking, violent odours of methane and volcanic ash crowding the world. The goblin climbed out of that mess and stood before me, shrouded in the brimstone cloud of her remains.

I think back to how I stood. I was half-crouched in the doorway, ready to turn and run, but impaled by what I saw; my hand was thrown up as if to ward off this vision.

'What a terrible ugly child you are,' said the goblin. 'What a violent, what a fiery monstrous thing!' I think it mocked me.

My mouth fell open, I couldn't speak. Slowly, slowly, I straightened up. I don't know if I was more interested or surprised or terrified.

'You must be wicked beyond words,' said the goblin in its rasping voice: 'Why did you call me?'

My own returned: 'I didn't. I'm not –'

'You did. And you are. I know, I take holidays behind your bathroom mirror. I know you better than you think.'

Speechless again, I stared, set to run still.

'You're going to have trouble explaining this,' the goblin declared, gesturing towards the bed. The smoke was clearing now. There was precious little of my grandmother left; just incomplete mummified flesh and her clothes, all shredded and burnt.

I nodded.

Its mouth stretched wider, revealing what I can only describe as badly fitting false teeth: 'Been burning granny's corpse again, have we?'

I shook my head on the verge of terror.

The goblin sat down on the bed and bounced on the mattress. My grandmother bounced too. 'Don't cry,' it said nastily. 'I can't bear children who cry.' It bared its teeth, fangs this time, and hissed: 'I eat them.'

The goblin was right about my temper. It suddenly flared and I stood up straight. 'Who do you think you are?' I cried out. My voice quavered and tears threatened, but with anger rather than fear.

'Gbrnztphlkx,' said the goblin. It laughed, a sharp series of k-sounds that grated on my nerves. 'Gbrnztphlkx, Gbrnztphlkx is my name. King of all the Goblins. And what is yours, horrible child?'

'Philip,' I said dully.

'What a frightening sound.' It sucked in air through its fangs. 'Worse than spiders, the hairy ones. Worse than millipedes in drains.'

'Well, you're worse than slug soup,' I said. 'You're worse than toad's brains in Tabasco!'

The goblin doubled over, quaking, wildly drumming on the back of its head with its long clawed fingers. It suddenly stood up and pointed at the bed: 'What are you going to do about this unspeakable mess? What will you say when your mother comes home?'

'Tell her the truth.'

'She won't believe you.'

'Yes she will.'

'No she won't. Not a chance. Too silly. Too strange.'

'She will!' I shouted. But I knew the goblin was right. My mother would hold me responsible. She blamed me for everything, and her temper was greater than mine.

Just then we heard the sound of a car approaching and stopping. Car doors slammed. The goblin dived wildly to the floor and scuttled under my grandmother's bed. When I plucked up the nerve to look, there was nothing; just puffs of dust and an old paperback that must have been there for ages, lying open, face down. I pulled it out. It was *Through the Looking Glass*, a book I had tried to read but didn't understand at all. The whole thing was suddenly too much for me. I raced for my room, dived into bed, pulled the cover over my head and pretended to be asleep.

I was too young to understand my grandmother's death, though I knew about death in theory. Instead of grief, I felt nothing. There was a numb place that would only become grief later, when I saw and shared the grief of the adults. My real problem was the goblin and the guilt that went with it. I was wicked. I had summoned the creature. I was the one present when my grandmother had died and caught fire. By my mother's logic, that made me inescapably responsible.

On the other hand, I was used to strange things happening around my grandmother. She had always been a very eccentric woman. She was frail and absent-minded; but when she forgot herself, nothing seemed impossible. For example, once when I was four and my grandfather was still alive, she had baked a turtle-dove pie. She said then, 'My nose tells me the pie is ready.' She opened the oven door, bent down and picked up the pan. She straightened up, lifted the steaming pie to her face and breathed in deeply. 'Smells good,' she said. 'Smells just right.'

As she turned towards the kitchen table, my grandfather entered. 'Frieda!' he called out in alarm. 'You're holding that thing without gloves! *You'll burn yourself!*'

It was quite true. Her hands were unprotected. And as he drew her attention to it, she screamed in pain and dropped the pie.

A couple of years later, I watched from the shade as she pottered about our garden. My grandfather and my father (who hadn't abandoned us yet) were standing beside a bench, discussing where to place it. The bench was a precast concrete monstrosity that had come with the house. It had two barrel-like legs; the seat was a concrete beam over two inches thick and at least two yards long.

'It should go in that corner,' said my father, pointing. 'Under the lemon tree. What do you think?'

My grandfather nodded. 'I would say so,' he replied.

Now my grandmother was roughly the size of an under-nourished eleven-year-old girl. As the men concurred, she straightened up from the seedlings she had been planting, wiped her brow absent-mindedly, and approached. 'There?' she asked. 'That corner?'

'Yes, there,' replied my father. My grandmother picked up the seat and carried it to the chosen spot. I remember the two men staring after her; I remember them sitting on the bench and opening a bottle of wine with the air of men who have seen something they'd rather not talk about.

Bearing this in mind, and similar events, Gbrnztphlkx wasn't as much of a shock as he might have been to someone with a more conventional granny. Perhaps her life had prepared me for the manner of her death.

'Jesus Lord, Philip,' screamed my mother. *'What have you done! Come here child!'*

I thought at first to remain sleeping; but I soon realised that the tactic would make things worse. I climbed reluctantly out of bed and went to my grandmother's bedroom where I had no doubt my mother would be. She was there of course; she gestured at the remains, her mouth working with rage and grief, and shrieked: 'What have you *done!*'

I can't say my mother didn't love me. That would be dishonest. I think she did love me fiercely, but when anger took her she was beyond reason.

'I was sleeping,' I replied. I rubbed my eyes and yawned to prove it. 'What's going on?'

'What's happened to Granny?' she asked as she dragged me to the site of my grandmother's death.

I tried to look shocked. I shrugged. I settled on removing all expression from my face.

'Dunno,' I said.

Then, thank heavens, Dan's comfortable bass rolled through the door: 'Easy on the boy, Alice, easy.' He was my mother's boyfriend, a tall, thin, leathery middle-aged man who in his manner of dress had never emerged from the forties. He parted his hair in the middle, slicked it down, and wore suits with flaring lapels. 'It appears,' he said, 'that Granny has – so to speak – passed away.'

'But this –' objected my mother, her voice sliding perilously up the scale of hysteria, her face patched crimson and white. 'But this –'

She pointed at the charred remains, placed her hands over her face and began to sob in helpless full-throated spasms.

Dan approached and saw more clearly. His eyebrows shot up, his eyes widened. They rolled ever so slightly and he said: 'It seems to be a case of spontaneous combustion.'

I stared at my mother in awe. Her shoulders shook and tears trickled out through her fingers as she lowed like a calf. Dan sent me to fetch a glass of sugar water for her; I took my time, and I don't know what passed further between them. There was much discussion, even after the funeral, about what precisely had happened to Granny, Dan stoutly insisting that I couldn't have had anything to do with it. I continued to play dumb and injured. I believe this gave me some advantage; as my mother's grief abated, even she saw how suspicious and unjustified her reaction had been.

In the end it was decided that something had gone wrong with the electric blanket, even though the thing wasn't switched on at the time. Nobody entertained the thought – not for an instant – that the King of all the Goblins had set my grandmother alight while using her corpse as a passageway from his own mysterious world.

'Jesus Lord, Philip, what have you done!' became my mother's battle-cry that long and difficult summer. So many things went wrong. But it was never me, it was always Gbrnztphlkx. He appeared when I was alone in the house, and was sure to cause some disaster or other. I began to dread being left alone, not because I feared the goblin, but because the consequences were so dire.

For example, one hot afternoon as I sat watching television – a rerun of *Gremlins* it was – I heard the broom cupboard creak, and out of the kitchen strolled Gbrnztphlkx.

'What are you watching?' he rasped.

'*Gremlins.*'

'Sounds interesting. Mind if I join you?'

'Do I have any choice?'

'Of course you have,' he said. 'Just say the word and I'll vanish from your life for ever.'

I knew he was lying; I had tried it before. He sat down on the couch, a box of popcorn suddenly in his hands. 'Want some?' he offered.

I shook my head. I didn't trust him. God knows what that popcorn really was. For a while nothing happened, apart from the loud sound of his chewing. The smell of hot butter filled our lounge. Then his chewing stopped. Snow White and the Seven Dwarfs had appeared; I glanced at the goblin. 'No,' he hissed, cowering back into the couch. 'No.' His teeth chattered.

'Can it,' I said wearily.

He ignored me, but relaxed when the gremlins tore their way through the screen. Then he was hopping up and down on the couch shouting, 'Way to go!'

'Do you mind?' I asked.

'Sorry,' he said, subsiding. 'Great movie! Popcorn?'

'You just like the gremlins,' I said sulkily. 'They remind you of yourself.'

'And why not?' he retorted. He wiped his eye, cleared his throat and asked (the corners of his mouth turning down): 'Has not a goblin eyes? Has not a goblin hands, organs, dimensions, senses, affections, passions? If you prick us, do we not bleed? If you tickle us, do we not laugh? If you poison us, do we not die?'

'Suppose so,' I said. 'Maybe you don't like being a goblin after all.'

We watched in silence for a while. I sensed that Gbrnztphlkx was annoyed. I repeated more loudly: 'Maybe you don't like being a goblin.'

'Nothing wrong with being a goblin.'

'Then why do you spend so much time here with people? Why don't you go back to wherever it is that you're king of?'

His teeth chattered audibly again, but this time with rage. He brought them under control and said carefully, distinctly: 'I just happen to be visiting. For a while. Because I want to.' Then he stared resolutely at the screen.

I wanted to annoy him. I flipped channels to a daytime soap. 'Well then watch some real life,' I said. 'This is a human movie. No insects in it.'

The goblin glared at me. 'Put it back,' he said.

'No.'

'Put it back.'

I flipped again, to a different soap. It was exactly the same as the first one.

'You'll regret this,' he said.

'Won't.'

But I had a sinking feeling that I would. Still, I couldn't stop myself. I flipped again, this time to a ballet. I think it was Swan Lake.

'Unbearable,' hissed the goblin. 'Such ugliness.'

'Naturally you don't like it. No insects.'

Gbrnztphlkx leaned forward gracefully and lifted a heavy glass ashtray from the coffee table. Effortlessly – it could have been a frisbee – he flicked it spinning into the tube. I felt blood drain from my face as the screen shattered and Gbrnztphlkx stood up saying, 'Nasty bad-tempered brat.'

His timing was impeccable. There was the unmistakable sound of my mother's car – her exhaust was holed – and the goblin poured forward and crawled into the destroyed television set, crunching through glass, setting off blue arcing blitzes of stray electricity and puffs of stinking smoke. He somehow turned round inside the set, stuck his face out and said, 'Pass me the rest of that popcorn will you?' Dazed, I complied. He took it and said, 'Goodbye sausage,' then crawled in deeper, backwards, and disappeared.

The door opened. That familiar challenge rang out. I just sat wearily in the couch, sighed, and said, 'It exploded, Ma. All by itself. I was just sitting here watching *Gremlins* and it blew up.'

I won't dwell on the consequences, particularly after both parts of the ashtray were found inside the tube.

I began to suspect that Gbrnztphlkx had something to do with electricity. I didn't know what exactly, but perhaps the solution to my problem lay in that direction. I discussed it with Dan one evening.

'Dan,' I asked, 'what's the opposite of electricity?'

He picked up his glass of brandy and stared at the ice. 'The opposite of electricity? Now that's an interesting question, Phil.' He swirled the ice around. 'Alice,' he called into the kitchen where my mother was making supper, 'What's the opposite of electricity?'

The beat of a blade chopping baby marrows stopped.

'Gas?' called my mother.

'Gas?' asked Dan, looking at me.

'I don't think so. Not gas.'

He waved his glass at me. I fetched the bottle and poured in more brandy. He sipped. 'Better,' he said. He sipped again. 'Opposite of electricity? Rubber maybe?'

I shook my head.

'No electricity?'

'Yes, obviously, but that's not what I mean.'

'Gravity?'

I shook my head again. He took a long draught and said, 'OK, I give up. What's the opposite of electricity?'

I just sighed and stared at the floor. Dan watched me for a while, a look of concern on his face.

Seeing no one knew the opposite of electricity, I took a new tack. 'Dan, what's inside a mirror?'

'It depends, I suppose, on what's outside the mirror.'

'I guess so.' I thought about it some more. 'Dan,' I asked, 'Do you think you could take what's outside the mirror and put it inside?'

'Maybe,' he replied. 'You never know.'

'I mean so that the outside thing that's now inside can't get out again?'

'Well, I'm just a land surveyor, you know. This is a bit beyond my expertise.'

I raised my face to him anxiously: 'But could you?'

He waved the glass at me again. I fetched the bottle and poured. 'And ice,' he said. I fetched him ice. 'What's the question again?' he asked. I repeated it.

'Maybe,' he said. 'Maybe there's a way to do it. Just maybe.'

We were called to supper then. I didn't try draw him out in my mother's presence, but I kept on looking at him hopefully. I wondered if he had forgotten. Once he looked up at me and winked. Later he said, 'I think you'd need a house of mirrors. You know, a mirror looking into a mirror, and that looking back into the first one, and so on. Reflection after reflection. You'd have to put that thing you need to catch in the middle of the mirrors and get it reflected so much it couldn't ever work out which part of itself was real.'

'You mean which part was outside the mirrors?'

'Exactly.'

'So it would stay inside the mirrors because it would think its real part was a reflection?'

'Quite so. Answer your question?'

I nodded solemnly. A wild hope flared in my heart.

I was alone the very next Sunday morning. Dan had gone fishing and my mother had gone to church. I woke up with a feeling of excited dread. I had plans for the goblin and almost wanted him to appear. The night before I had pried the mirror off the inside of my cupboard door. It was about two foot square, stuck on the door with double-sided tape. I took it to the bathroom and propped it against the wall, under the towel rack. Most of it was hidden by a towel. I raced to the kitchen, where I grabbed a couple of rusks for breakfast, to the bedroom for my book (*Dinosaur Tales* by Ray Bradbury), and back to the bathroom. I was going to spend the morning there; Gbrnztphlkx inevitably turned up wherever I was. The chances were quite good too because I hadn't seen him for a while.

I ate my rusks and settled down on the cold floor with *Dinosaur*

Tales. The book absorbed me. I am a slow reader, but page after page went by.

Something prickled at my attention. I wasn't aware of it at first. Then I felt something, a presence; then I heard it. Each time I turned a page, I heard the rustling echo of a second page turning. I looked around wildly. Nothing. I turned a page; the noise followed. I stood up quickly, my heart hammering. Only then did I see Gbrnztphlkx lying in the dry bathtub, legs crossed, a look of happy absorption on his face, reading a book called – I peered at it carefully –*selaT ruasoniD*. I thought it must be a book in goblin language. He looked up at me suddenly as if taken by surprise and boomed a greeting: 'Good morning, clown! Spending a morning reading in the bathroom, are we?'

'You startled me,' I complained, letting go a shuddering breath.

'Of course I startled you. It's my job to startle you.' His voice went rusty and squeaky at once: 'Startle, startle. What shrapnel language you speak. It cuts my tongue to grind out startle.'

I ignored him and turned to the basin and Dan's shaving equipment.

'Eng-glush,' muttered the goblin from the bathtub. 'Barbaric garbage language. Stupid book too. Dinosaurs? Ha, no such thing. Not even backwards.'

Followed by the sound of a book being torn apart. I winced, mindful of the strength required to do that. Then some indescribable noises: he was stuffing shredded paperback into his mouth and chewing it.

I didn't allow myself to look back at the tub. I ran hot water in the basin and began whipping up a lather. As I said, Dan hadn't emerged from the forties, and still used a shaving brush and soap stick. Through the looking glass I saw Gbrnztphlkx's head pop up over the tub. He burped loudly. 'Shaving?' he cried. 'Shaving?'

I ignored him and began applying the lather.

'Too young,' he said. 'Baby's bum, your cheeks. No need to shave.'

I peered at his reflection, still applying shaving soap to my face with grandly exaggerated sweeping movements. 'Seems to me,' I said, 'that you don't need to shave either.'

'What!' exclaimed Gbrnztphlkx, stepping out of the tub. 'Of course I need to shave. Goblins shave all the time!' He ran his hand over his cheeks and jaw. 'Five o'clock shadow!' he rasped.

'Time for a shave.'

I began applying lather to the top of my head.

'You don't shave like that,' said Gbrnztphlkx, 'A goblin baby knows you don't shave like that.'

'Course you do.' I lathered my left ear vigorously.

'No you don't, fool. You shave like this.'

He shoved me aside, snatching the utensils from my hands. 'Like this,' he said. He whipped up a tremendous foam and applied it generously. Then he picked up Dan's safety razor and began shaving, stretching his marble-smooth black skin with his free hand, sticking out his jaw, pulling down his upper lip as he dragged the blade all over his face. 'Most goblins shave at least twice a day,' he said. 'Usually more often.'

I turned round, sticky with lather myself, and retrieved the hidden mirror. With trembling hands I held it up behind him. 'What do you think of your shave now?' I asked. Gbrnztphlkx turned round and saw what I was doing. He spun back, and there was I reflected, standing behind him, the mirror in place. He saw the reflection of himself reflected back again. '*No!*' he grated fiercely, but too late; he was caught in my house of mirrors.

His body began to flicker and buzz with furious energy and I thought wildly, 'You're nothing but a trick of light!' His voice warbled in and out of phase at the same panic tempo, buzzing and grinding and squeaking horribly. I shook with adrenalin, but held fast against the psychic violence of his going. He gave off a final prolonged buzz that went faster and faster, higher and higher, becoming inaudible, a pressure that hurt my ears, made them ring – and the King of all the Goblins disappeared.

Or so I thought. But when I lowered my hand-held mirror and straightened up, what did I see in the fixed bathroom mirror? Of course in hindsight it is obvious, predictable: Gbrnztphlkx stood before me echoing my movements, not my own familiar reflection. But it wasn't predictable then, and the hammer-blow of shock almost knocked me flat.

Clever, said the goblin. *Tricky little swot*. There was no sound; I heard his voice in my thoughts. I swivelled wildly down to the mirror on the floor. He was there too, grinning up at me: *Now what have you done, horrible child? You'll have trouble explaining this to your mother, won't you?*

'No I won't,' I said. 'When she sees you, she'll believe me. Specially when she sees both of you. All of you.'

Liar, he said. *She'll kill you*. But his chagrin was all too clear. I walked out of the bathroom, letting out a long, shaky breath.

I went to the kitchen to wash off that sticky lather. I didn't feel like doing it in the bathroom.

My triumph lasted as long as it took to splash cold water over my head and face. As I straightened up, dripping, I thought I heard music, faint music. A woman singing? Yes, that was it. A woman singing in the back of my mind. I shook my head hard, but the singing continued. As it grew louder, I heard it outside too. It was a lovely complex tune, extremely high, full of colour and movement. I had never heard such gorgeous music before. It burst into full physical volume from various places in the house. Every room, I realised, that contained a mirror. I rushed back to the bathroom. There stood the reflected Gbrnztphlkx singing, eyes cast upwards piously, palms pressed against each other horizontally before his midriff, his mouth wide open, stretching ever wider, Adam's apple bobbing up and down furiously. Needless to say, his image in the smaller mirror on the floor did precisely the same. And what was he singing in such uncharacteristic gorgeous voice? I know now that it was the famous Queen of the Night aria from *The Magic Flute*; and I still can't hear that opera without a strange pricking of my thumbs. You've worked out by now, I suppose, what happened next. Of course, of course: top C shattered all the mirrors in the house.

With the goblin's usual finesse: just as my mother arrived home from church. I heard her scream *'Jesus Lord, Philip, what have you done!'* with such violence that she might have shattered all the mirrors in the house herself, had any been intact.

I just waited where I was for the wrath of God to descend. But for once it didn't. She was at her wits' end – she told me so later: 'Philip, I am at my *wits'* end!' – burst into harsh racking sobs that tore me apart with guilt, and slammed the bedroom door behind her. She spent the day there, leaving me more than enough time to gather all the shards and every last splinter. When Dan came home that evening, something about the awful silence of the house must have alerted him, because he stepped in warily, looking about him as if he expected some kind of intruder, a skunk perhaps. 'And?' he asked. 'And?'

'They just broke,' I said. 'By themselves.'

His eyes widened slightly, his eyebrows rose. 'They? By themselves?'

'All at once,' I said. 'By themselves.'

'Windows?' he asked, looking round. 'No, not the windows. Lights? No, not the lights. The crockery?'

'The mirrors,' I said.

His mouth opened and closed a few times and then he said: 'Ah, the mirrors.' He rolled his eyes: 'Well, I never really liked the sight of my face anyway.'

He lifted his brace of dangling cob: 'You wouldn't mind gutting these for me, would you?'

I shook my head. 'Don't mind,' I said.

He gave me the fish and went into her bedroom. Their voices, low and intense, went on for a very long time. I went out and sat on that bench in the dark garden, and wished my grandmother were still alive.

They sent me to a child psychiatrist. His name was Doctor Alport. His head was astonishingly round and bald, a living cannon ball with large intelligent eyes which he preserved behind thick spectacles. When I was alone with him in his office for the first time, he took a square of white writing paper and unscrewed his fountain pen. I had never seen a fountain pen like that before; it had a lever that could suck in the ink and squirt it out. He squirted ink on to the paper, glancing at me from time to time to see if I noticed his trick. Then he folded the paper over this inkblot, and squashed out a shape. He lifted the paper, blew on the ink, and turned it towards me.

'What do you see, Philip?' he asked in a kind, bored voice. He blinked behind his glasses. 'What do you see in the inkblot?'

I saw a camel. But I saw no point in dithering, so I said, 'I see a goblin.'

He leaned forward intently. 'A goblin, you say? Good, good. Tell me about this goblin. Just let the ideas run freely through your head. Say what comes to mind, don't worry if it sounds silly or anything like that.'

'It's a black shiny goblin. It only comes out when I'm alone and breaks things. No one else has ever seen it. Its name is Gbrnztphlkx –'

'Gerbinzfilx?' said Doctor Alport cautiously. 'Is that the name did you say?'

'No, Gbrnztphlkx, you have to roughen your voice to say it the way he does, and you have to go faster.'

Doctor Alport pursed his lips.

'Anyway, he comes out of the broom cupboard or disappears under the bed, stuff like that. He breaks things just before someone comes home. He's the King of all the Goblins. I can't stop him. It's not me breaking all these things. He can live in mirrors too and get out by singing really loud. He used to take holidays in the bathroom mirror – that's how he got to know me – until he broke all the mirrors in the house.'

Doctor Alport was still holding up the piece of paper. He looked a bit upset. He asked me many more questions about the goblin and I answered them as truthfully as I could. It was a relief to talk about Gbrnztphlkx, and I was grateful that there was an adult who would listen to me. Afterwards I went out to the waiting-room and my mother went into his office. They closed the door. I don't know what they said, but I know it turned into an argument, because I heard the all too familiar rhythms of my mother in her rage. Then the office door blew open and she took my hand and dragged me out of that office, her high-heeled shoes thudding dully into the carpet and loudly on the stairs.

When we were in the car I asked: 'What did he say, Ma?'

'He's a stupid fool!' she snapped. I held my peace.

That night I eavesdropped on her and Dan when they thought I was asleep. I heard the words 'paranoid schizophrenia' and 'institutionalise'. I didn't know the meaning of those long words. Her voice rose in indignation: 'The idiot can't tell the difference between a lunatic child and an honest liar with too much imagination.'

They didn't take me to Doctor Alport again.

It was a long time before I was left alone in the house. Autumn came, the cooler weather bringing a sense of relief. Yet I slept badly and ate badly and lost weight. There were dark rings under my eyes. My mother had me tested for iron deficiency and I was given doses of anti-worm syrup. The problem wasn't worms of course. I knew I would have to be alone sooner or later; I knew Gbrnztphlkx would return then. And finally, the thing that I anticipated with such dread happened. My mother and Dan began to trust me again. They felt sorry for me. They took my straitened emotional condition to be one of remorse, but it was really foresight.

I knew I had to be prepared; after the mirror trap had worked out so badly, I decided to try an electricity trap. I took a long piece of flex and connected it to a plug at one end, and separated the wires at the other. I stripped the separated ends and soldered them on to crocodile clips. In the middle I placed a simple switch, the type used on bedside lamps. I kept this with me at all times.

And what was I doing when Gbrnztphlkx rang the doorbell the third Saturday afternoon I was alone? (I was expecting him; it was Indian summer, a day of searing listless air.) I was seated on the couch with crocodile clips attached to my earlobes. The wire ran over the back of the couch, and was plugged in behind it. The socket was switched on at the wall, but the switch in the middle was off.

'Come in!' I shouted. 'It's open!'

The goblin came in holding a gift-wrapped box. 'Long time no see,' he remarked.

'It's been a while,' I agreed.

'What's that?' we both said at the same time.

'It's a gift for you,' he replied first.

'This is something that people do that goblins don't know about,' I said in turn, pointing to my ear. 'And the gift?'

'Oh that,' he said, slightly embarrassed. 'Just chocolates. I know I've put you to some trouble. I've been feeling bad about it.'

'Oh you shouldn't have.'

He shrugged and handed me the box. I tore open the wrapping. They were Springer chocolates, little chocolate bottles containing real brandy. I really like that kind. 'Fantastic!' I said.

'Think nothing of it. Go ahead, try one.'

'No thanks, not right now. I've just eaten and I'm quite full.'

His eyes kept wandering to the clips on my ear. I could see he was burning with curiosity.

'Would *you* like one?' I asked, proffering the box.

'Not just now, thanks.'

I waited, very polite. He sustained a silence equally polite.

He broke first: 'Mind if I ask you a question? Nothing very important. Just a trifling thing . . .'

I shrugged. 'Please go ahead. Ask whatever you like.'

'Those clips on your ears?'

'Yes, what about them?'

'Oh, nothing. Nothing important.'

'Sure you don't want a chocolate?'

'No, quite sure, thank you.'

'Well, thanks for popping in. Very nice of you to bring this little gift. You really shouldn't have. Most kind.'

The goblin crossed his arms, a long taloned hand dangling from the wrist. His foot began tapping, as if by itself, and his ears twitched. He uncrossed his arms.

'Why don't you take a seat?' I invited. 'My mother isn't out for long. She's just gone out for some milk, I think. I'm sure she'd love to meet you.'

Gbrnztphlkx sat down with a bad grace. Then he blurted out, quite upset by the strength of his curiosity: 'What is it, what is it that people do that goblins don't know about? Those clips on your ears? What is it? There's nothing people know about that goblins don't. Nothing. Can't be.'

'Oh, that,' I replied airily. 'I'm sure you know all about it then.'

He looked terribly frustrated. Time to strike, I thought: 'It's just something we human beings do when we have a really difficult and interesting problem to solve. It's an ancient ceremony called "charging the batteries". As you goblins know, it gives us certain magical powers.'

'Of course,' said Gbrnztphlkx, 'I know that.'

'Of course you do. So I don't have to tell you more about it.' I yawned and stretched, and said, 'Well, I've just about finished "charging my batteries" now. Would you like to try it? I believe it would work for goblins too, though I'm not quite sure.'

Gbrnztphlkx yawned as well – it was a tremendous studied yawn that took a great deal of time to pass through all its phases – and gazed at his talons. 'Oh, I don't think so,' he said eventually. 'Seeing I know all about it.' Then, as an afterthought: 'Oh well, perhaps just a little. It's been a while since I – what did you say? – "charged my batteries".'

'Why not?' I said, as casually. 'Now the first thing you do is sit down here next to me.' He did so. I took the clips off my ears and held them before him. 'Here. You just press the clips open like this

– see how they open? – and put them on your ears. One on each side, that's right. Just like that.'

'And then?'

'You wait for a bright idea.'

'Is that all?'

'That's all.'

He looked doubtful. I shifted a bit further away from him, making sure there was no point of contact, and threw the switch. I heard a crackling noise rather like his name, and he slumped down.

I stood up in shock. What had I done? Had I killed him? At one level I hoped so, I really did; and yet I felt great anguish because I might have committed murder. I see that moment in retrospect as the death of my childhood. My angst was misplaced. It wasn't murder I had committed, it was cynical practice; I had treated a live being as an object and so became something of a goblin myself.

I leaned over the supine creature. Gbrnztphlkx was perfectly still. There was no sign of breath; I wondered whether he had ever had a pulse in the first place, and whether it was safe to touch that electrified flesh (if flesh it was). I let out a long, shuddering breath and as I began to straighten up, I was arrested: one goblin eye opened, the lid simply popping up, nothing else moving in that outrageous face; intelligence returned, great intelligence; and slowly his obsidian lips parted, releasing a puff of smoke and a strong smell of burning, and he croaked, 'You're right. Goblins know nothing of this.'

I only had time to think, 'Now what happens next?' before it happened. His hands swept up faster than a striking snake and his forefingers jabbed against my forehead, one on each side; I can only guess that he had stored the current – yes, what irony, like a charged battery – and it surged back into my brain.

My mind became a carnival of all sounds, all colours and shapes possible, all scents and movements, a complete history of things grotesque. I have said that language is an instrument of order, but here I learned the inner speech of goblins. When I had done speaking in tongues of chaos my body was still flopping like a landed fish, my head banging on the floor. I retain only one understandable image from the moment before darkness flooded in. Gbrnztphlkx picked up his box of chocolates and said, 'You don't mind if I take these back do you? You won't have much use for them for a while.'

Perhaps my soul made a polite inward surge as if to say, of course not, help yourself, and then I was dead to the world.

I came to with a giant florid tear-drowned face filling the sky and I was wrapped in something strong and warm: my mother's face, my mother's arms. She had found me unconscious with the clips attached to my ears and assumed quite reasonably that I had tried to commit suicide. (She didn't know that it was Gbrnztphlkx's little joke.) Apart from a monstrous headache, there were two other strange side-effects. One was that I couldn't open my mouth. It was simply impossible. I tried to talk to my mother and could only make strange gagging moon-calf sounds. It drove both of us completely hysterical, and she wept and wiped her tears off my face, shouting, 'Oh my poor boy, what have I done to you!' and similar troubling endearments. Then Dan arrived – he had been taking groceries out the car – and took charge.

First he took my mother out the room, I believe to their bedroom, and made her lie down. He returned and unplugged my electricity trap and removed the crocodile clips from my earlobes. He said slowly and carefully, making distinct lip-movements, 'Phil, can you hear me? If you can, stop making those sounds, OK?'

I stopped making those sounds.

'Good,' he said. 'I can hear myself think. Now what seems to be the problem?'

I began moaning and gagging again, trying to explain. He put his hand up before my face and shook his head. I went silent again. 'You can't open your mouth?' he asked. I nodded vigorously, wild-eyed. Then he applied a simple remedy. He pressed down on my jaw with his palm and increased the pressure carefully until with an audible snap and a jolt of pain, my upper and lower teeth parted. 'Open wider please,' he requested and peered around inside. 'Bit dark in there, but I think you've melted your fillings. Soldered your teeth together.' I opened and closed my mouth many times and took in great relieved breaths of air.

The second side-effect was a swollen red lump on either side of my forehead where I had been jabbed by the goblin's forefingers, as if horns were trying to emerge.

For at least a week my mother was wonderfully nice to me. Then human nature began to assert itself and she took me aside and gave me a talk on the Devil (though still making sure to keep her voice down). She said that the Devil was not a creature with a forked tail and horns – she glanced uneasily at my forehead, as if she were unsure – but spoke to us in a still, small voice which said very reasonable things, but which must be resisted with all our might. I replied that I was sure she was right, but the only devil I knew either appeared in the bathtub when it was empty, came out of the broom cupboard or rang the doorbell like anyone else. And he wasn't very reasonable at all. Her lips began crumpling and before she could say, 'My poor baby, what have I done to you?' I conceded that it wasn't really the devil, only a goblin, not an evil one, just somewhat mischievous and unpredictable. She looked so stricken and fiercely loving and defeated that I felt sorry for her and quite guilty about all the trouble I had put her through just by being born and continuing to remain alive through all the fortunes of that season. I promised not to commit suicide again, and there the matter rested.

In the middle of winter I visited my grandmother's grave. I rested against my bike, heated by the ride despite the chill air. It wasn't a plush cemetery. Straggling buffalo grass filled the spaces between graves, and a copse of sad bluegums lined the boundary. But it was quiet there, and it seemed for a moment that I could hear her voice explaining things about darkness and light I couldn't understand. She never talked like that when she was alive, so I was sure I was just imagining it. I laid the bike down, sat on her gravestone and tried to picture her face. But after a while I was thinking about other things. The handlebar was loose still and there was a girl at school I liked but she wouldn't speak to me, not even look at me, and Dan was getting quite old, his hair was mostly grey. Then I thought I heard my grandmother laughing and she said in my mind, her voice strangely young, but as kind as I always remembered it: *I'm not a figment of anyone's imagination.*

Nearly a full year passed before I came against the goblin king once more. He returned during one of those shattering highveld summer storms where lightning strikes close and the battering of thunder sets your ears ringing with pain. But there were other noises that night, a skittering about on the roof and odd bangs and thuds. I put on a raincoat and went outside, walking backwards away from the house, peering up anxiously, shielding my eyes against the downpour. There he was prancing about on our galvanised iron roof, shaking his fist at the bruised sky and shouting furiously. I couldn't hear what he was saying; I still don't understand how he kept his footing on that slick, streaming sheeting.

'Gbrnztphlkx!' I shouted. 'What are you doing up there?'

'Is it you, horrible child?' he shouted back. 'I contest the wind and the rain! The King of all the Goblins does battle –' The wind took his words, and I lost them.

A violet flash of lightning made me wince but at the same time released my own wickedness so that a voice seemingly other than my own, older and with greater authority roared out: 'King of the Goblins? Where are your subjects? Goblin flunkey more likely!'

The thunder drowned out everything; then his voice surged back: '– can you understand the strength of mind it takes to behold a creature as appalling as you? You are the *substance of nightmare*!'

I had to lean against a blast that nearly shook him off the roof. He recovered and danced higher up, against the chimney. He turned away from me, raised his face to the sky again, virtually screaming. I heard something like, 'Blow, winds, and crack your cheeks! rage! blow! You cataracts and hurricanoes, spout till you have drenched our steeples, drowned the cocks!'

A squall of rain hit us, cutting off vision; I had to turn away, face downwards as wind and rain drowned out everything, holding me in a vortex of blindness. It passed and his voice floated down in this brief pause in the storm, only to be interrupted again: 'And thou, all shaking thunder, strike flat the thick rotundity of the world, crack nature's moulds, all germens spill at once –!'

When I had cleared the water from my hair and eyes and could see again, he was on top of the chimney. The voice of the wind rose shrieking, and Gbrnztphlkx leaned forward steeply into it, supporting himself on the TV antenna which – it might have been an illusion – slowly gave way under his weight. The wind dropped, a dramatic pause, and his voice sank into the space it created, hissing and rasping as only a goblin's voice can: 'You sulph'rous and thought-executing fires, vaunt-couriers of oak-cleaving thunderbolts, *singe my black head* –'

You probably won't believe what happened next. It seemed that the forces of nature heard his challenge and answered. When the lightning struck it was with such violent repetition that I thought it would never end. His body on the chimney was wrung about manically, slammed through death beyond death; the house was plunged into darkness, then lit inside by a series of ghastly phosphorescent flashes; finally, a blinding explosion of such force that I was thrown to the ground and couldn't breathe for ozone.

It took me a while to realise that I wasn't actually dead myself. There was no trace of the goblin. I went back into the house and shook myself off. Of course there was no power. I found my torch, took a towel and a couple of blankets and huddled down in the passage, a place without windows. Dan and my mother didn't return that night. I wasn't worried because I knew he would have too much sense to try and drive home through such a great storm.

They returned at first light and found me asleep in the passage, at peace with the world and myself. So was the world; the storm had blown over. Not so our house. The wiring was entirely destroyed, the new television set was a pile of slag, and all the mirrors throughout were blackened, the glass irregularly shattered and melted in places. I expected that familiar cry, *'Jesus Lord, Philip, what have you done?'* to ring out, but it never came. Yet I couldn't stop myself saying, 'It wasn't me, Ma.' She looked at me strangely, and I added: 'It wasn't the goblin either, for once. He's gone.'

Dan lifted his eyebrows and rolled his eyes, ever so slightly. 'Ha,' he said. 'Goblin? I thought it was the Easter bunny.' I kept quiet, but thought to myself: one day I'll tell you what really happened, the whole thing, and then you'll roll your eyes.

Gordimer's Cat

ACHMAT DANGOR

'Why get your mother to come and spend Christmas in the city? That's like trying to change the tide of history,' Patrick told Nicole. 'Everywhere in the world people want to go the other way, away from the city.'

He poured himself a drink, getting ready to 'just flake out', as he put it, in his armchair and read the paper, starting from the back, with the sports news, and work his way towards the front pages where he would be too tired to do anything but skim over the political reports.

Who blamed whom for what?

By the time he was confronted by the rape and murder stories, he would have to get up to help Nicole. Bath baby Michael or set the table, depending on whose voice he heard first, Nicole calling from the kitchen or the baby crying in its cot.

'What about you – you want a drink,' he asked Nicole, and then leaned back against the kitchen counter when she shook her head as he expected she would.

'You know, everybody wants to have a place in the country they can go to over Christmas, some little plaasdorpie where time is slow and you can leave your door open at night and listen to the crickets, be in touch with nature and all.' Patrick said, in one long breath that held at bay the next deep sip of whisky. He paused to take another gulp. That's how he drank the only drink he would have at the end of the day, in quick slurps. Nicole took the opportunity to speak.

'Every year, for ten years, we've driven to Mafikeng, picked up Rosie and whichever boyfriend she was busy with and drove off to

Buurmansdrift,' she said, waving her finger to stop Patrick, who had swallowed that big sip, from interrupting her. 'And I had to listen to you complain, every year, about how primitive it all was, Mama's home at Buurmansdrift. The toilet was nothing but a big hole underneath you, that you never knew whether a scorpion or a snake was waiting to bite your arse as you sat down.'

'Ya, well . . .'

'Heat, dry and dusty, dusty and dry, whichever way you want to put it, remember? . . .'

'Well, I still think it's therapeutic, long empty days, being able to think. Here, all we have over Christmas is more crime and violence.'

'Listen to the blerry Mister-from-the-suburbs! Anyway, Joburg is empty then.'

'Yes, because people leave, run away . . .'

'To Durban or Cape Town, to the sea, to something bigger than three houses, a butcher shop . . . and a church . . . on a back road to Botswana.'

She turned away and began to slice the vegetables laid out on a wooden board. That was usually his job. Fascinated by the smoothness and skill of her somewhat bony fingers, he didn't offer to take over from her.

'Anyway, I think we should give Mama a break,' Nicole said. 'I think she's burying herself alive in that place.'

'So, is Rosie coming as well, and Frankie what's his name . . .?'

'Frankie Apollis, yes.'

'Christ, can you see us spending a whole week here in Joburg with Frankie mister damn Apollis and his little Rosie?'

'Hey, you sound jealous. Sometimes I think if she wasn't my sister . . .'

'She's too neurotic for me.'

Their conversation resumed its calm, somewhat distracted tone. She busied herself with dinner, he sat in his chair, and had only reached the inner page World Results when young Michael screamed, that yelping scream which instantly roused Patrick from whatever state of distraction he was in. Michael's helpless child's voice was like a silent whistle, above the range of normal hearing. A restless newborn baby, Michael tossed and turned like an adult. It was Patrick who heard, in his deepest sleep, the child stir, and it

299

was he who stumbled through the darkness to take the infant in his arms and rock it back to sleep.

Now, with the child bathed and dinner eaten, Patrick and Nicole sat for a while in front of the TV to watch the news. Then tore themselves abruptly from the threatened after-dinner stupor and slipped away to their own sanctuaries, he to pack the books he would need for the next day's lectures while she organised her diary or worked on some or other urgent document. Their reunion began in the bathroom where a light-hearted skirmish took place around the basin. Though they had a good income between them – he lectured applied mathematics at a technical college and she was an attorney – their recent move from the township into one of the oldest suburbs in the city had put them in 'white man's hock for ever' Patrick said. There wasn't enough money to build that second bathroom, en suite. Shit, these hundred-year-old houses!

'It's your Calvinist nature, really,' Nicole teased him.

It was true that spending money on something that was not essential was difficult for him. Or, perhaps he enjoyed the intimacy forced upon them by a single bathroom cum toilet. Here, pacts were made, disputes resolved and new ones started, here the subtle preludes to sex began, and here, Nicole insisted, Michael was conceived after ten barren years.

'It was the angle,' she had told him in the doctor's rooms. 'I was bending over to rinse my hair, remember?'

'We have an overhead shower, Nico,' Patrick had shot back, trying to hide his embarrassment. Their doctor, an old family friend, smiled and said that conception worked on the same principle, whatever the angle.

When they were in bed Nicole crept close up to him, but he knew she did not want to make love. An anguish that Nicole could only half articulate, had surfaced in her. She often 'felt' things, and because she didn't understand them well enough to speak about them, she descended into a melancholic state that demanded from Patrick days of cajoling – provocation even – to try and get her to snap out of it.

'I don't like Christmas time,' she said.

'Why?' he asked, immediately regretting his querulous tone.

She turned away.

'Because things happen at Christmas,' she said from the darkness on her side of the bed.

The day before Christmas Mama Edna, Rosie and Frankie Apollis arrived in Frankie's souped-up ninety-eighty-something Toyota. Since their Easter visit to Mama's house Frankie had added false racing vents to the front of the car. It brought balance to the false rear spoilers, Patrick observed silently as the car. drew up in the driveway.

'Who needs a blerry Christmas tree,' he muttered, earning himself a withering 'don't start' look from Nicole. They greeted and hugged, smiled, and helped to carry in the luggage, gifts already disguised in gaudy paper, and more food than they would ever be able to eat over the festive season. Frankie had brought his own beer that he immediately demanded should get pride of place in the fridge. Patrick helped Frankie to settle in, he and Rosie got Patrick's study because it was the larger of the two, while Mama Edna was to sleep in Michael's room. The baby's cot had been moved into Patrick and Nicole's bedroom. Nicole was busy with a sensitive case, third force stuff, and didn't want to have to move papers around too much.

Rosie, seeming to address herself to Patrick's sudden and inexplicable resentfulness, announced that they could only stay until the day before New Year because Frankie's family had this traditional New Year's Eve dinner which they were duty bound to attend. Mama of course could stay on. Patrick remembered his manners and offered everyone a drink. But the women were already in the kitchen, on the pretext of getting the Christmas lunch going. Their clannish, womanly intimacy that mother and daughters had forged years ago in response to their withdrawn, morose father, was being re-established.

Patrick reconciled himself to being deprived of Nicole's affections for all of that week. Frankie, in the mean time, suggested they go for a walk. Check out the neighbourhood, see how the 'real' larnies live. In the December heat the streets were cool archways of tall trees.

'Nadine Gordimer lives there,' Patrick said, pointing to an old house behind a high wall.

'Who?'

'The writer. Won the Nobel Prize.'

'Oh ja, because of her politics.'

On the wall they saw a sleek, three-legged black cat walking regally, pause to lick a forepaw.

'Shit,' Frankie said, look at that. 'It's a crippled black cat. Somebody's going to have bad luck.'

The cat jumped down from the wall into the garden. Patrick wondered how it was able to do that with only three legs. Bored with looking at high walls and snarling back at dogs, Frankie suggested they go back and have a drink. Using an all-purpose Swiss-army type of knife, he opened a quart of beer. Patrick thought that the breweries had long ago stopped using these archaic mementoes to drunken township days and that they belonged in an apartheid museum, but accepted the glass of beer which Frankie had poured and suggested they go out into the garden. Drinking beer while sitting on grass seemed like the only tradition he had ever had.

They settled under the huge magnolia tree which Rosie, on one of her few forays into the garden 'just to check that F is behaving', described as 'gorgeous'. Frankie added his praise, saying that it provided just the kind of shade a drinking man needed. Michael lay on a blanket gurgling, trying to touch with his fat little hands the shafts of sunlight woven into the shadows of the tree, then fell asleep. The place was quiet. No neighbours milling about, chatting as they too prepared for a Christmas in the sun. It had a different kind of peace, silent and distant almost. He missed the cheerful bustle the Christmas brought to the townships, everything beginning to wind down, people tackling with great zeal chores stored up especially for the Christmas break. Soon the energy would have been spent, and an even more pleasurable phase of laziness commenced. The collection of empty bottles, only recently carted to the dump, would begin to grow again.

In Patrick's suburban garden empty beer quarts lay on the lawn like spent cannon shells. He felt queasy, even though he had drunk far less than Frankie who began to speak in low, mordant tones about the 'situation in the country'.

'It's really shit being a Coloured these days.'

'If he says, just once more, that, we were too black then and we're too brown now, I'll kill him,' Patrick whispered to Nicole when he went in to put Michael down and to relieve himself. He went into the toilet, vaguely aware that Nicole's face had on a tight mask. When he came out of the toilet he saw Rosie had been weeping. In the back garden Mama Edna sat upright in a deck chair, as tense as a bird ready to take off.

Under the magnolia tree, Frankie had enough energy to let off one more diatribe against these 'blacks who were our brothers in the struggle – until the struggle was won!' then fell asleep with his mouth open. Patrick wondered how such a thin man could keep his pee in for such a long time. He hadn't been to the toilet all afternoon, at least four quarts of beer notwithstanding. Nicole came out and asked Patrick to move Frankie's car. They were going for a drive, in her car. He sat waiting in Frankie's car that was unbelievably clean inside and smelled of lavender, while Nicole reversed out into the street. Rosie was at the back and Mama Edna in front, leaning forward like someone getting ready give directions in a place she no longer remembered.

By early evening Patrick had bathed and fed Michael, wakened Frankie from his 'tiep' with the offer of some coffee, then guided him to the toilet – finally – and prayed that the guy's aim was good. He hated having to clean vomit from the floor. He sat on the veranda sipping coffee, looking anxiously along the road for Nicole's car to appear. He had this Nicole-like feeling of dread. It was dark when they returned. All three had been crying. Nicole squeezed Patrick's hand, a gesture that said, 'don't ask, not now'. Rosie announced that they were going to evening mass and that they would have Christmas Eve dinner instead of lunch the next day. Mama wanted to go home in the morning.

Mama Edna looked drained, but lighter somehow. As if the heaviness of her years had been lifted. Frankie didn't mess on the floor and had sobered up enough to bath and shave without slitting his own throat. He too wanted to go to church. When he was alone, Patrick drank a whisky in the quiet of the house, trying to decipher the mystery the three women were harbouring. He set the table, warmed the food. They came back from church, the women taking mantillas from their heads and carefully folding them like it was some long practised family ritual. Frankie loosened his tie and opened another quart of beer. Their Christmas Eve dinner was a subdued affair, livened up only once by Nicole offering a muted toast to peace and goodwill. Michael screamed loudly and

Nicole went to tend to him. Rosie served the dessert and Frankie talked about the service.

'I'm not a Catholic myself, but the service was beautiful. They put on a nice show.'

Mama Edna said she was tired and was going to bed. She hoped she had not spoiled their Christmas. Soon Frankie and Rosie went to bed, saying they were making an early start. Patrick washed the dishes, made sure that doors were locked and outside lights switched on. Having completed what Nicole called his 'paranoid patrol' he brushed his teeth and got ready for bed. He found her, half-undressed, standing over Michael's cot, a dreamy look on her face. He too had this cloying love for their son. Comes from having a child when you're into your late thirties.

Nicole took off her clothes and uncharacteristically got into bed naked. Propped up against the headboard she stared at the ceiling, and anticipating Patrick's 'what was that all about' question, began telling him about the revelations Mama Edna had made that day.

'Mama took us to the place where she lived when she was twenty years old.'

'Mama lived in Joburg?'

'Malaycamp.'

'Christ . . . there's nothing there any more.'

'Patrick, just listen, please . . . she was a student nurse, lived in a boarding house and met this man.'

Patrick had wanted to complete the last part of the sentence for her, it was that predictable.

'Now before you judge, just listen. He was a bit older, maybe twenty-five, Indian . . .'

That too he could have predicted. Young Coloured girls from the sticks loved men with soft, lush beards. Only they couldn't be white men in those days. Then hated himself for a moment. Here he was just like all those other small town Coloured men he had always despised, thinking that Coloured girls who went with white or Indian men were weak and self-hating, whores even. God help the woman if the man was black.

'They used to go out, to the cinema, they went dancing at some famous club in Malaycamp, imagine, my timid Mama. Then suddenly he went quite funny and secretive, asked if he could stay in her room for a while. He remained the gentleman throughout, never imposed himself, never wanted to go all the way, sexually,' Nicole continued.

Nicole spoke slowly, the way Mama spoke to them when they were children, as if they were too innocent to understand some of the things of the world she had to make them aware of. She closed her eyes and imagined her mother and this young man lying chastely side by side. Who is Mama kidding? she said to herself. Then dismissed this disloyal thought. A thick, black beard. She could never imagine her mother with such a man. She had been married for nearly forty years, to a man so clean his face seemed barren.

'He stayed for a whole week, not leaving her room, sneaking to the toilet when Mama's landlady went out. Not once did he insist on making love, though they got close, Mama says.'

'Your mother told you all this?'

'Yes, and more. Mama couldn't stand it any more, she thought maybe he couldn't do it. So, she took the initiative. Seduced him, or aroused him, at least. Yes, that's the word she used. They made love and he wept afterwards, and was on his knees asking for forgiveness.'

'He was married.'

'No, he was on the run from the police. He was in trouble . . . it was soon after Rivonia . . . Communist Party and all that.'

'Christ!'

'He was to leave the country soon, just before Christmas. And so he wept and she wept, for days, until he left. Later Mama found out she was pregnant and she knew there was no way she could contact him. She had the baby.'

Patrick was unsure whether he should offer to get Nicole the drink he felt she needed. But the darkness outside their room seemed too dense. And he might run into Frankie foraging for a drink. Why did he dislike this man so much? Perhaps because he spoke his mind and didn't hide his feelings. Patrick wished he could do that, tell Nicole that it was a nice story but not unique. Then it struck him that baby in question might have been Nicole. So what? He always thought she looked different from Rosie.

'So, you are the daughter of an Indian who fathered you in a one night stand then went off into exile . . .'

'Oh Patrick, sometimes you are so insensitive. Mama took us to meet her daughter – our other sister – today. The baby was adopted soon after being born.'

She slid down into the blankets, her eyes pressed shut.

'So,' Patrick wanted to say, 'you met your sister today. What about the man? Has he returned, is he famous, in the Cabinet maybe, a leader of some sort, has he had the decency to contact Edna, do you get to meet him too?' but turned and saw the rigid shape of Nicole's back. Now he wanted to touch her, tell her he was sorry, that this was the only way he knew how to deal with pain, someone else's or his own.

But Nicole was asleep. Sheer exhaustion had forced it on her. This house had a way of slowing things down, sighing and breathing, until the shadows sunk down on it like heavy eyelids, forcing everything to submerge. Patrick turned on to his side and closed his eyes. What the hell, tomorrow is Christmas and the sun will shine and we'll open presents and have enough time to seduce each other and get drunk, and afterwards, we'll take Michael for a walk in the park. Maybe we'll stop on the way and ring the bell and Nadine Gordimer will open her gate and he'll ask to see that black cat and enquire whether she knew that her cat brought omens to the neighbourhood?

Maybe they'll just take a drive to the townships and go and have a drink with friends and Nicole will tell her mother's story and everybody will cry with her and then laugh, saying, 'You know, it's incredible how wicked the old people were in their days!'

'Life will be OK,' he murmured to Nicole's still rigidly sleeping back.

Hijack

COLIN JIGGS SMUTS

Jesus, my arse is sore. That guy really hurt me. But at least I
have the hundred bucks.

They're insisting I get up. They say I have to get out for the day.
This is a place only for sleeping, they say. Have I still got my money?

I feel my back pocket. Shit, those Big Guys took fifty bucks!
Fuck them! I got beaten up for those bucks and now they've gone
and stolen half of it.

'Where's Jabu and Mandla?' I shout, jumping up.

'They gone, man,' replies Tshepo.

'They stole my money!' I shout.

'Hey, man, you're lucky they left you with some,' Tshepo says.

'You saw them, why didn't you wake me up?'

'And get fucked up? Are you mad?'

Oom Piet, the caretaker of the parking garage, comes towards
us and shouts, 'Out with you! You should've been out of here long
ago.'

'They stole my money, Oom Piet.'

'Now look here, Johannes, I told all you guys, I don't want
trouble here. Just pay me for sleeping here and put those filthy
rags you sleep on in the room. Ooh, but you stink. Fuck off now,
the white people will be here soon!'

Tshepo and I wander around the Bronx, looking for Jabu and
Mandla. They are not at any of the usual haunts. They must've
gone to town or Braamfontein. I have my okapi in my pocket.

'I'll kill them!' I threaten.

'Relax,' Tshepo tells me. 'You at least have something. They
didn't take it all. In this life you must share.'

307

'Share? Do they ever share with me, with us?' I ask without expecting an answer.

'Hey Johannes, I'm hungry, man,' Tshepo says. 'Can't we eat something? You're not going to keep that money in your pocket like a bank are you?'

As we enter Fontana the security guard stops us with his baton.

'Here to steal again,' he says, poking the baton in my face.

'Who steals?' I ask him as I whip out the money to show him.

He lets us in. The other customers, black and white, look at us with disdain, telling each other that we shouldn't be allowed in. Another security guard is behind us, checking out our every move. Just as well we have money today; they seem determined to bust us. We buy two hamburgers and Liquifruit. After we've paid we stand at the shelves near the front entrance where you're allowed to eat your take-aways.

The security guards are still watching us, one behind us and the other at the door. But fuck them, we are paying customers!

Later, we're continuing our search for those bastards when Tshepo says, 'Hey, man, I need to kak.'

'Well just hang on,' I tell him. I know there are certain flats and hotels where the security guards will let us in for fifty cents.

'I can't hold it, man,' Tshepo complains. 'Let's go into the alley.'

Behind the Summit Club we find this closed shutter door. We go in and have a nice sit-down. The place is a strip club, bar, restaurant and whorehouse. Yes, you can fuck the strippers or the dozens of whores who hang out at the place. That is, if you have the money. There are also boys on offer if that's what you want. If you don't fancy the prices inside there's plenty of cheap competition to choose from on the pavement outside.

We finish our sit-down just in time. An SAB truck pulls up to deliver booze at the Club and the driver and his mate come after us with sjamboks. Suddenly the mapoyisa of the Club join the chase. Holding up our tattered pants, trying to button up our stinking arses we run like hell with blows, kicks and lashes pelting us. Once we hit Banket Street and run through the crowds, they lay off.

'You know, I swear those bastards just like playing like white men,' I tell Tshepo as we catch our breath. 'The white man used to treat them like this and now they're taking it out on us!'

I was twelve years old. I had been on the streets for three years. My mother had four children and I was the eldest. We all had different fathers. Ma seemed to care only for the kid she had from the latest man. Otherwise she left us at home. This was the family home in Central Western Jabavu where four families lived in one large four-roomed matchbox each with their own door. We all shared the communal tap and toilet. I didn't like living there. Everybody fought with everybody else. Each family had its own fights, and with the neighbours in the four rooms, plus with the others who stayed in the next four-roomed. And sometimes it got violent. A lot of us ran away because we were accused of starting the trouble.

All my three uncles had been in jail and my two aunties were prostitutes. They hated my mother; they said she thought because she sold herself in Hillbrow to whites and foreigners that she was something. They also complained that she slept with coolies and bushmen but never with black men – unless they were from Nigeria. They had to sell themselves to the local tsotsis and migrant workers in Soweto who didn't pay like the people in town. They were jealous of my mother.

You know, most of the people in those houses didn't work. They're all involved in some or other scheme like stealing cars, burgling houses, all sorts of things. They even stole from the rich black people in Dube and Selection Park.

But, hayi, the real things were in town where the whites stayed. And they're always fighting and accusing each other. Some even impimpi on one another to the police, to the gangs. Hey, it was terrible. And when you were sleeping at night, they came in drunk and if you were in their way they kicked you. Sometimes the aunties brought their customers home and they told you to go out so they could earn some money. Sometimes they didn't even bother. But if you dared to sleep on the bed they smacked you on to the floor and just started doing it while all of us kids were watching.

Jesus, I wanted to try that too. But my sister and cousin smacked me on the hand and told me I was being rude. But one day when I was alone with my cousin Rachel, we tried it.

It was really fun. Her smooth cookie, ha ha, no hair, like I've seen on the big women. It was tight but I found some vaseline and that made it easier. I didn't have sperm then, but it was nice. My first real sexual experience. A few weeks later when the blood came, Rachel got scared and thought it was because of what we had done. She kept washing herself and changing her underwear, trying to make it go away. But that's not easy if you live on top of each other as we did.

'What's wrong, what's all this blood,' her mother asked.

She blurted out that we had done it! They called her a whore. I was called a jagse hond. They whipped me so bad, I didn't go back for a year.

I liked going to see my father because he always gave me something. He stays in Meadowlands and has a nice house and car. He's married with three other children. Actually he doesn't really like me turning up there. I should rather phone him at his work or pass on a message to his friends.

He always gave me five or ten rands. Once he even bought me shoes. They looked just like Nikes. He knew this guy in the Smal Street Mall who he said was a friend who gave him a special deal.

But most times I don't hear from him. You see like him, the people at the house said I was a big boy and I must also help support. And if you stole something you thought was valuable and took it home, and they couldn't sell it, they beat you up and told you you were useless and just lived off them.

The teacher who was the soccer team manager in Zondi, where I was at school, promised to take us to Swaziland if we won all our matches.

Well, we did. So we had to raise money for the Combi to take us there. Each boy had to bring in two hundred rands and we had to buy new kit from our manager, plus boots. The team manager printed these papers at school where we had to ask people to give ten rand a time as sponsorship for our trip.

Hey, I tried. But most of the people I knew couldn't spare even five rand. Eventually I asked my father for money.

He said he would try and help but that I should first approach the white lady at that school in town – 'The one your mother's white boyfriend took you to. She likes you,' he said. 'She will probably take all the tickets plus buy the kit.'

Hayi, this white lady was becoming difficult. She wasn't as

nice as when I first went to the school. Then she would do anything for me. Buy me shoes, give me lunch, awu it was nice. If I stayed away from school and told her it was because I did not have busfare, she would give me money.

One day she came to school and this big fat coloured woman was not nice. She kept telling us to keep quiet or she would punish us. When I put my hand up to go to the toilet she just told me I was rude. I suppose because I was the poorest in the class and the most shabbily dressed, she and some of the kids looked down on me.

When I couldn't hold it any more I pissed into an empty Coke bottle lying around in the classroom. The boys and girls who saw me all giggled. Just as I finished the fat one became aware of the giggles.

She looked up and said: 'Johannes, causing a disturbance again?'

'No, teacher,' I replied hiding the bottle under the table.

The next day Sally, the principal, took me upstairs to go see Mr Paton, the director, and Shaun, the politician who just wanted to know if you supported the Party. It seemed like the Party was the only thing he knew.

I put the Coke bottle on Sally's desk.

When she came back, she sniffed.

'What's that terrible smell?' she asked.

The class broke into giggles, muttering my name. With a very stern look she came over to me.

'Johannes, what is this all about?'

'Well, Ma'm,' I said, scratching my head, and I told her what happened. '. . . and I kept the bottle to show you how bad they treat me when you are not here.'

I took a chance. I thought she would call Mr Paton and the politician to come and sort me out. Instead, she told me to take the bottle to the toilet, to empty the pee down the urinal and then throw the bottle in the dustbin. After I had done that she spoke about how people need to talk to each other, how students must talk to their parents and teachers about their problems.

'What Johannes has done is not right,' she said. 'But he felt he had to make a point.'

During the break she and Mrs Honey went upstairs to discuss the matter in her office. As I was leaving that day, she called me aside and told me that what I had done was wrong and that I must never ever do it again. She said she had me on the waiting list for those two women who came by every week and asked the children funny questions about their lives. That Friday morning, I was the first to see those funny ladies.

You see, it all started when my mother met this strange-sounding white man with this bald head and blue, blue eyes. Hayi, a real white man. He was from a place called Germany. I heard that it was the same place that Hitler came from, a mad man who liked to hold up his arm with a flat hand in salute, like the PAC, but he didn't like Jews and black people.

There we were sleeping at Highpoint in the parking garage when I heard Oom Piet say, 'Is this the one you are looking for?'

I reached for my okapi. I knew Oom Piet was an impimpi but why was he selling us out? He must be with the police. I'd have to get away fast. I hoped Tshepo knew what was going on otherwise I'd have to leave him behind.

Oom Piet kicked me on my thighs and said, 'Wake up! Wake up! There's a white man who wants to see you.'

'Wait, wait,' said this funny voice. 'Be gentle.' Now's my chance, I decided and I jumped up with my okapi flashing. I lunged out in all directions and started running for my life.

'Johannes, Johannes, stop!' the woman called out to me.

I recognised that voice. It was my mother! I stopped just as I was about to run up the car lane and looked back and there's my mother, with this strange white man, running after me with Oom Piet hobbling behind.

'It's OK,' my mother was shouting. 'He's not from the police, he's my friend and we're here to take you home.'

I put my okapi back in my pocket and walked back towards them in the garage looking to see if there were police or any other people watching me. If this was a trap I'd make a move down the fire escape or down the other floors. My mother broke into SeTswana, telling me it's all right, she had a home, this was a good white man, we were all going to live together.

Oom Piet shouted at me, also in SeTswana, that I was crazy to run away from my own mother. The white man held out his hand and said, 'Hello, Johannes, I am Horst. I have been looking forward to meeting you.'

'Awu!' I thought, keeping my mouth shut.

I couldn't believe it. This white man had a house in Moletsane and, man, it was posh! He had bought it from a colleague who had moved to the white suburbs. Well furnished, with TV and video and enough to eat and only us. Hell, man, it was only a four-room but it was the first time that I slept in a bed by myself. And my brother and sister had their own beds too. My baby brother slept with my mother and Horst.

Hell, it was the nicest time of my life. You know, he would buy us Chicken Licken or Kentucky on a Friday night. And he would make sure we all got to school, taking us himself.

He didn't have a car. I found this quite strange. I thought it was natural that every white man owned a car.

He would take us by taxi or train. Can you imagine travelling with a crazy white man in a black taxi or third class on the train and people are asking who is this crazy mlungu with you, holding your hand? I used to get so scared for him, I thought they were going to try to rob and stab him. Hey, but I used to have good shoes, clothes and books and he even used to take my mother with him and ask the teachers and Sally how was I doing and go over my reports with them.

Man, I really loved that white man. More than my own father. The only other man I loved like that was Uncle Omry. I even felt equal to those well-off kids at the school.

Horst would even wait for me, to take me home or to see me into a taxi. You know I don't know what he did. He told me he sold insurance. I'm not sure what that means. But Sally told us it was to protect you if you got robbed or burgled or if you died. But I don't think he was a crook, not like my family. He had to pay at this funny school which is the only one that would take me. With no school record or a bad one like mine, no school wanted to take me. My younger brother and sister got accepted because they had never been to school before. So they were in township schools near our home.

I liked calling that place 'home', it was the only home I ever knew. Until those crazies, those bastards who said they supported the PAC and Azapo – and some even said they were ANC supporters – said they couldn't have a white man staying in Soweto. They almost killed Horst. They threatened to burn the house down with all of us in it.

My mother ran away with the three small children. I had to lead Horst over fences, down alleys and through the Avalon cemetery into Kliptown to escape.

I later heard that they ransacked our house and stole everything. Horst paid the electricity and service charges and that's what upset them. They said he was breaking the boycott by paying and that he was an impimpi for the system! How you could be a spy for the system with an ANC government in power in 1995 and Madiba leading the Masakane campaign to get everyone to start paying for services, I never understood!

I hear now one of those thugs occupies the house and does not even pay. I hear he's the local chairman of the Civics Organisation.

Horst was so frightened, he went back to Germany three days later. But he promised Sally that he would pay my fees and send me money. He told me I must study and become a somebody. You know he went to John Vorster Square to lay charges and those useless policeman told him there's nothing they can do. He must lay charges at Moroka Police Station!

I told Horst, I know the Big Guys, they will get our house back, they will take those bastards out, I know where to contact them. He got very angry with me and told me I must never think like that, I must never contact those people or go back to that life ever again! I said yes, but I felt he didn't understand how things work here.

We went back to the crowded one room in Jabavu. They were not happy to have us. Soon afterwards my mother found a new man and moved in with him. She took my sister and two brothers with her but said I was big, I must stay behind and look after myself. This man was like the others that she had before. They were not like Horst, they didn't want to make a family and didn't want me around.

My brother and sister tell me, when I see them, that they miss Horst. This man is horrible to them. He treats our mother very badly. He even beats her. When I'm big I'm going to fuck him up!

At the funny school it wasn't going easy. The Fat One, she was really a Humpty Dumpty, with a big fat tummy hanging down, she looked permanently pregnant. She was always picking on me and making me feel like I didn't belong there, like the other children were better than me.

'This is not the street, Johannes. We have respect and decency here,' she kept telling me.

But I noticed she never did that if Sally was around or the other nice teacher, Mr Botha, who liked the Bible. Hayi, he liked the Bible, that one! When Sally came into the class and he was talking about the Bible we could see that she disapproved because this school had no religion, no prayers, no grace when you had your lunch. When we had assembly, Sally just told us about what was happening in the country, our behaviour and things like that.

This Botha was a funny guy. Maybe that's why he was a teacher at this school. They were always having people speaking or making movies of us or taking photos. One day they had people who showed us a video about sex and Aids and safe sex and all that. They also told us where to get condoms and that it was free with no age restriction. Now me, I'd been doing it. You know, if you make money, even the girls in Hillbrow, the Bronx, the big ladies will give you. Awu it's nice, man.

There is this clinic near Park Station. So that afternoon I went there and they said I could take as many condoms as I want. I took ten. You see, I liked that movie and that talk. And I saw people dying from Aids in the Bronx hospital and in Soweto. The next day I had a bulge in my pocket with all the condoms. You see, whether you stay at the family home or on the street, you have to have protection. Hayi, the guys and the girls thought I was main time at that school when I showed them what was in my pocket.

'Hey, man, it's better to do it bare back, that Aids thing is for white people and moffies,' the guys would say.

Anyway Mr Botha wanted to know what was this bulge in my pocket. So I told him and showed him. Ha, ha, the class laughed. Mr Botha was so cross he took me to Sally. Hayi, more trouble. Sally told me to please not exhibit my condoms around the school because it wasn't right. Ha, ha, I think she even ticked Mr Botha off about bringing me to her and not talking to me himself.

The truth is, I was so upset about Horst leaving and my mother going to stay with another man who didn't want me around, I decided to leave the school and the hell-hole I lived in and go back to the streets and live in the Bronx with the majitas.

Hey, but things had changed around there. Mandla, Jabu and Tshepo were now into the big time. They didn't steal from shops or mug people any more; that's for small-time tsotsis. They were still into those white ladies and men who take you home to their nice houses, shower you, feed you and then fuck you. But they're not satisfied with a hundred bucks any more.

'Now we demand more and if they don't want to pay we moer them, take what we want in cash and all the video machines and TVs, plus we even take the cars,' Mandla boasted. 'Ha, ha. We sell the cars quickly.'

'They don't seem to report us,' Jabu added, 'because the gatas don't come around looking for us. But the most exciting is when we take a house and tie up the people. And if the cherries are lekker, you know what we do. Then the Big Guys ask for their credit cards and their secret numbers. We have to hold them there while the Big Guys go out and draw all the money. Hey, it's easy, man, and the gatas don't even worry. The Big Guys know how to bribe them.'

'But the real easy money is in the cars,' Tshepo chipped in. 'When an order comes through you have to check out the car on order and go for it. But it can be dangerous because some of these drivers have guns.'

'Guns?' I asked. 'Then what happens?'

'Ka, ka,' the guys laughed. 'We have guns too, man. And we know how to use them. Sometimes we have to shoot or they will shoot us. But once you've got the car, you have to take it to the Big Guys quick-quick. But they work with us and are always nearby. We also know how to drive, but they always send a real sharp driver. Hey, we make a thousand, maybe more, just on one car. And when we're flush even the big women want us, and the skimpies beg to sleep with us. Hayi, even the white women want us when we've got bucks. And you know there's a lot of rich blacks now. We go for them too. It's the New South Africa!' Jabu laughed at me listening to them with round eyes.

The guys even had a flat where they stayed, compliments of the Big Guys. It was one of those one-room flats, with a toilet and bathroom and a space for a stove which was supposed to be the kitchen. But they shared it with lots of other boys working for the Big Guys. I think there were ten guys altogether staying in that flat. And, Jesus, was it filthy! The toilet stank, the bathroom was filthy, everything in the place was filth. And sometimes the water and lights didn't work. I don't think they paid the Council, but someone knew how to connect the wires.

There were so many fights in the place, a heavy vibe hung in the room. The whole building was like that; once I even saw a man lying dead in the passage. Women were always screaming and there were things breaking, like someone was trying to break every window in the building. Compared to this, my hell-hole in Jabavu seemed calm and the house we stayed in with Horst was like heaven. They introduced me to one of the Big Guys and assured him that I was one of them but needed to catch up as I had not been in the system for a while, two years in fact. He told us that he would have to consult with the other Big Guys and come back to us the next day. So all I could do in the mean time was head for Oom Piet for a place to sleep.

Nothing had changed, except the boys sleeping there looked younger and Oom Piet was his usual self, but had grown a bit older.

'Hell, Johannes,' he said. 'I thought by now you were in high school being a respectable person. Why are you back here?'

I told him the story about what happened to Horst and my mother. He said he had read about this white man being chased out of Soweto.

'But you shouldn't come back here, you know. Things are getting worse. Are you also taking these drug things like Mandla and them?'

I had noticed that at the flat the guys were smoking dagga, crack, and there was beer everywhere. I refused these things. One of those talks and video shows organised by Sally at the funny school had really put me off the stuff.

Uncle Piet said I could stay there that night for free. 'But remember, you owe me,' he told me.

The next day I was accepted by the Big Guys but I would have to start on the streets first, to get some training. I had to go with two guys who knew the operation. Sauer Street was their area, mainly between Jeppe and Bree. The operation was to hit the moegoe whites, but if blacks, coloureds or Indians also seemed to think they were white we hit them too. The only guys we never interfered with were the taxi guys. They would shoot you if you tried to grab something from them or their passengers. Most of

317

them were part of one syndicate or another. Man, I tell you, in the Syndicate we have the Big Guys, the police, businessmen, even people in government!

So what we did was we walked among the cars and if we saw a radio, a cell phone, a bag, jewellery on the person, anything of value, we grabbed it. Of course that's if they had the windows open. If the windows were closed we just took a brick and blasted the window or even the windscreen. No shit, I felt so proud at first, as if I was a genuine MK, a revolutionary fighting against these white oppressors who had everything and us, the true owners of the land, as the PAC says, the dispossessed! And for those who had guns, or sprays or even alarms in their cars, we had our okapis. Some guys even had guns. And they never hesitated to use them. Shit, it was either us or them. Hey man, every now and then the gatas came around and what did we do? We just faded away. The Big Guys heard from our brothers in the force that they were coming and we just got redeployed to the northern suburbs.

But it's all changing now in the suburbs. There are so many blacks staying there, people who have forgotten who they are. They have become like real white people. I hate them. I hear they also say, like the white people now, we don't go further south than Rosebank! Hey, man, that's why I support the PAC, Azapo, and Woza and outfits like that.

Madiba likes white people. He's not concerned about us, who are suffering, he's only worried about them and their skills and about them leaving the country. But what about us? We are still starving!

Shaun, the Politician, also says Madiba is wrong but Thabo Mbeki is going to change all that, he is really on black people's side. But I don't know, that guy smokes a pipe and seems so far away.

I was the runner. The one ou had to approach the car, that was me. If the person gave shit, like a gun or a spray or closed the window, the second guy had to hit him with a brick and the third guy would then come with the knife or gun. By then I or the second guy would be through one of the broken windows grabbing whatever we thought was valuable. Sometimes we would have to break the side window. Some of those larnies would forget to lock their boots and in a tick we'd have them open and off we went with the goods. And the Big Guys were always waiting in the side streets with their cars, ready to load up and move off. Hey, man, it was a perfect operation.

Did you see me that one Saturday in *The Star*? I was right there. All the guys recognised me! Front page, centre page, it was all me!

But the Big Guys didn't like it. They told me to play it cool, park in the shade for a while. They reckoned their connections in the force had told them if they busted me it would be a main time number and take the heat off them because I was featured in every photo. So I was confined to the flat or hell-hole for a week. They asked me didn't I have relatives in the countryside they could send me to. I only had family in Jabavu and they were known thieves, so that was not a good idea.

So I was confined to hanging out with these thugs who would take you out at the slightest chance and even more so if the Big Guys checked you. Shit, I had to watch my few possessions like a hawk. Sometimes I'd wake up at night just to feel if the two small bags with all my stuff were still there and to make sure by feeling my face that I was still alive!

Ja, the Syndicate was organised. Even if you didn't make the storage vehicle, another guy would just grab your stuff and stay cool while the cops were chasing you. And when they caught you and found nothing on you, although they had seen you take the stuff, they had to let you go. And even if the gatas caught you, hey, man, the Syndicate was organised, you were out again in the next hour, especially if the cops recognised that you were part of the Syndicate. The most I stayed inside was overnight. You know, the politicians think we are kids, they said we should have 'special protection'. Hey, but that was a joke! They had all these nice people who said, we are people and we must be treated properly. Oh fuck, we were all out of there in such a short time, it was funny. Ha, ha. But that Boer ANC chap, ou Karel, quickly changed the law and now we get busted like the big ouens.

But don't fuck with the Syndicate. They take you out, boy, there's no mercy. Don't try to steal or do a side deal. Man, you're fucked. But of course within the organisation, if you're connected, you can get away with anything. You see, the trick is to link up with a bigger guy who's on the rise. And if he thinks that he can trust you and you will do anything he says, whatever he gets, he's got to pass some on to you. You check. Hey, man, if the guy fucks up, you can even overtake him. Just fuck him up. That's it.

I soon got promoted in the Syndicate. I was taught to drive and use a gun. Man, I was proud. I was soon promoted to the same unit as Jabu, Mandla and Tshepo. No bullshit! We did heavy numbers. You know, we took this guy out in his driveway in Bryanston. I felt sorry for him. He tried to press a button, which we thought was an alarm and Mandla panicked and shot him. There was no time, we just pushed him aside and Jabu drove the car straight to Alexandra to the connection. We were out of there in five minutes, with five hundred each in our pockets. I felt like a millionaire. I even bought groceries from OK and took them home, just to boast!

Rachel is offering it to me. She tells me her mother's clients like her and her mother often asks her to help her out. They pay another fifty bucks just to have it with her. But she wants to help her Ma, so she agrees. My aunt also thinks I'm a tycoon and she is also offering it to me, never mind the neighbours in the three other rooms. My three uncles are praising me as a great family member because I gave them money to buy beer. They never saw so much money at one time on a family member.

But shit, now I can't sleep tonight; they'll kill me just to get hold of my money. But I'm sharp. It's quite a night in the house because of the beer and the food I've bought. I get up and say I'm going to the toilet. I slip out of the yard and head for the main road where I take a taxi to town. It's better to deal with those tsotsis in town than to try and sleep or have sex with your relatives who will take you just for what you have in your pocket!

One time I was arguing with my one aunty and I told her she's a whore. You know the whole lot beat me up so bad that I lay on the floor for three days. And every time they saw me, they would give me another kick and tell me I was an ungrateful bastard.

This was when I went back to the school. I turned up at the school all battered and bruised, blue eyes and all! Sally took me to the doctor around the corner. She insisted I lay a charge. Jesus, was that a battle! You know the cops at Jabulani all knew my family! They were either in cahoots with my uncles with the stolen goods or fucking my aunties. For protection! It was only when Sally complained at John Vorster Square that a case was registered. And of course only when Uncle Omry came home was I able to go back again.

You see, I didn't even know about Uncle Omry. They told me he was dead. Meanwhile he had escaped and had become an MK soldier. But when he returned, he wasn't a big ANC, a general or anything, just him. He was looking for his family, his mother, his father and brothers and sisters. What did he find? His mother dead. His father had given up the family home and now stayed with his skimpie and his children and their children in a whorehouse, a den of thieves! Oh, did that man cry!

We tried to repeat our success on that Bryanston man. We were watching this man with his lovely BMW in Parkmore. We noticed he was English from walking past him in front of his house. You know the Syndicate was so sharp, they could get those cars into second-hand car showrooms so fast, with papers and all from their cop connections and sell them as legal. We handled orders from politicians in the Transkei to orders as far away as Zambia. I even heard some of the Big Guys talk about Kenya and New Zealand.

But this day when we decided to take the Englishman's BM we didn't notice that he had his little girl in the car with him. She must've been three years old. She was strapped to a baby seat on the back seat. As he was waiting for his gates to open, Mandla approached his window and, aiming the gun straight at him, said, 'Get out, we want your car!'

The guy had a gun next to his seat. He shot Mandla right through his brains! Jabu who was at the passenger door fired a shot hitting the guy in his face but he still managed to shoot back at Jabu, dropping him. Tshepo, who also had a gun, ran out and finished the Englishman off. I was panicking behind the wheel. Tshepo was now taking aim at the little girl in the back seat who was crying and shouting, 'Daddy, daddy!' I think the wife inside the house must have let the alarm off.

I rushed out and grabbed Tshepo just as he was about to shoot the girl and shouted, 'Let's get out of here before we are also dead!' My God you couldn't believe the amount of blood that was all over the car and in the driveway. This white man slumped over the steering wheel with brains blown out, shattered with glass and blood all over. And Mandla and Jabu lying in pools of blood with their heads and stomachs blown away!

I drove recklessly and Tshepo kept holding the gun up, making us so easily noticeable. I headed for Marlboro, to disappear there into Alex. In no time the cops were after us. There were helicopters above us and very soon I realised we were being chased by a cop car. We should've noticed the kid in the back. That always turns the public on. We should've canned the hijack for the day.

The police were gaining on us. I tried to take a corner but I rolled the car. We managed to get out and I shouted at Tshepo to follow me into the deserted factory building and I noticed out of the corner of my eye that he had the gun with two hands in a stiff aimed position waiting for the police to come around the corner. I'm by now on the first floor and trying to catch my breath. I watched as he fired as the police car turned the corner. He missed. Jesus, that was it! They opened fire and as he fell they drove over him, smashing into the factory wall! God, I ran, and ran, through the building, out the other side, into another building, holding my gun in front of me. Whenever I came across some bastard, I warned him; out of my way, or I will shoot! After about three blocks, I saw the Alex Clinic. I calmed down for a few minutes. I had to get out of there. There was going to be big shit there that night. I dropped the gun in the grass as I walked out of the last factory and headed for the nearest taxi rank. I headed for Oom Piet and spent the night there.

He was glad to see me and I told him everything's cool. He wanted to know where the other guys were and I explained, just hanging out, they wanted to have a good time in Alex. He wanted to know, how come I'm sleeping there that night, seeing that I'm now a member of the Syndicate. No, I told him, I just wanted to check some old friends. The next morning I headed for the funny school to see Sally.

I walked into the school and they're all staring at me. The students, the teachers, everybody. They called Sally. I could see she's shocked to see me. But I only realised later that I must have looked in a state. I was still in the same clothes after the getaway. Jesus, I must have stank! She quickly hustled me up to her office and told me to relax, she wouldn't be long and she would speak to me. She organised some tea and sandwiches for me.

I confessed everything to her. I cried. I told her how Mandla, Jabu and Tshepo died. Oh my God, I don't want that life, I confessed! Please take me back, help me to learn, help me to become somebody, I don't want to die like that, I pleaded. This place, you and Horst are the only ones that have made me feel like a human being, please, you must help me, you must allow me to come back, please, you must!

She told me that as I was involved in a crime I should report to the police and if I believed I had done nothing wrong, I should prove that by going to the police. If I claimed I did not shoot or harm anybody but was only with the guys as I had told her, I had nothing to fear. After more pleading that they would really kill me if they found me because the man was dead and the child was in the car, she told me to hang on while she went to consult with the director. Now this director, Mr Paton, was like the school, funny looking, always dressed in jeans, didn't say much. I often wondered what his job there was. I noticed the Politician and the white secretary, who seemed to be jolling the Politician, were always speaking.

After about an hour she came back and told me I can rejoin standard five where I left off, provided I obey all the rules, do not try to influence the other boys and girls, do all that is required of me and don't dare step out of line!

I had never seen her so stern, I realised she really meant business. I wiped my tears and told her how grateful I was to be given another chance. She told me it's not her but Mr Paton who is giving me the chance as she still thinks I should go to the police. She suggested that I went home and made up with my family and tried to do the right thing. That's when I met Uncle Omry.

Omry was one of the youngest members of the June 16 Uprising. He was twelve or something when it all happened. I could see the whole family were going on like a ghost had risen. They didn't seem too pleased to see him. I learned something interesting: he had also attended the funny school and he knew Mr Paton whom we called the Coolie. He said he was like a father to him, hid him when he was on the run, supported him here and abroad when he fell out with the Party. He said he was going to get the whole family right, he was going to get a job and see to us all. But we all had to live moral lives, to help build our new society. He had fallen out with the Party and told us to be aware of the new elite who were just like capitalist dogs. But we now had the space to make our voices heard. We must build a Socialist State. 'Viva Socialism!' he would shout. 'Forward to a people's revolution!'

Hell, he was glad to hear that I was at the funny school. The next day he went with me. He was invited into Mr Paton's office. Hey, man, the guy even took him to lunch and gave a special party for him at the school! Quite soon Uncle Omry became a drama tutor at the school on Saturdays. He also told me to stop saying 'the funny school' and calling Mr Paton a coolie and the others bushmen, larnies and darkies! Jesus, he was only supposed to be there on a Saturday but he went with me every morning and stayed until I finished. It seemed like he and Mr Paton had lots to talk about.

It was not long before he had a full-time position at the school as a programme assistant and drama tutor. I must tell you, I really began to see the place in a new light. This school had produced my blood uncle, a real MK who fought the Boere, hell I was proud of him.

But I wondered why Uncle Omry didn't get a position in government, and why he wasn't on the gravy train. But Uncle was bitter. He told me he fell out with Mbokodo who he said were like the military police in the Boer army. He said Mr Paton had always taught him to ask questions, never just to accept. And he saw so much corruption by these guys who were in charge of security and the leadership in exile that he led a march in protest against them in a camp in Tanzania.

That was the end of his MK career, despite all the medals, including the Isithwalandwe decoration for bravery. He managed to escape as the security were trying to kill him and ended up in a squatter camp in Dar es Salaam. There he met a beautiful woman who was a refugee from her family who were trying to force her into a traditional marriage. He had no choice but to contact Mr Paton who managed to send him American dollars and that helped him to survive. He was also in contact with the foreign embassies and was negotiating with them for scholarships in their countries.

But 1990 changed all that and like most exiles he found himself coming home, under the United Nations High Commission for Refugees. He told me he couldn't go to the Party for help because those same Mbokodo who had tried to kill him in Dar es Salaam were all in important positions now and were frightened that he would expose them and other people in leadership positions. They were still after him and would kill him if they got hold of him. He said his best bet was to try the UN for a scholarship.

However, back home, Uncle's attempts at trying to get our family normal again soon led to a crisis. He insisted that all the children went to school. Learning, he said, was the fountain of life. An ignorant child was like a rock on the side of a road, that did not grow. He also demanded that all my uncles and aunts found jobs, any work to make an honest living. He refused to allow any strangers in the house to sleep with my aunts. If he saw stolen goods he would go mad and tell them to take the stuff away or he would destroy the goods or take them to the police station.

He was a walking preacher, always giving a sermon. But his sermon was: Now we have a bourgeois democracy, the black elite will rise, but the working class and the downtrodden must take up the cudgels to fight for a true workers' socialist revolution. We kids loved it, we felt so safe with him. But that was what produced the crisis.

He was supporting the entire family on his meagre salary from the funny school. He bought everything. The place was small, just one room, but the breakfasts were as nice as Horst had provided. Hell, we had porridge during the week and on Saturdays and Sundays cornflakes. If one of the aunties had not cooked when he came home, he would cook. Most of all, he felt anger at our grandfather who was staying with a woman in a squatter camp and had become an alcoholic.

You see, my grandfather was fair, he looked like a coloured. My grandmother was dark. All the other children were fair, except Uncle, who looked liked grandma. The old man used to call him 'my kaffir son'. I used to wonder whether my mother attracted the white men because she was so fair. I was also dark skinned. My mother had become pregnant by my father while she was still at school. All her other children were from white men. Is that why I was left behind? Because I looked like a kaffir?

Every now and then Mbokodo would come after my uncle and he would have to run. They were scared that he would reveal to the Party or the Truth and Reconciliation Commission how they tortured him because he exposed their corruption and fascist practices which were just like the Boers.

And you should have seen the plays that he put on at the school. He put me in some of them. They were all about women, mostly about granny. Hell, they were sad. We all used to cry and the audience, especially the other kids, thought we were faking it and would laugh. The older girls who took the lead parts really liked what he was doing. They felt he was telling the world about how black women suffer.

'Hey, man, you must lay off, I think that's too much for the kids. That's really heavy stuff!' I heard Mr Paton say to Uncle after we came off stage one day.

It was after his longest stay away from home, running from Mbokodo, that the aunties and uncles decided that maybe he was dead and not coming back again and they resorted to their old ways. Did we children suffer! While he was there we had a say. We could add our objections. Now we were just beaten up again as in the past if we dared open our mouths. And then he turned up.

All hell broke loose. Aunties were entertaining the police from the Jabulani police station that night. The police didn't care, they were drinking and fucking our aunties with all of us kids watching! Our uncles were smoking dagga and had their girlfriends with them. Uncle walked in. Jesus, he shouted at them, how could they be doing this in front of children, in front of each other, was this what the new South Africa was about, where the upholders of the law were the most corrupt breakers of the law! The captain told him, 'Keep quiet, otherwise I will lock you up for the night.' Uncle shouted at him, 'You corrupt fascist bastard, get out of my house!'

The shit really hit the fan. The cops, aunties and uncles all attacked Uncle. The captain told my aunties to lay a charge of assault against him. So they all went down to the police station. I panicked and somehow managed to get into one of the police cars. You could see my aunties and uncles felt really bucked at driving in the smart police BMWs. And all the while the cops at the back were hitting Uncle in the face. They locked him up at the police station and came home and carried on their party.

I ran to a friend and pleaded with his dad to let me use the phone. I phoned Sally and she phoned Mr Paton. But there was nothing they could do. Uncle spent the night in jail and the next morning after a call from Mr Paton and a faxed letter to say what a good person he was, who after years in exile had just lost his temper, he was allowed to go, but never to come back to the family home ever again. He was not even allowed to come and collect his suitcase. I had to take it to the school.

Over and above that, one of the cops told him he knew him and that the Party guys would like to see him. That really put the fear of God into Uncle. He found a place with one of the tutors at the school through Sally, who really seemed fond of him. Mr Paton seemed upset with him for messing it up!

And then the Mbokodo turned up at the school. And Uncle ran. All the way to Mafikeng. He met a captain, a former colleague of his who took his story to the Party and those Mbokodo were 'disciplined' and Uncle is now in the army. I hear he is a lieutenant. But I haven't seen him since. Sally keeps telling me he's OK. He obviously keeps in touch with her.

I think he has taken a decision not to have anything more to do with us. I don't blame him. But just like Horst, the hopes in my life keep disappearing from the scene. I hardly ever see my mother and brothers and sister. And my father tells me that at fifteen I'm big enough to look after myself.

You know, my whole family is now in jail! One night the cops all turned up there with liquor and Kentucky. They were after a good time. Aunty Mabel, who is the youngest, in her twenties, didn't want to do it with the captain. He had already had sex with my other aunty soon after he came in and Mabel was jealous as she thought she had attracted the captain away from her sister. She had been putting off the advances of the black sergeant who had been trying to have sex with her. I had also noticed Uncle Gabriel sleeping with the white sergeant on the floor. Thank goodness Uncle Omry had moved Rachel and Sophie out of the house. The captain suddenly hit Aunty Mabel violently and she retaliated by stabbing him in the chest just above the heart. Now there was total chaos. The two policemen rushed the captain to Baragwanath hospital. In a short while two carloads of policemen turned up and proceeded to beat up every one of us and trash the house. I managed to run away.

I took a taxi and spent the night at Oom Piet's. The next day I went to school and told Sally what had happened. She put me up for a week.

I went home to find only Uncle Dullah there. He was the eldest and an alcoholic. He drank blue train: methylated spirits. He was so fucked that he couldn't even steal any more, just wake up and drink spirits or chibuku and listen to Abdullah Ibrahim music – that's why he was called Dullah.

I finished my standard five that year. Sally had arranged with the school to grant me a bursary, but that was already in place after Horst had left. And being a relative of Uncle Omry also helped because the school did not charge fees if the child or a relative of a staff member attended. Sally gave me money for food and transport and occasionally bought me shoes or shirts. She also gave me a job on a Saturday as a type of assistant to look after the small kids at playtime and do some messages. In between I could participate in the workshops with the other kids my age. For that I got paid fifty bucks a week, which helped. I had learned drama and dance, but I always used to feel awkward on stage, like I couldn't move my body as well as the other kids. I used to feel it was because I was so poor and had started all these things so late. But I tried.

The next year Sally got me into Athlone Boys' High School. Mr Paton got this short white lady who I had seen at the school to pay my fees. I still worked at the school on Saturdays and Sally helped me with money for food and clothes as in the past, but life was hard. I was in high school now and also wanted to have smart clothes and cassettes and CDs and money to go to a jol. I had to get some extra money. But the question was how. I only knew how to steal in shops or rob people. But I couldn't do that now, in town, in my school uniform. That's when I got the idea. I could drive, I had the connections, I could handle a gun. Hijack!

When I had returned home, I had found a gun. It looked like a police revolver. But they were so common that if the police didn't sell them to us, we just took them from the cops and shot them if they resisted. It must have been left there by one of the policemen.

I checked out the Big Guys in Soweto. They were paying one thousand rand a car now with a scale going up to five or even ten thousand if you managed to get a real big Merc.

I then had to check out areas of operation. This was going to be a solo move. I had to get away with it. I didn't want to end up like Mandla, Jabu and Tshepo. The memories of their bodies drenched in blood still haunted me. It couldn't be areas like Corlett Drive and Louis Botha Avenue where hijacks were common. It had to be a quiet area where nobody operated. I decided on the Southgate/Mondeor areas. They were near Soweto and I could get back on the highway quickly. The plan of action was simple: stand in the shadows early evening at quiet stop streets, preferably at traffic lights. Make sure the driver had not noticed you. Target women especially. Move quickly but without attracting attention. Point the gun through the driver's window. This is a hijack, get out and you won't be killed! It worked. And I do it whenever I need cash. I thank my ancestors.

*

Life is good now. I'm doing well at my studies, there's food in the house and I can jol and dress decently. I even have a CD player. I can also talk to the other kids about having the latest disc or kit. I even give Uncle Dullah a couple of rands.

Well, now I'm in matric. Through Mr Paton, I have applied to do a degree in public administration at Wits University. I will get a bursary with fees and books fully paid. I will also stay in residence on a full bursary. You see, I am from the formally disenfranchised majority, part of what is called affirmative action. I will finally be able to move out of the 'family' home. Just in time. My aunts and uncles are beginning to be released from prison and returning home to carry on as before. Maybe I won't have to hijack any more.

You know, I have started to listen to the English station on SABC to improve my English and this morning this father phoned in to thank a hijacker, who had taken his daughter's watch and money in Mondeor, for not harming her! Ha, ha! I rolled over on the bed, I couldn't stop laughing. That hijacker was me! You see, I'm not such a bad guy. I'm like Robin Hood. I only steal because I have to live. I'm poor. I don't do terrible things to people.

After I qualify, I'm going to become a politician, I'm going to join the gravy train. I've already joined the Party's youth movement. I'm a fully paid-up member of the Party. I'm going to be just like the Politician: women, power, money, ha, ha, ha, ha, ha!

Ululants

ZAKES MDA

'Tears are very close to my eyes,' says Bhonco, son of Ximiya. 'Not for pain . . . no . . . I do not cry because of pain. I cry only because of beautiful things.'

And he cries often. Sometimes just a sniffle. Or a single tear down his cheek. As a result he carries a white handkerchief all the time, especially these days when peace has returned to the land and there is enough happiness to go around. It is shared like pinches of snuff. Rivers of salt. They furrow the aged face.

He is different from the other Unbelievers in his family, for Unbelievers are reputed to be such sombre people that they do not believe even in those things that can bring happiness in their lives. They spend most of their time moaning about past injustices and the bleeding of the world that would have been had the folly of belief not seized the nation a century and a half ago, and spun it around until it was in a woozy stupor that is felt to this day. They also mourn the suffering of the Middle Generations. That, however, is only whispered.

Bhonco does not believe in grieving. He long accepted that what has happened has happened. It is cast in cold iron that does not entertain rust. His forebears bore the pain with stoicism. They lived with it until they passed on to the world of the ancestors.

Then came the Middle Generations. In-between the forebears and this new world. And the Middle Generations fleeted by like a dream. Often like a nightmare. But now even the sufferings of the Middle Generations have passed. It is a new life and it must be celebrated. Bhonco, son of Ximiya celebrates it with tears.

NoPetticoat, his placable wife, is on the verge of losing patience

330

with his tears. Whenever someone does a beautiful thing in the presence of her husband she screams, 'Stop! Please stop! Or you'll make Bhonco cry!'

She dotes on him though, poor thing. People say it is nice to see such an aged couple – who would be having grandchildren if their daughter, Xoliswa Ximiya, had not chosen to remain an old maid – being so much in love.

It is a wonderful sight to watch the couple walking side-by-side from a feast. He, tall and wiry with a deep chocolate face that has gullies; and she, a stout matron whose comparatively smooth face makes her look younger than her age. Some times they will be staggering a bit . . . humming the remnants of a song, their muscles obviously savouring the memory of the final dance of the feast.

The custom is that men walk in front and women follow. But Bhonco and NoPetticoat walk side-by-side. Sometimes holding hands! A constant embarrassment to Xoliswa Ximiya: old people have no right to love. And if they happen to be foolish enough to harbour the slightest affection for each other, they must not display it in public.

'Tears are close to my eyes, NoPetticoat,' snivels the man of the house dabbing his eyes with the handkerchief.

'Big men like you shouldn't be bawling like spoilt babies, Bhonco,' says the woman of the house, nevertheless putting her arm around his shoulders.

A beautiful thing has happened. They have just received the news that Xoliswa Ximiya, their beloved and only child, has been promoted at work She is now the headmistress or principal of Qolorha-by-Sea Secondary School.

Xoliswa Ximiya is not just called Xoliswa. People use both her name and surname when they talk about her because she is an important person in the community. A celebrity, so to speak. She is highly learned too, with a BA in Education from the University of Fort Hare, and a certificate in teaching English as a second language from some college in America.

'They will not accept her,' laments NoPetticoat, as if to herself.

'But she is a child of this community,' says Bhonco adamantly. 'She grew up in front of our eyes. She became educated while others laughed and said I was mad to send a girl to school.'

'They will say she is a woman. Remember the teacher who left?

331

He was a man yet they did not accept him. They made life very difficult for him. What more for a woman?'

'They made life difficult for him because he was uncircumcised. He was not a man. How could he teach our children with a dangling foreskin?'

'I tell you, Bhonco they won't accept her. They will give my baby problems at that school.'

'She is not a baby. She is thirty-six years old. And if they don't accept her it will be the work of the Believers. They are jealous because they don't have a daughter who is as educated,' says Bhonco, making it clear that the discussion is terminated.

It had to come back to the war between the Believers and Unbelievers. They are in competition about everything.

The early manifestation of this competition happened a few years ago when the Ximiyas bought a pine dining table with four chairs. The family became the talk of the community since no one else had a dining table in the village those days. But Zim, of the family of Believers, had to burst the Ximiya bubble by buying exactly the same dining table, but with six chairs. That really irked Ximiya and his supporters.

Since then the war between the two families has become a public one. The good neighbours await with bated breath the next skulduggery they will do against each other.

The Cult of the Unbelievers began with Twin-Twin, Bhonco Ximiya's ancestor, in the days of Prophetess Nongqawuse almost one hundred and fifty years ago. The revered Twin-Twin was the one who elevated unbelieving to the heights of a religion. The Cult died during the Middle Generations for people then were concerned with surviving and overcoming their oppression. They did not have the time to fight about the perils of belief and unbelief.

But even before the suffering of the Middle Generations had passed – it was obvious to everyone that the end was near – Bhonco son of Ximiya, resurrected the cult.

He does not care that only his close relatives and himself subscribe to it. Nor does it matter to him that people had long forgotten the conflicts of generations ago. He holds to them dearly for they have shaped his present, and the present of the nation. His role in life is to teach people not to believe. He tells them that even the Middle Generations would not have suffered were it not for the scourge of belief.

Beautiful things are not celebrated only with tears. So Bhonco tells his wife that he will go to Vulindlela Trading Store to buy a tin of corned beef. NoPetticoat laughs and says he must not use the promotion of her baby as an excuse. He needs something salty because he had a lot to drink at the feast yesterday, and now he is nursing a hangover. Whoever heard of sorghum beer giving one a hangover, Bhonco wonders to himself.

'While you are away I'll go to the hotel to see if they have work for me,' says NoPetticoat as she adjusts her ghiya turban, and puts a shawl over her shoulders. But her husband cannot hear her for he has already walked out of their pink rondavel.

NoPetticoat supplements the income from her old age pension – or nkamnkam as the people call it – by working as a baby-sitter at the Blue Flamingo Hotel. Often tourists come to enjoy the serenity of this place, and to admire birds and plants, or to go to the Valley of Nongqawuse to see where miracles happened. They book at the Blue Flamingo, and leave their children with part-time nannies while they walk or ride all over the valley, or swim in the rough sea.

NoPetticoat is occasionally called by the hotel management whenever there are babies to look after. However when many days have passed without anyone calling her, she walks to the hotel to find out if there is work. She has to do that since she discovered that the managers call her only as a last resort. Their first choice are the young women whose bodies are still supple enough to make red-blooded male tourists salivate. Almost always when she goes without being called, she finds that indeed there are babies to look after but the message has been sent to some shameless filly to come for the job. Invariably she fights her way and takes over.

Bhonco drags his gumboots up the hillock to the trading store. His brown overalls are almost threadbare at the elbows and at the knees. He wears a green woollen hat that the people call a skull-cap. He does not carry a stick as men normally do.

Under his breath he curses the trader for building his store on the hill. However, the breathtaking view from the top compensates for the arduous climb. Down below, on his right, he can see the wild sea smashing gigantic waves against the rocks creating mountains of snow white surf. On his left he can see the green valleys and the patches of villages with beautiful houses in pink, powder blue, yellow and white.

Most of the houses are rondavels. But over the years a new architectural style, the hexagon, has developed. On the roofs of these voguish hexagons corrugated iron appears under the thatch, like a petticoat that is longer than the dress. This is both for aesthetic reasons and for stopping the termites. But Bhonco does not believe in this newfangled fashion of building hexagons instead of the tried and tested rondavel.

From where he stands he can also see the Gxarha River, the Intlambo-ka-Nongqawuse – or Nongqawuse's Pool and the great lagoon that is often covered by a thick blanket of mist.

Indeed Qolorha-by-Sea is a place rich in wonders. The rivers do not cease flowing, even when the whole country knells a drought. The cattle are round and fat.

Bhonco was born in this village. He grew up in this village. Except for the time he was working in the cities, he has lived all his life in this village. Yet he is always moved to tears by its wistful beauty.

Vulindlela Trading Store is a big stone building with a red corrugated iron roof. It has a long concrete stoep on which there is a number of wooden yokes and green ploughs and planters chained together.

Behind the store is the trader's family home, an off-white rough-cast modern house with big windows. Between the house and the store a car and a truck – both of them Mercedes-Benz late models – are parked.

Bhonco looks at the television that the trader, John Dalton, has put on a shelf that he has built against the wall of the store's veranda. It plays videos of old movies, and children are always crowding here, watching 'bioscope', as they call it. Some of these children are herdboys who should be looking after cattle in the veld. No wonder there are so many cases these days where parents are being sued because their cattle have grazed in other people's fields.

Bhonco slowly walks into the store, and demands to see his friend, the trader. When Missis Dalton says he is away on business, Bhonco insists that he wants to see him all the same. He knows that he is hiding in his office. Dalton has no choice but to skulk out of his tiny office to face the stubborn man.

'What is it now, old man?' he demands.

He is a stocky balding man with hard features and a long rich beard of black and silver-grey streaks. He is always in a khaki safari suit. He looks like a parody of an Afrikaner farmer. He is neither an Afrikaner nor a farmer though. Always been a trader. So was his father before him. And his grandfather was a trader of a different type. As a missionary he was a seller of salvation.

Dalton is a white man of English stock. Well, let's put it this way: his skin is white like the skins of those who caused the sufferings of the Middle Generations. But his heart is a Xhosa heart. He speaks better Xhosa than most Xhosas in the village. In his youth, against his father's wishes, he went to the initiation school and was circumcised in accordance with the customs of the Xhosa people. He therefore knows the secrets of the mountain. He is a man.

Often he laughs at the sneering snobbishness of his fellow English speaking South Africans. He says they have a deep-seated fear and resentment of everything African, and are apt to glorify their blood-soaked colonial history. And he should know. His own family history is as blood-soaked as any . . . right from the days of one John Dalton, his great-great-grandfather who was a soldier and then a magistrate in the days of Prophetess Nongqawuse.

'Don't call me old man. I have a name,' Bhonco protests. Although he is old, and to be old is an honour among his people, he has always hated to be called old man since his hair started greying in his late twenties and people called him Xhego – old man – mockingly. Now at sixty-plus – or perhaps seventy, he does not know his real age – his hair is snow white.

'It is well, Bhonco son of Ximiya. We are not at war, are we?' Dalton tries to placate the elder.

'I do not fight wars with children. It was your father who was my age-mate. And ah, the old Dalton looked after me. He was a kind man, your father.'

'You didn't come here to talk about my father, did you?'

'I came to ask for ityala . . . for credit . . . I need a tin of beef. And some tobacco for my pipe.'

Dalton shakes his head, and takes out a big black book from under the counter. After a few pages he finds Bhonco's name.

'You see,' he says, 'Your ityala is already very long. You have taken too many things on credit, and you have not paid yet. You promised that you were going to get your old age pension soon.'

Dalton's wife, who is simply known as Missis by the villagers, thinks it is necessary to rescue her husband. She firmly steps forward and says, 'He is not getting any more credit, John.'

Bhonco does not take kindly to this interference. He screams at the trader, 'Let's leave women out of this!'

Fortunately Missis understands no Xhosa. She is a Free State Afrikaner. Dalton met her when he attended the cherry festival in Ficksburg many years ago. She was the cherry queen, although it would be hard to believe that now – what with her rotten front teeth and all. The trouble is that she eats too many sweets. The saving grace is that she hardly smiles. She still finds it difficult to understand her husband's cosy relationship with these 'Bantoe' rustics.

Bhonco adopts a new tactic and becomes very pitiful.

'Ever since Nongqawuse things were never right,' he laments. 'Until now. They are becoming right a bit now, although not for me. They are becoming right for others. Me . . . no . . . I am still waiting for nkamnkam.'

'This is my seventh year waiting. My wife came here as a child . . . she is many years younger than me. But she now gets nkamnkam. I am very very old, but the government refuses to give me my pension.'

Then he goes into a litany of the troubles he has gone through working for this country. He began to work half a century ago at a textile factory in East London, then at a dairy, then at a blanket factory, then . . .

He even went to work at the docks in Cape Town for more than eight years. He got permanently crippled – although it is impossible to see any sign of that now – when his sister pushed him down a donga, shouting, 'When are you going to mourn for your father?' Since then he was never able to work again.

Why won't the government give him nkamnkam like all the old men and women of South Africa who are on old age pension today? Is it fair that now, even though ravines of maturity run wild on his face, he should still not receive any nkamnkam?

'Maybe it is not fair,' says Dalton. 'But how are you going to pay me since you get no nkamnkam? Are you going to take your wife's money to pay for your tobacco and luxury items such as canned beef?'

'Did you not hear? My daughter is now principal. I'll pay you.'

It is late in the afternoon when Bhonco arrives home. NoPetticoat is busy cooking the evening umphokoqo – the maize porridge that is specially eaten with sour milk – on the primus stove. When the white man has smiled – in other words, when NoPetticoat has been paid at the Blue Flamingo or has received her nkamnkam – she cooks on the primus stove rather than outside with a three-legged pot.

'I didn't know that the white man has smiled at you,' says Bhonco, as he puts the can of corned beef on the table. 'Otherwise I wouldn't have humiliated myself begging for ityala from that uppity Dalton.'

Before NoPetticoat can admonish him for piling debt on their shoulders, Xoliswa Ximiya walks in. She looks like the 'mistress' she is – which is what pupils call unmarried female teachers – in a navy blue two-piece costume with a white frilly blouse. She has her father's bone structure and is quite tall and well-proportioned – which is good if you want to be a model in Johannesburg, but works against you in a village where men prefer their women plump and juicy. And indeed this is the language they use when they describe them, as if they are talking of a piece of meat. She has a charmingly trustful face, and brown-dyed hair that she braids with extensions in Butterworth. But people never stop wondering how she is able to walk on the rocks and gorges of Qolorha-by-Sea in those high heels.

She has just come to see how her parents are doing. She takes it as an obligation to see them occasionally. Her parents – especially her mother – were not happy when she moved out a year ago to stay in a two-roomed staff-house in the school-yard. At first they put their foot down that no unmarried daughter of theirs would stay alone in her own house. It was unheard of. They had to relent when she concocted something to the effect that as a senior teacher she had to live at school or lose her job. It really frustrates her that her parents insist on treating her like a child.

Bhonco and NoPetticoat are all over Xoliswa Ximiya, congratulating her on her promotion.

'You are going to be the best principal that school has ever had,' says her father proudly. 'At least you'll be better than that uncircumcised boy the community kicked out.' Such talk makes her uncomfortable. But she ignores it and announces that in as much as she appreciated the honour of being principal of her alma mater, she would very much like to work for the government.

'But you are working for the government now as a headmistress, are you not?' says Bhonco.

'As a teacher are you not being paid by the government?' asks NoPetticoat.

'I want to be a civil servant. I want to work for the ministry of education in Pretoria, or at the very least in Bisho.'

'Bisho! Do you know where Bisho is from here? And Pretoria! Pretoria! No one in our family has ever been there,' cries Bhonco. He is choking with anger.

'You want to kill your father?' asks NoPetticoat.

'I know where Bisho is, father,' responds the daughter in a cold sarcastic tone. 'It is the capital town of your province. I have been there many times. And Pretoria is the capital city of our country. I have not been in Pretoria, but I have been much further, father, where none of my family has ever been. I have been in places far over the oceans.'

'You see, Bhonco, you should never have allowed this child to take that scholarship to America,' says NoPetticoat tiredly.

'So now it's my fault, NoPetticoat?'

'If you like towns and cities so much, my child, we have never stopped you from visiting Centani or even Butterworth,' NoPetticoat tries to strike a compromise.

'I do not care for towns and cities, mother. Anyway, Centani is just a big village and Butterworth a small town. Don't you understand? People I have been to school with are earning a lot of money as directors of departments in the civil service. I am sitting here in this village, with all my education, earning peanuts as a school teacher. I am going. I must go from this stifling village. I have made applications. As soon as I get a job, I am going,' says Xoliswa Ximiya with finality.

It is an ungrateful night, and sleep refused to come to Bhonco. His eyelids are heavy, but sleep just won't come. Oh, why do children ever grow up? How huggable they are when they are little boys and girls, when their parents' word is still gospel, before the poison of the world contaminates their heads. He envies NoPetticoat who can sleep and snore in the midst of such emotional turbulence.

When nights are like this even his scars become itchy. He rubs them a bit. He cannot reach them properly since they are all over his back. And the person who usually helps him is fast asleep. Why he has to be burdened with the scars of history, he does not understand. Perhaps that's what prompted him to bring back from the recesses of time the Cult of the Unbelievers.

Yes, Bhonco carries the scars that were inflicted on his great-grandfather, Twin-Twin, by men who flogged him after he had been identified as a wizard by Prophet Mlanjeni, the Man of the River. Every first boy-child in subsequent generations of Twin-Twin's tree is born with the scars. Even those of the Middle Generations, their first males carried the scars.

You can give Twin-Twin any name. You can call him anything. But a wizard he was not. Bhonco is adamant about that. He was a naughty man. Even after he died he became a naughty ancestor. Often he showed himself naked to a group of women who were gathering wood on the hillside, or washing clothes in a stream. He was like that in life too. He loved women. But Prophet Mlanjeni got it all wrong. Twin-Twin was not a wizard.

The ancestor's name was Maxhobayakhawuleza. A patriarch and a patrician of the Great Place of King Sarhili. He was the father of the twins, Twin and Twin-Twin. Twin-Twin was the first of the twins to be born, so according to custom he was the younger. The older twin is the one who is the last to kick the doors of the womb, and to breathe the air that has already been breathed by the younger brother.

Twin and Twin-Twin were like one person. Even their voice was one. Mothers who eyed them for their daughters could not tell one from the other. And because they were close to each other like saliva is to the tongue, they relished playing tricks on the maidens.

The patriarch lived his life with dignity, and brought up his children to fear and respect uQamata, of uMvelingqangi, the great God of all men and women, and to pay homage to those who are in the ground – the ancestors.

The twins were circumcised together with the son of the chief, and therefore became men of standing in their community. They became men of wealth too, for Maxhobayakhawuleza did not want them to wait for his death before they could inherit his fields, cattle and overflowing silos. He divided the bulk of his wealth between them.

Twin-Twin, the first born twin who was younger than the second born, loved women, and was the first to marry. And then he married again. And again. Long before Twin could think of taking a wife.

Yet the brothers remained close friends.

Then the news of Mlanjeni reached the homesteads of Maxhobayakhawuleza, Twin and Twin-Twin – as it reached the ears of every homestead in the land.

Mlanjeni the Man of the River. He had not reached the age of nineteen yet, but his head was not full of beautiful maidens, stick fights and umtshotsho dance. Instead he was brooding over the evil that so pervaded the world, that lurked even in the house of his own father, Kala. As a result he refused to eat his mother's cooking, for he said it was poisoned. He decided to fast because food enfeebled him. Women also had a debilitating power over him. So he kept himself celibate.

In order to stay pure and undefiled he eschewed the company of other human beings, and spent his time immersed to the neck in a pool on the Keiskamma River. There he lived only on the eggs of ants and on water-grass.

'That son of Kala has something in him,' said Maxhobayakha-wuleza to his twins. 'He is a child, but he already talks of big things.'

'I have heard his father talking with him about his behaviour,' said Twin-Twin. 'Yet he will not listen.'

'Kala is right,' said the patriarch. 'What does a boy who has not even been to the circumcision school know about witchcraft and disease?'

When the time came, Mlanjeni went to the circumcision school. Both Twin and Twin-Twin were among the amakhankatha – the men who taught the initiates how to be men.

Maxhobayakhawuleza was the ingcibi – the doctor who cut the foreskin. They saw that Mlanjeni was very thin and weak. They did not think he would survive the rigours of the mountain. But he did, and went out to become the new prophet of the Xhosa people.

And the Xhosa people believed in him, for it was clear that he had contact with the spirit world, and was charged by the ancestors with the task of saving humankind from itself.

As his teachings unfolded people knew that indeed he was the next great prophet after Nxele, the man who revealed the truths of the world thirty years before the Man of the River. And both of them spoke against ubuthi, the evil charms that were poisoning the nation, and against witchcraft.

Whereas Nxele made revelations about Mdalidephu the God

of the black man, Thixo the God of the white man, and Thixo's son, Tayi, who was murdered by the white people, Mlanjeni venerated the sun, and prayed to it.

Nxele used to talk of the great day that was coming, when the dead would arise and witches would be cast into damnation in the belly of the earth. But his career was stopped short by the British who locked him up on Robben Island. Before he surrendered he promised that he would come back again. Alas, he drowned trying to escape from the island.

'Can it be that Mlanjeni is the reincarnation of Nxele?' Twin wondered. 'After all the Xhosa nation is still awaiting the return of Nxele.'

As Mlanjeni was praying to the sun, it scorched the earth. There was famine in the land. Cattle were dying. And those that still lived you could count their ribs. As the Man of the River was waning away from his fasting, men and women of the land were waning away from starvation. And he told them that is was because of ubuthi.

'Leave ubuthi alone,' he preached. 'As long as there is witchcraft among you, there will be disease and death among people and animals. Cast away ubuthi! You do not need ubuthi to invite good fortune or to protect yourselves! Cast it away, and all come to me to be cleansed!'

'This sickly boy is Nxele himself. Nxele has returned as he promised he would,' said Twin.

'No, he is not Nxele,' responded Twin-Twin 'Mlanjeni is a prophet in his own right.'

This developed into a serious disagreement between the twins, to the extent that they took up sticks to fight each other. Women screamed and called the patriarch. When Maxhobayakhawuleza arrived he was happy. His sons had never disagreed on anything before in all their lives, let alone fought against each other. Now, for the very first time they had a disagreement.

'I was becoming worried about you two,' he said, taking the sticks away from them. 'Now you are becoming human beings.'

People came to Kala's dwelling to be cleansed by his wonder child. They came from all over Xhosaland, even from beyond the borders of the lands that had been conquered by the British. Those who had poisonous roots and evil charms disposed of them and were cleansed. But still, some people held tight to their ubuthi, and lied that they had got rid of it.

Mlanjeni erected two witchcraft poles outside his father's house and those who wished to remove the suspicion of witchcraft walked between them. The innocent walked through without any trouble. But terrible things happened to those who had ubuthi even as they approached the poles.

From early dawn hundreds of people gathered outside Kala's house. Among them were Maxhobayakhawuleza, his wives, his other children from the junior houses, Twin-Twin and his wives and children and Twin. People had come because word had spread up to the foothills of the Maluti Mountains that Mlanjeni cured the sick, and made the lame to walk, the dumb to speak and the blind to see.

People said he was a man of great power. He lit his pipe on the sun, and when he danced drops of sweat from his body caused the rain to fall.

The Man of the River appeared at the door of his hut, and after one word from him people saw the star of the morning coming down from the sky and placing itself on his forehead. Another word from him, and the earth shook, and the mountains trembled. He disappeared into the hut again. And people began to sing a thunderous song that echoed in the faraway hills. They sang until the sun rose from behind the mountains and moved to the centre of the sky.

Mlanjeni emerged again, raised his spear to the heavens and touched the sun. The sun came down to touch his head, and went through his body until it was bright like the sun itself. People prostrated themselves, shouting, 'Mlanjeni! Mlanjeni is our true Lord! The Man of the River possesses the secret of Eternity!'

One by one some began to walk between the poles. The clean were unscathed. The unclean were struck by weakness and fear as they approached the poles. Then they writhed on the spot, unable to move. The people shouted, 'Out! Get out witchcraft', until the victims staggered through the poles to Mlanjeni, who gave them some twigs that would protect them from further evil and keep them pure.

Twin-Twin rushed to his wife, who was then writhing on the ground in agony. He was shouting, 'No! No! My wife is not a witch! There must be a mistake.'

A group of zealots grabbed him and dragged him to the donga below Kala's homestead. There they flogged him with whips. They beat him until he was almost unconscious. Then they went back |to the Man of the River expecting his praise.

'He is a wizard. That is why he was defending his wife who was clearly identified as a witch by the poles,' said Mlanjeni feebly. 'But you had no right to beat him. I have said it before, no person should ever be harmed for being a witch. Witchcraft is not in the nature of men and women. They are not born with it. It is an affliction that I can cure.'

Twin-Twin's weals opened up and became wounds. After many months the wounds healed and became scars. But occasionally they itched and reminded him of his flagellation. At the time he did not know that his progeny was destined to carry the burden of the scars.

For a long time he was angry at the injustice of it all. He was not a wizard, and was sure that his wife was not a witch. Yet his own father and twin brother were blaming him for stupidly defending the honour of a woman who had been exposed as a witch by none other than the great prophet himself. And now both Maxhobayakhawuleza and Twin were ostracising his wife from the senior house. It did not escape Twin-Twin that that was the second time he had quarrelled with his twin brother, and on both occasions the prophet was the cause.

He continued to defend the prophet. He was just as furious as the rest of the men of Xhosaland when the British decided to hunt the prophet down since they claimed they did not approve of his witch-hunting activities.

Twin-Twin suppressed the bitterness in his heart and went with Twin, his father and a group of mounted men to meet the white man who called himself the Great White Chief of the Xhosa, Sir Harry Smith. He watched in humiliation as the Great White Chief commanded the elders and even the chiefs to kiss his staff and his boots. And they did. And so did he.

The Great White Chief was running wild all over the lands of the Xhosa, doing whatever he liked in the name of Queen Victoria of England. He even deposed Sandile, the king of the Ngqika Xhosa. This rallied all the chiefs, even those who were Sandile's rivals, around the deposed king.

The people had had enough of the Great White Chief. Mounted

men went to the Keiskamma River to consult with the prophet. Mlanjeni ordered that certain types of cattle be slaughtered, and doctored the military men for war so that the guns of the British should shoot hot water instead of bullets. The Great War of Mlanjeni had begun. Both Twin and Twin-Twin fought in the war. And so did Maxhobayakhawuleza, who was still strong enough to carry a shield and a spear. It was an ugly and tedious war that lasted for three years, during which the Khoi people of the Kat River Valley discarded their traditional alliance with the British and fought on the side of the Xhosa. The frustrated Great White Chief was heard on many occasions talking of his intention to exterminate all Xhosas.

'Extermination is now the only word and principle that guides us. I loved these people and considered them my children. But now I say exterminate the savage beasts!' he told his field commanders.

Twin and Twin-Twin, who continued to keep close to each other, fought under General Maqoma in the Amathole Mountains. It was by and large a guerrilla warfare. They ambushed the British soldiers when they least expected it. The great size of the mountain range made things very difficult for the Imperial forces, and gave the Xhosa armies many opportunities to destroy the enemy soldiers.

It was at one such ambush that Twin and Twin-Twin – accompanied by a small band of fellow soldiers – chanced upon a group of British soldiers who were cutting off the ears of a dead Xhosa soldier.

'What are they doing that for? Are they wizards?' asked Twin-Twin. 'Or is it their way of removing iqungu?'

Iqungu was the vengeful force generated by war medicines. A soldier who died in war could have his iqungu attack the slayer, bloating and swelling up his body until he died. Xhosa soldiers therefore ripped open the stomachs of their dead enemies to deceive the iqungu. This was considered as savagery of the worst kind by the British, whenever they came across their dead comrades with ripped stomachs on the Amathole slopes.

'It is not for iqungu,' explained Twin, who seemed to know about the ways of the British from fireside gossip. 'It is just the witchcraft of the white man. They take those ears to their country. That's what they call souvenirs.'

The twins saw that the leader of the soldiers was a man they had met before. John Dalton. He had been one of the soldiers accompanying the Great White Chief during the boot-kissing ceremony. He had been introduced then as an important man in the Great White Chief's entourage of soldiers. He spoke some Xhosa, so he was the interpreter.

Then to everyone's surprise the soldiers cut off the dead man's head and put it into a pot of boiling water.

'They are cannibals too,' whispered Twin-Twin.

The British soldiers sat around and smoked their pipes and laughed at their own jokes. Occasionally one of the soldiers stirred the boiling pot, and the stench of rotten meat floated to the twins' party. They could not stand it any longer. With blood-curdling screams they emerged from their hiding place and attacked the men of Queen Victoria. One British soldier was killed, two were captured, and the rest escaped.

'It is our father,' screamed Twin. 'They were going to eat our father.'

It was indeed the headless body of Maxhobayakhawuleza.

'We were not going to eat your father,' said John Dalton, prisoner of war, in his perfect Xhosa. 'We are civilised men, we don't eat people.'

'Liar!' screamed Twin-Twin. 'Why would you cook anything that you are not going to eat?'

'To remove the flesh from the skull,' explained Dalton patiently. He did not seem to be afraid. He just seemed too sure of himself. 'These heads are either going to be souvenirs, or will be used for scientific enquiry.'

Souvenirs. Scientific enquiry. It did not make sense. It was nothing but the witchcraft of the white man.

While they were debating the best method of killing their captives, a painful and merciless method that would at least avenge the decapitated patriarch, the British soldiers returned with reinforcements from a nearby camp. Only Twin and Twin-Twin were able to escape. The rest of their party was killed.

It tortured the twins no end that their father met his end in the boiling cauldrons of the British, and they were never able to give him a decent burial in accordance with the rites and rituals of his people. How will he commune with his fellow ancestors without a head? How will a headless ancestor act as an effective emissary of their pleas to Qamata?

In the mean time the Great White Chief was getting even more desperate. He was unable to win the war outright. The British fire-power was stronger, but the guerrilla tactics of the Xhosa soldiers were paying off. Chief Maqoma and the Khoi chief, Hans Brander, were giving the Imperial armies a hard time. People were disappointed with Mlanjeni's prophecies. None of them was coming true. The Imperial bullets did not turn into water. Instead many Xhosa men were being killed every day.

But when the Xhosa were about to give up, the Khoi people kept them fighting. At least they had muskets, although they were running out of ammunition. General Maqoma and Chief Brander destroyed more than two hundred farmhouses and captured five thousand cattle from the colonists.

Khoi women prostituted themselves to the British soldiers in order to smuggle canisters of gunpowder to their fighting men. It was with one of these Khoi women, Qukezwa, that Twin fell in love and later married.

The Great White Chief would stop at nothing to win the war. If he could not defeat the Xhosas in the field of battle, he was going to starve them into submission. He ordered his soldiers to go on a rampage and burn Xhosa fields and kill Xhosa cattle everywhere they came across them, instead of spending their time hunting down guerrillas in the crevices of the Amathole Mountains. When the troops found unarmed women working in the fields they killed them too.

The great fear of starvation finally defeated Maqoma's forces, and the Xhosas surrendered to the British. They turned against the Man of the River, because his charms had failed. Yet other nations continued to believe in him. Messengers from the distant nations of Basotho, Nbathombu, Amampondo and Amampon-domise visited him, asking for war charms and for the great secret of catching witches.

Six months after the war the great prophet died of tuberculosis.

Although the twins' wealth remained intact – they had hidden most of their herds in the Amathole Mountains – they were disillusioned with prophets. They were devastated by the death of the patriarch who ended up as stew in a British pot.

Mlanjeni's war, however, had given Twin a beautiful yellow-coloured wife, and Twin-Twin the scars of history.

In the Centre of a Circle

PETER HORN

I was gang-raped. But what does that mean to you? It is of little use that we say what we see. What we see is never in what we say. Just as in school: there is never only one writing lesson. Yet in all the many writing lessons you only learn to write down the same twenty-four letters which are supposed to describe all there is in the world. There is just one alphabet for it all, but that alphabet does not say it at all. For you to understand what happened to me, you would have to know already, you would have to understand before the words come out of my mouth, reluctantly, hesitantly, but then the words would be superfluous and useless and we would understand each other without them.

I do not know how to talk about this, and it does not help to eat words and spit them out in your face. What does it mean, if I say I was gang-raped? Another sentence making the air vibrate, another collection of black letters on a white page. Words are not words of things. They don't get near the shame and the hurt, and shame and hurt are merely words, too. Words are like traffic signs which tell you where to turn left or right, but that is about it. Warm noises without meaning. Not much more meaning anyway than the roar of the motorcycles and their hooters and their police whistles. Not much more of a meaning than the tracks in our front garden, churning up the sandy soil and uprooting the flowers. Perhaps less. Marks in a garden which we had thought belonged to us. A safe place. Yet one of them could drive right through that and demolish it in less than a minute.

Because they have come back. After what they did. They have come back and circle and circle round that emptiness of noise at

347

the crossroads where they have ripped the stop signs from their metal poles and thrown them into our front garden. But that does not stop me. They have come back and their wheels are spinning as they race along our road, the pack thickening and thinning as they weave their way around the streetlamps, over the kerbs, along the white line.

My eyes are black holes, and the men and their gleaming machines disappear into that black hole, trancelike, flying dark angels, their inscriptions flashing for the last time in garish colours before they disappear forever, the wheels rotating in emptiness. Somewhere they continue to exist, squashed, inaccessible, mute, atoms without meaning. But I do not know any more what eyes are or whether I have eyes.

Their helmets look like strange masks. The strident colours and bold inscriptions on them which are indecipherable from this distance made them look like medieval armour adorned with various coats of arms. When their dark visors are down their faces are wiped out behind the curve of the glass, their heads are featureless except for the bold colours on them, the visors are like the surveillance ports of robots from a science fiction film. Their uniformly black leather clothing sports the same bold colouring and lettering as their helmets, and some wear steel chains slung over their shoulders or around their necks like an exotic kind of jewellery. Their motorcycles without the silencers sound like bull-roarers, and from time to time one of them sounds his horn which then emits a strident noise like a rusty trumpet in distress, while others are blowing their police whistles, making an unbelievable din.

As they circle the intersection the roads leading to it are curiously empty, no cars seem to move along any of the four spokes radiating from the cross, no pedestrians walk about, even the windows appear shut like empty mirrors, although there are faint movements of curtains behind most of them, furtive eyes appearing and dis-appearing. An aura of anxiety pervades the scene.

From time to time one of the cyclists veers from the circle, and performs a series of dangerous manoeuvres along one of the four roads leading to the intersection. Lifting up the front wheel he balances himself precariously on the hind wheel, attempts short jumps, drives on to the pedestrian walkways, crashes through the flimsy gates of the small gardens in front of the houses and flats, and ploughs through the tiny flower gardens kept there by some of the more aesthetic inhabitants of this bleak and uniform environment until he gets stuck in the heavy sandy soil and has to use his feet to push himself out. A window opens shortly and a shrill voice protests the violation. There is a sound like a shot, but it could have been a back-fire from the labouring engine of the motorcycle. The window is shut hastily, and the cycle careers back on to the road.

One of them with his feet on the back saddle and perched precariously over the handlebar performs a death-defying race along one of the roads, until, about three hundred metres down he jumps into his seat in one fluid movement without stopping the cycle, turns the cycle with a monstrous roar of its engine and returns to the circle with a number of sweeping movements from side to side, nearly colliding with a parked lorry in the process. Those who return into the circle are greeted by raucous laughter and a devilish din of hooters and whistles.

My eyes are useless, they reflect only what I know. I want to become a beam of light, an intense light which penetrates those dark visors and illuminates their faces, the black holes of their eyes, blinding them so that they are helpless on their roaring machines. I want them to smash into walls and be broken like wooden dolls, arms and legs dangling from their useless bodies. I want to tear out my eyes. I want to cut off my ears. I want to plug my nose. I want to vomit.

My problem is that they know who I am. Their problem is that I know who they are. In spite of their helmets and their blackness. I had seen their faces, and they were boys of the neighbourhood, teenage boys, of my age, I had gone to school with them, and they know me. That is why they are back and why they perform with all that noise at the crossing in front of our flat.

Of course, I knew that it was dangerous to go to the café after dark. Everybody knows that in our street. The noise of their bicycles and their horns tells its own story and you need nobody to tell you stories about what these boys do to keep you indoors.

But I said to my mother: I can go everywhere I like. We have had a democratic election. We are a free nation now. We have a democratic government. This is a non-racial and non-sexist society.

Women have rights here, or do they, human rights. I don't allow a bunch of bullies to dictate to me where I can go and when. I am weak, I know that. That is what they are counting on. But when one is weak, the thing that gives one strength is to take them down a peg or two, or perhaps right to the bottom. They parade in the street to instil fear in us, but one needs to strip them of that which instils fear. One needs to see that they are really laughable. One must teach onself to see them as they are, or worse than they are. One must look at them from all points of view and then see that they are really bags of hot air. That sets you free. So I went down the street to the café.

Everything was mine that evening, it all belonged to me. I had the street to myself and the full moon behind its cloud was a lightness as I had never experienced before. I had the sound of my shoes on the road, and I had a tremendous sense of fear.

As I walked up to the door of the café they arrived with their infernal thunder and started to circle me. At first they moved around me like actors on a stage who had forgotten their words. The only words they had were their machines and the roar of their engines. Their dark visors were down and their faces were invisible behind the curve of the glass, their visors immutable except for the reflexes of the streetlights playing on them, their heads were featureless grotesque extensions of their bodies in black leather. Some were wearing steel chains gleaming in the night. Their motorcycles without the silencers made an infernal noise, and from time to time one of them was sounding his horn, while others were blowing their police whistles.

I panicked. Fear can't be cured, it seems. If you go out into the street, you will surely finish up by finding out what it is that really frightens you. Despite my brave thoughts when I left home I was afraid. I was shit-scared.

Then one of them opened his visor and shouted over the din of the engines:

– Hey, you over there!

I ignored him and attempted to move towards the café, but the circle drew tighter around me, and then one of the cycles spiralled inwards towards me, chasing me as I tried to escape him, round and round. I lost one of my shoes and hobbled on my stockings on the harsh cement. Then he caught up with me and his hand encircled my waist, as he drew me towards him.

– It seems this chick does not know the rules.

His speech echoed through the hollows of his helmet. Whatever he said next was swallowed up in a fury of engines being revved and hooters being blown.

– Women belong in the kitchen and in the bedroom. Didn't you know this?

Another one shouted from the circle:

– Hey, we are here to protect the morals of this street. Girls who wander about at night are up to no good.

The one who held me said:

– You ought to know the rules, chick.

The circle started to move again with much noise. For a moment they did not seem to know what to do with me.

– You should be at home peeling potatoes, chick, the one said. But he knew he was repeating himself. Then he pulled me up on his cycle and started to move.

Just then two dogs came running out of the darkness. Darting here and there, in haste, then standing still, the one dog sniffing the other. Then again in full flight. Then a tense moment of stillness. Sniffing. Then the dog started to mount the bitch and started to fuck her with fast furious movements of his hind-quarters, clasping her body with his front paws.

– The dog says fuck her, said the one who held me.

- Yes, that is what he says, laughed the others. So that is what we need to do.

I too heard the dog say this, but the dog spoke in the voice of my mother and my father and my brothers and my grandfather and my grandmother and my great-grandmother and my great-uncle. When dogs speak they always speak with the voice and the authority of our ancestors. They always speak male. All our ancestors, male and female, speak male. Even our female ancestors speak with the important and husky voice of their male ancestors: whoof whoof, bow-wow, fuck her. They say what they have heard. Again and again. Like Missis in school.

Then the one who was holding me put his motorcycle on its stand, pulled me towards him, threw me over the saddle, lifting up my skirt. The scream of tearing fabric, as he ripped pieces of clothing from my body. I waited endlessly, shivering. I started to go blank, until I felt the pain, recurring endless pain and revulsion. I felt the cycle move underneath our motions, and for a moment I was afraid it would tilt and smash on my leg. Then I was all by myself.

My body is inside. The skin no longer guarantees myself, it gives way, it splits, urine, blood, excrement flow from my tortured body. Loathing, filth, waste, defilement, sewage, muck, shit, the spasms, the repugnance and the retching that thrusts me to the side and turns me away. The shame of being in the middle. What the eyes see and what the lips touch, a gagging, a spasm in the stomach, the belly, tears and bile, I spit out myself, forehead and hands perspiring, a sight-clouding dizziness, a nausea turns me inside out, guts sprawling. I do not want to listen. I do not want to see. But I scream.

Gestures and things, voices and sounds, stammering, vibrato, tremolo and overspilling: the grand opera of the erections parading with much noise in a circle around me. Concordant, discordant. The revving of the bikes. And within it a murmur arising from a constellation of voices that assemble my proper name: whore. Nobody said it. It was not in my consciousness. But suddenly it was there, brought to the light of day by whispering voices. It was an order: You will be a whore! For us! We will make you! Sentences running through me, coming from another planet. Voices saying: she is a whore! All in an instant: they spoke and I heard, and I could not forget who I was to be for them. It was there in the noise and the silence, their laughter, and in the cries which spewed forth from my mouth without ending. Protesting and submitting to the order the cries entered the mix of other noises, became part of the unspeakable violation.

There are dead spaces and dead times, when the whole world shrivels, when passions die and the body becomes a machine, when everyone can see that that woman is dead, that I am that dead woman, a broken machine, never to be repaired, death is the figure of that bundle of splayed limbs on the road, like a doll with broken bones thrown there by a tornado, lifeless. My body is a set of locks, valves, bowls, wheels, gears – broken. These things used to have a name, but I have forgotten all names. I no longer have a brain or nerves or a chest or a stomach or guts. All I have left are a torn skin and broken bones. A corpse, a cadaver, a cropper, this is a cesspool, and death. My body cannot extricate itself from that waste sprawled on the cement. I faint. I wake. I do not know where I am. There is a space around me which nobody wants to step across.

They stare at me. They stare at what they have done to me. Close-up. White clowns, moon-white, angels of death. Faces reflect the streetlights, holes in pitiless darkness. Faces are horror-stories. There is something absolutely inhuman in the human faces staring at me, a white wall with black holes, chalk faces with eyes cut out, before they disappear behind the dark visors of their helmets. One of them, I know his name but I will not say it, because I, too, have learned to forget my own name, one of them, leaning on the handlebars of his cycle, looked at me and looked at the blood on the white cement, there in front of this café, and his face was white as he contemplated these three drops of blood, and maybe he saw a face as he was deep in a kind of catatonia, or maybe it was just me. They are saying something, but I can't understand it. They are speaking the same tongue but a different language. I forget what people are saying to me, I no longer know where I am going or where I am coming from, or to whom I am speaking. But I can understand the fear in their laughing voices. The smell of death and rotting animal flesh is in the air and will cling to them for ever. They know I am their fate from now on: the body of the ruined queen, tortured, I have become an animal, retribution and justice are out of the question, but they will have to live in the stench of the goat's sty from now on. I have become the goat they kill and then send off into the desert. But the goat returns to haunt them with the smell of horror.

That was yesterday. Or was it? There is no yesterday, today and tomorrow any more, is there? There is only now and now and now.

The noise is there again. The noise is still there. That noise which comes from the circle in the road: now again. It is like a warning cry. Like a message to flee or to stay and admire. Everybody understands what it means. It is a threat. It is like the roar of a lion in the night. It is like death. Anyone speaking about what happened to me to the police would have had it. It said: this is our turf, and we do what we like. But it is also a cry for help: please betray us, please somebody punish us. A roar of despair: don't you see that we are waiting for it, and that there is no meaning in it at all. They don't ride on their bikes for the fun of it. I know that they know that there is no fun in it. They are foolish, but not that foolish to believe that riding those bikes is fun. It is much too serious for that. A rumble and a buzz, blinding lights. A clarity that gushes from every wall. I understand what the circle means: it was empty. There was nothing in the circle. They were still looking for something or somebody to fill that circle, but at the same time they threaten everybody who approaches the circle.

Suddenly I start to laugh hysterically, for a long time. I laugh because of the emptiness. I can't stop laughing, because of all the times I had been frightened by the emptiness. I laugh and laugh. Tears running down my face. Moving with ever greater rapidity. A flight not to be arrested. I swim through everything: through head and arms and legs, and behind the sockets of my eyes there is a region, unexplored, and there is no logic whatsoever, no justice, no right or wrong, just destruction and abolition pure and simple, a passion for abolition. I give birth to myself, to another self, in a convulsion of horror and laughter, I vomit myself into being. I am breaking through the walls and head towards the emptiness in the middle. There are no acts to explain, no dreams to interpret, no memories to recall, no words that have any significance. There are colours, sounds, intensities. I close my eyes, my ears, my mouth: because there is nothing further to see, to hear, to say.

Scatter the Ashes and Go

MONGANE WALLY SEROTE

'Jerry, when are you leaving?' I asked.

Jerry looked at his watch. He stared into the distance. Then he said, 'An hour.'

'I will take Oupa in about four hours,' Vusi said, taking a gulp of beer from his glass. Jerry stood up noisily and vanished into the bathroom. Water ran. The heat was piercing. Even the wind was hot.

Vusi and I met Ralph. Comrade Ralph. Ntate Ralph. He had grey hair. He was short and his shoulders were bent. His gait was slow, heavy, almost a limp. He had a very bright smile. But you knew, he was watching and listening carefully. He wore light blue overalls. Black boots. He had arrived in a bakkie. We had met before. I did not know that he was now placed here. I did not know him as Ralph. I knew him as Raymond. I had met him elsewhere, on another front.

'He arrived today,' Vusi said.

'You did not land in jail?' Ralph asked me, responding to Vusi. 'No.'

'Haai, you fellows, man. I never know whether to think you love jail or jail loves you, you always end up there.'

'I hope I won't,' I responded.

'He has to cross tonight,' Vusi said.

'That's him?' Ralph asked. As he said this, I knew he knew I was the one who must cross. He had given no sign that he and I had met before. He knew long before that I would be crossing, and going home. I knew he knew this.

'Fellows come here, go home, and land in jail, straight into the

355

hands of the Boers. Why? You fellows must be careful. This is a long vicious war. Better to spend this time alive out of jail and working for freedom . . .' he laughed, throwing his head backwards.

'They are waiting to receive you, they are comrades of long standing. The area has been mobilised, they need backing. Have you been briefed?'

I nodded.

'You will leave tonight.'

I looked at Vusi. He was watching me. Ralph got into his bakkie and drove off. Vusi laughed.

'What?' I asked.

'Ralph, he's a funny old man.'

It was very quiet. The birds sang. The heat buzzed. The trees were still. Now and then a goat or sheep bleated, a cow bellowed, a dog barked. But it was very still and quiet. Occasionally, I heard voices, voices of women in the distance. Sounds travelled far here. That was why we whispered when we talked.

'He spent twenty years in prison,' Vusi said.

'He's one of those?'

'Ja.'

'He's based in one of the villages here?'

'Ja, he sells vegetables from that bakkie. He is so committed to it that at times I can't say whether he is more committed to selling vegetables than to the struggle.'

'He crosses the border all the time, backwards and forwards, he knows his area.'

I reminisced about the last time I had seen Ralph, when he was Raymond. He was wearing a shirt and a tie, and was meeting with ministers of the country we were in.

'He was like a diplomat then,' Vusi said.

'Where are his children?' I asked.

'You know him then?'

'I do.'

Vusi did not answer. He looked away into the distance.

'You know there is something I now and then try to understand. Women?' I said out of the blue.

'Women?'

'Ja.'

'You want to understand women? Why?'

'I have been with Ralph and his wife. Now you know, I have lots of time and respect for Ralph. But his wife, she treats him like a small boy. She has so much contempt for him.'

'And you think that is because she is a woman?'

'I have never seen men close to him treat him like she does.'

'Really . . .'

'Once when I went to their house, she virtually threw his plate of food at him. We had just returned from home. We had engaged the Boers. We had had to walk twice the distance we were supposed to. I knew he was dead tired. He greeted her. She did not respond. He kept smiling, talking to his daughter whom he adores. As he sat down, the plate of food came flying at him. He asked whether there was food for me. She did not answer. She threw another spoon at him. He caught it and gave it to me. Eat, he said, that's what will tell you that you are still alive! For the three hours that I was there, they hardly said anything to each other. He had this monologue with his little daughter while his wife went to and fro, throwing her buttocks around.'

'But that's not women, that's *a* woman,' Vusi chuckled.

'No, man! This happens a lot with women.'

'Are you saying it would not happen with men?'

'I have not seen it. She strikes me as being very evil. She blames him for having gone to jail and for leaving her. She does not agree with his involvement now. She wants him to stay home, sell vegetables, and look after children. You can't run a revolution and run a family, that's all there is to it,' I pronounced.

'Rubbish, a family is a base for a revolution,' Vusi countered.

'Whatever you mean by that,' I said. 'But the truth is you can't do both!'

'Don't you do revolution so that families can flourish?'

'Yes. After the revolution families will flourish, but you can't run a revolution and a family simultaneously, that's that,' I concluded.

'Are families not oppressed? Are women not oppressed? Are all of us, all blacks, not oppressed? What is the best? A life under oppression for ever, or a life in a revolution and in a family working for change? Which is the better of the two?' he asked rhetorically.

'Obviously the latter,' I said, 'but not everyone thinks that way.'

'We should help people to think that way, like we taught them to reject oppression.'

'Ja, I agree. Men and women must be taught.'

'I . . .' Vusi was about to say something, but stopped. He was listening carefully; I also picked up the sound of footsteps.

We disappeared, hiding in the bush. A shepherd appeared from behind a bush, looked around him. He then looked down, obviously at our footprints and examined the bent grass where we had been sitting. He paused. We waited, watching him.

'Let's retreat,' I said.

We began to crawl backwards. We were a couple of metres away from the shepherd. Eventually he drove his sheep past Vusi after looking in his direction. We moved out of the trouble spot and again we waited.

After a while we saw Ralph's bakkie driving slowly on the main road. There were two people in the car. Ralph and someone else. Vusi said it was Ralph and the shepherd. He was right.

'This man will take you across,' Ralph said. 'You will go with him, from now on you are in his hands.'

I went home that night. I had been away from home for fifteen years.

When I arrived back from South Africa, I was met by the shepherd. He took me to Ralph, who took me to Vusi.

Vusi cooked what he called the South African meal. Rice, cabbage, potatoes, carrots, meat, beer. Jerry and someone else was there. We sat in the heat of the foreign country, eating and drinking, and we talked. That night Vusi took me to see the woman he loved.

'Meet Oupa,' Vusi said. 'Oupa, this is Warona.'

'Where are you?' I greeted her.

'We are here, and you?' she said with a pretty smile and happy eyes. She struck me as a sharp person. She must have a good job, judging from her house, her clothes and manner.

There was a silence after this. This told me that she knew what business Vusi was involved in. She therefore knew my business too. She asked no questions. I accepted the silence as normal. Vusi made tea. We sat down to drink.

'Warona works for Government,' Vusi said.

'Is that so?' I said, not knowing what else to say. 'What work do you do?' I asked.

'Protocol,' she said. My mind went through the meaning of

this word. It was a bit difficult to fathom.

'I am a lecturer in Swaziland,' I said.

'What do you lecture in?'

'English,' I replied.

She looked at Vusi. Vusi's face was blank.

'I have been to Swaziland many times through my work,' she said.

'It's a nice place, Swaziland, but I find it confusing politically.'

'You do? Why?'

'Monarchy, traditional leaders; political leaders; relations with South Africa.'

'Well, you are South African,' she said. 'You may be confused by that country's relationship with yours, but how they rule themselves is their business.'

'You think so?'

'Yes.'

'But there is the fact that Swaziland exists. It exists in the twentieth century and in the Southern African region. Because they do not take this into consideration, it is a confusing place.'

'You are right,' she said, 'but its people have the right to decide what they want to take into consideration. They have the right to exercise their right.'

'Yes,' I insisted, 'but if their right confuses us, we should say so.'

'I suppose so,' she said. 'It is a beautiful country, I agree,' then she looked at Vusi. Lost in his thoughts, he was not part of us. Warona smiled at him.

'Love, what have you been doing?'

'Working,' Vusi said.

'You look tired.'

'No. I am listening to the music.'

Just then, I realised it was Stevie Wonder playing 'I just called to say . . .'

A servant entered the room politely, and set the table after greeting us. I was going to say, thank you, I had eaten, but had to take my cue from Vusi who sat down at the table and began to eat. We joined him.

'Warona becomes offended when I say I have eaten and can't eat any more,' Vusi said.

'Have something, meat or gravy,' Warona said.

'I love her, I don't want to offend her with small things,' Vusi said.

'It's not small things,' she said. 'Vusi must not always come here after having eaten somewhere else. He will just have to eat more.'

'It's punishment then?' Vusi asked.

'No, encouragement for you to eat here, and not elsewhere, is that you know you will be coming here,' she said.

I thought, Oh, so she has accepted that he may or may not come.

'I don't know what I am doing with you. Oupa, you know, Vusi comes and goes as he wishes. At times I never know whether he will be coming or not.'

'Why?' I asked.

'Ask him.'

'It's my ANC work,' Vusi said.

'At least there's news that Mandela will come out soon, some of us will write to him to let our men go,' she said and laughed.

'You won't write a letter, with your work, you may whisper in his ear at the airport,' Vusi said.

'I would if I had the chance,' she said. 'Sweet, finish at least that piece of meat.'

I got the sense that she must have been married before. Vusi had once told me that women here had children at a young age. I had not seen any child. But something told me there was something like that. Something also told me she was a very independent woman. No, not something. The furniture. Her dress. Her car outside. The work she did. But what did she have to do with the likes of Vusi and myself?

'It's rough for the ANC here,' I said.

'Are you in the ANC?'

'He's trying to recruit me,' I said nodding towards Vusi.

'And . . .?' she asked.

'Difficult. I understand what he is saying, I have to think about it.'

'He has the right to think about it, not so, sweet?'

'As long as he does not think for ever,' she said. 'But that's his business.'

'It's rough to be ANC,' I said.

'It is,' she said, 'but it will be over.'

Steven with bus, Doornfontein, Johannesburg, 1960

Concession store, Knights, Germiston, 1965

Nyassa miners going home after serving their twelve-month contract on a gold mine, Mayfair railway station, Johannesburg, 1952

A company house for a white miner, New Modder, Benoni, 1965

'Boss Boy', Randfontein Estates Gold Mine, 1966

Butch Britz, Master Shaftsinker, No 4 Shaft, President Steyn Gold Mine, Welkom, 1969

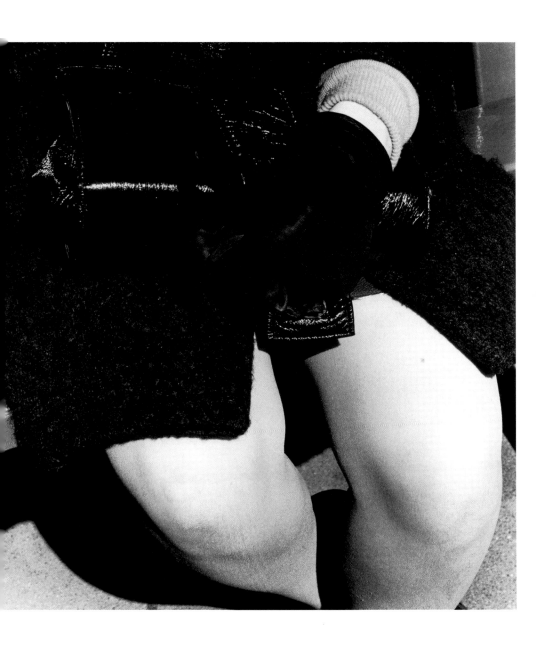

Woman on a bench, Joubert Park, Johannesburg, April 1975

A domestic worker on Abel Road, Hillbrow, Johannesburg, 1973

'When?' I asked.

'It will be,' she said with finality. 'And then I will know more of Vusi.' She said, 'You must mean a lot to him as you are the first person he has brought here.'

'Am I?'

'Yes.'

'Is that a form of pressure on me to join the ANC?'

'No. I would not recruit you, all I'm saying is just that; also that he is a very closed person.'

'Are you two discussing me?'

'No, not really, I'm talking to Oupa,' she said.

We returned to the lounge section of the room. Warona was tall. She had a strong frame. She must have been told that she was a beautiful woman. But even as she knew it, she seemed to be casual about it. She was warm. I understood how she and Vusi could be together. I could imagine what they did when they were together. But also, so much remained unanswered.

'She wants me to leave the struggle once we are free, but I tell her she must remember that she has a country and I don't, so I can't make promises like that,' Vusi said to me later. 'I love her, and it is painful that we don't agree on this.'

I left Vusi. I left him with Ralph, Jerry and the hot country. I had met Warona once in the three months that I stayed in her country.

I looked Warona up when next I returned. I knew that Vusi had crossed the border and was in South Africa. I had been there a while now. I knew that when he and I met, he would ask me if I had passed through the place; he would ask me in a way that would tell him whether I had seen Warona.

The place had become dangerous. There had been a raid, a cross-border raid. Twelve comrades had been killed. Vusi was there when it happened. I knew that Warona was still alive.

I thought hard before I decided to see Warona. The only reason I wanted to see her was that I knew she still loved Vusi. I had heard that after the raid she had protected him.

I planned to meet her but to make it look like a coincidence. We met early one evening as she went to the shop. When she came out of the shop and was about to get in her car, I approached her from behind.

'Haai,' I said. 'I think we have met before.'

She looked at me, unlocked her car, opened the door, got in, closed it.

'Who are you?' she asked.

'Oupa,' I said.

'Where did we meet?'

'With Vusi in your house,' I said.

'Me?'

'Yes,' I said.

'Can I help you?'

'No, I wanted to greet you. If you have time, I would like a word with you?'

'What about?'

'Can I get in? You can drop me off somewhere.'

'What do you want to talk about?'

'I am taking a chance talking to you here. I will be seeing Vusi soon. Can I get in?'

'OK.' She unlocked the passenger door. 'Get in,' she said.

There was soft music as she switched on the ignition.

'Well,' I said as she reversed, 'I wanted to see you for two reasons. First, I will see Vusi soon. Secondly, just to say hullo. If you have something to say to Vusi you can tell me.'

'I have nothing to say to Vusi,' she said as the car sailed forward slowly. 'Thanks for coming to say hullo . . . Is that all?'

'Yes. If you have nothing to say to Vusi, you can drop me at the next corner.'

We reached the corner in silence. The car stopped. I got out.

I told Vusi this story when next I saw him.

'Was she angry?' he asked.

'No.'

'How was she?'

'What do you mean?'

'I mean, was she all right?'

'Healthy. Beautiful. Polite. All that.'

'No man, don't be a fool, I mean was she, what? OK? Did she say anything?'

'It is as I have told you,' I said.

We drove silently through the town.

Three months later I left South Africa. I met Warona again.

'Vusi sends his love,' I said.

'Is that so?' she responded.

'He said I must give you this,' I held out my hand.

'What is it?' she asked.

'A letter and a present.'

After a while she took the present and the letter from me. I did not see her read the letter or open the parcel. Something about her told me I should leave her alone.

I met Vusi in Zambia. He asked me about Warona. He had had no chance to see her on his way back from South Africa. He had not passed through her country. I told him Warona had said nothing. I had not seen her open the letter or the parcel.

'Why?'

'It was best to leave her alone.'

'Why?'

'I just knew, I can't explain.'

'You mean she was angry?'

'No. I don't know.'

'What do you mean?'

'Just that.'

'Was she suspicious?'

'I don't know.'

'What do you mean?'

'Just that.'

He looked at me. His eyes searched my face in the most penetrating manner.

'What are you saying?' he asked me.

'Look, what do you want me to say? Maybe she was suspicious. Maybe she has a new love, maybe she is angry – I met her briefly.'

'Why?'

'What?'

'Why did you meet her briefly?'

'Because I felt she wanted me to go.'

'Where did you meet her?'

'In her car.'

'Did you make an appointment?'

'No, I walked up to her.'

He pulled at his cigarette. He thought for a long while.

'I will see you,' he said.

'When?'

'Well, I am leaving,' he said.

'You are leaving?'

'Yes, on a mission.'

Our eyes met. I saw sadness and a trace of tears in his eyes.

'OK. Look after yourself,' I said.

He walked out the door. I watched him through the window. He walked quickly. A lone man on the street with a mission. For some reason, I thought about the time when he and I were at home on a mission. I had seen Vusi. I had seen Jerry. I had seen many who were on missions. We walked those streets, the South African streets. We were hunted people.

Somehow we belonged and yet, we did not belong. My quiet shepherd had tried to explain this to me. He had said that we were a new breed of South Africans. But I had also, on my first time of entering South Africa in fifteen years, seen a new breed of South Africans. They were the nation. Both blacks and whites were in their own way a new nation. We fitted into this, and also did not fit. So with the whites: they fitted and also did not fit. What was new, was not what could be seen, touched or heard. It could only be felt.

Coming from outside, I had become blind to the 'whites/non-whites' signs. They had long been removed. I did not even notice that they were not there. Having been in many African countries, where the majority of the people were black, I did not notice that Johannesburg and other cities, which were completely white before I left, had become black. It was only when people pointed this out to me that I noticed the change.

Being a reader, and having been closely in touch with all kinds of developments in my country, and through my involvement in the underground structures of my movement, I was not surprised by the low quality of life in the townships. And the extremely low quality of life in the rural areas, where poverty, disease, illiteracy, were tangible, could be smelled. It could be sensed in the eyes and manner of the people. Their lives had had to adjust, as a body does when it is whipped, frowning, cringing and staggering. There seemed to be a permanence about it.

I had seen all this in the camps too, when men and women arrived to join MK. They were from all over South Africa. Despite the distances and the many stops they had made before they reached

Angola, the frowns, the cringing and the smell of suffering were still with them. They made those of us who had severed ourselves from this by choosing exile share anew what we had once experienced and known.

We absorbed this as they were absorbed by MK. No one came to the camps and remained as he had been when he arrived. MK itself was constantly being transformed. It became multilingual, almost creating a new South African language. It was both rural and urban in experience and so became a new, unrecognisable South African body. Through it, women, men and youth became alike in the way they walked, their clothes, speech, living quarters, the types of food they ate and the hours they kept.

As this process of adjustment took place, you could hear and touch human resilience adapting to the demands and the rigours of military life. You saw it in the eyes of the people, in the way in which they looked at you. You heard it in their vocabulary, in the words they spoke, in the manner in which they used words to tell of where they came from, where they were, and where they hoped to go.

They were ready to live as people rather than die as slaves. It did not happen instantly, nor could one walk out of it as one does from night to day or day to night; it happened, and at times one heard it as one would hear a breaking twig, or a stone dropping into water. Sometimes it was not that quick; it happened in the sound of water flowing along as a river.

Entering South Africa after fifteen years of absence, of adjusting to MK, without the minute-to-minute adjusting to despair, was like walking in the night then suddenly finding it was day. In a sense, you were outside something and in another sense you were inside something you had to be out of. It was a process of learning to live with change.

Once, the shepherd Morongwa, Vusi and I talked about this. We had time to talk. We were staying in a hole we had dug, camouflaged and turned into a habitable pit. At night we came out and entered life. In the early hours of the morning, we returned to the life of animals. So we talked, smelled each other's lives, anger, hopes, fears, disgust, weakness. We stared at all this; touched it and heard it.

We talked about why we did it. Vusi said Morongwa was the

best among us. He would not use a car; he sat in it as if he expected it to threaten his life. But on his feet and walking, he was tireless. Military life had given us some measure of this, but for him it was a way of life. We heard his speech adjust to Zulu words and accents from Setswana, to English and Afrikaans. Sometimes he seemed as uncertain as a trapped animal, but in the camp confidence and control emerged.

Was it this which nourished laughter, smiles and gaiety in Lydia, Ralph's wife – who, otherwise, had the face of a fish lying on the sand? Ralph, when Marongwa was at his house, had this strange posture; the look of entering an unknown light and a strange place. He became quiet. He slid back to become part of the furniture; even his little daughter sensed this uneasiness as she clung to him, absent-mindedly playing with his beard and sucking her thumb.

Lydia was oblivious to all. She was aware of Morongwa, but pretended that she noticed nothing.

'Which is what, his wife or daughter?'

'His daughter.'

'So there is nothing between them.'

'You mean between Ralph and his wife?'

'Yes.'

'If there was nothing they would not be together.'

'We seem to be going in circles here. I'm trying to say Ralph looks pathetic and you are saying he is cherishing something.'

'His daughter,' Vusi said.

'If he leaves, he must leave the child behind.'

'Not necessarily.'

'Let's not play with words. Where would he take the child? He's hardly ever at home. He is a hunted man. Don't you see that the only place he can have a little peace with what he values and loves, is there. The price is, he must bear that woman.'

'That's pathetic!'

'It may be, but what else is there for him to do?'

'But how can Ralph still love Lydia then?'

'Vusi, don't be foolish. You know I often hear people talk about love, wife, family and children. I wonder whether people know what they are talking about. This is society. When you marry, if you have children and build a family, you are linked to society. That is one thing. The other is that you have created life, as man and as woman. When you have children, you have linked that to the innocent, who are wholly dependent on you; your nurture, trust, love, passion and compassion. You are asking me why Ralph is not tired of all this. That is what you are asking me. Remember, there was a time when they, Ralph and Lydia, thought nothing would part them but death. Marriage for them was the struggle of two people to become one . . .'

Vusi laughed at all this. His laughter was loud and even derisive.

'Morongwa, you are obviously an expert on these matters, you sound like a priest!'

'Well, if you ask me, I will give you my view.'

'I agree with your view. But all I'm saying, which you seem to refuse to agree to, is that Ralph looks pathetic.'

'But so does Lydia!'

'Both of them look pathetic then! That's all I'm saying.'

'But you are also saying if they are so pathetic, why do they not part? I'm saying if it was a process for them to come together, it will be a process for them to part.'

'OK.'

'Sometimes when I'm with them, I know they have parted a long time ago, and of course I ask myself the same questions that you are asking me, and I can see that even though they have long parted, they seem not to know this.'

'You sound like someone who has thought a lot about this.'

'Ralph is a good man. Lydia is a good woman. I love them. They have accepted me because of my love for them.'

'You love them?'

'Yes, I don't only respect them, I love them,' Morongwa said.

Vusi was silent as he dished up. He concentrated on what he was doing as if he had never done it before, or it was the last thing he would ever do. He sighed heavily as he gave us each a plate, and prepared to sit on his sleeping bag and lean against the rough wall of the pit.

'Oupa, you have been very quiet,' he said to me.

'I have been trying to read.'

'Have you?'

'I tried.'

'It's eleven now. We have three hours.'

'Ja.'

From the pit you could hear the lone sound of a car on the main road about half a kilometre away. At times, this sound was the only contact we had with real life. Life as it was led by people out there.

We often forgot where we were. At times, when there was lots of movement around, we became conscious, alert and ready.

We knew that the pit, our home, was quite safe. It was well chosen, and well camouflaged. I had been to it many times to prepare it. Once I had chosen it and planned it, I went there with Vusi and Morongwa. It took us three months to complete it. In that time, I came to know Vusi. I also came to know Morongwa. We came to know one another.

It is not often that this happens. The military creates and builds relations according to hierarchy and orders, and according to rules which give authority. Sometimes it is orders for life to be taken. But the military is systematic, with both the individual and the collective, in building carefully, cementing and sealing its hierarchy, rules, systems and relationships. At times, it leaves out the human element. At other times it recognises it, grudgingly making allowances for it.

If the human element is understood, a machine emerges. It is a system which can hone sharp razor blades to cut at a flash, coldly, brutally, ruthlessly set out to work and accomplish. As it does this, its parts, the human beings, change. They can grow and develop. They can degenerate. MK had all these elements in it. It gave you many eyes, many ears, touch and smell; it gave you vision and understanding. It welded you to a past and to a future which shaped your life.

The three of us had completed nine months of systematic work. The likes of us should be there. We knew this. We brought MK with us. MK was emerging not far from us. If you listened you could hear the songs; if you watched you could see it in the eyes and gaits, in the villages and near the townships. If you could read the writing on the wall you could sense the convulsions. If you had vision, you knew the future would be different.

We thought a lot about Ralph because of who he was. And since we had hopes, we loved life. That made us wish him well. But we could see that all was not well. We knew Lydia and we knew Ralph. We wondered about them. We wondered about their talkative little girl and wanted the three of them to have a life in an unfolding future that we touched and shaped with our own minds. It was so ripe!

But I was worried. In the village and in the township, I sensed that when we met people we were hero-worshipped. The way people talked to us; looked at us; listened to us; it was not natural. I understood why they behaved this way. How would you react, if you met and talked and touched people, yet did not know where they stayed, how they came to you.

You knew from everything which happened in the old town, in the houses and streets that they brought change. You yourself, sang songs you knew, but which had different meanings. You saw and heard dances and songs which moved people, which united them, which stirred hope and encouraged and tore fear away. You heard people who you had known for a long long time, some you knew when you were still little, they talked and did things you would never have thought they would say or do. They were fired. They leapt high in dance and spirit. What the TV told you about, that it happened in the cities, the big cities, now happened here, with you, all around you to the extent that even the Boer in the town, whom you feared, feared you. You thought. You sensed. Even as the Boer threatened, was fired with anger, and could kill, and you knew he killed, you also knew that this was not because of the confidence of the past. It was something new. It was fear. It was insecurity. It was, as they said, the desperate love of a past life, clung to, and slipping away.

The radio said today that the ANC and the Boers were talking. They were talking through second and third parties. The Boer President was still wagging his finger on TV and in newspaper photographs.

Vusi said the more the Boers talked to the ANC, the more MK must hit hard.

I found that I pondered over Vusi a lot those days.

A thought crossed my mind. Vusi, not so long ago was an ordinary black South African. His life, the story of his life, was enough to break anyone's heart. But now it gave me great joy. It was the story of ordinary black South Africans. He was one of those you see covered with a large canvas on highways after kombi accidents: cars fly on highways, blind: smashing into trees, into each other, into buses and other cars. They overturn after tyre bursts at speeds faster than spitting. People die, and are covered with newspapers in the street; they are robbed; they fill the prisons, police stations, police cars; they overflow in hospitals on mattresses on the floor, covered with bloody sheets; they make ugly corpses in mortuaries; they are the ones whose wives, sisters, children, brothers search and search for; they disappear from the face of the earth for ever.

Vusi is now thirty years old. His ginger colour can be very seductive. His almost hazel eyes, with their unshakeable stare, attract you. You stare back at them until you see his tight mouth, which, in a gentle but firm way, says he is staring because he is searching for clues from you about you. Something about him tells you that he is, or that he can be, a very hard man. When he sees you staring back at him, his eyes seem to focus. They become riveted on yours, as if eternally, and his face, mouth, cheeks, nose, become granite. He creates a very uncomfortable atmosphere. I have seen many people fold up and fall under this stare. His stare and something which he does when he stares – his shoulders either lift up or broaden as if in preparation for battle. His voice softens, almost in mockery, and he moves forward, leans closer to you, when you expect him to move backwards. All this is natural.

Vusi came to MK when he was twenty-four.

I have known him as he grew to become thirty. I have watched him read. I have seen him listening. I have heard him ask questions, differ from others, and assert his views. It is these things which have made me wonder, made me angry, made me ashamed of being South African. Vusi is not and will never be an ordinary black South African. He speaks Zulu, Xhosa, Tsonga, Afrikaans, English and makes you wonder which is his mother tongue, which he is fluent in, where did he get all those accents? But Vusi is natural in everything he learned. His ginger colour, the evidence of the crossing of tracks, increases the confusion. He would, according to us South Africans, have been better talking Afrikaans, being a coloured. But then he does not. He despises anyone who thinks that he should.

When he is with Warona, he is vulnerable. He is a lover. He loves life and says so in every way possible without meaning to. In this world of manoeuvre and manipulation, I fear for him; he is generous, thinks love is reasonable and he is full of praises. I do not know why people say, when they talk about certain types of women, like

Warona, that they are tough cookies. She is, for what that is worth. She is going to live, and nothing will stop her. She is right, but then, she fumbles in love matters. She has this will, which is as sharp as a needle, for a car, a house, nice furniture, security. Who does not?

Vusi will go back to Warona's country soon. He has to report to Ralph. I can see, by the way he occasionally broods, that that is where his mind has been lately.

I remember the heat of Warona's country. It is a heat which is unbearable. It pounds the skin; it pounds on energy like a blazing fire; it pounds on the distance of the eyesight; it is thick to the extent of creating mirages on the vast sand, and on the dried out trees, and their white, sharp thorns and on the tough and rough and tricky goats which climb trees and nibble the little green leaves. It is a dry, sharp and penetrating heat.

I have often wondered what it does to a brittle, sensitive and soft thing like the human brain. It does nothing, I know. This heat is of the people there, and they are of it. They are of it, and of the sand. They love goat meat and watermelon, whose sweetness they do not eat but drink, making its red turn white, with its pips and its peels scattered about as if they had been flung like empty bottles.

What is it that has caught Vusi's heart there? It was when I asked this question that I came to know how black South African women had been pounded, beaten down, and left for destroyed. In that other country, women swear at you, strip you naked with their shrill voices and by reading the size of your buttocks and the size of what enters them, in the open crowded square which they call the Mall. They have foul tongues which they wag at you, when their love and passion deserts them or overwhelms them. I have always been very afraid of them.

I have watched Vusi with them, and through Warona, in their arms, naked like a child who is oblivious of its nakedness, running around. I have seen their eyes shine from within, deep black skins, which sometimes seem blue; I have seen them flash their bright white smile at a distance at the sight of him; I have seen him walk to them, hands flying in space, shoulders open, his feet fast as if flying above the ground and I shuddered, wondering if he was going to fall. But then, Vusi is Vusi; he has his stare, his mouth, and I know MK has touched him, body and soul.

He was more stand-offish with South African women. He seemed not to know that he was a man and they, women. For such language exists. It is in the eye, in the gestures; it is in the shrugging and touching of one's body which one is not aware that the other is watching. It is also in the laughter and the smile, as it is in the word.

Vusi lacked all these with South African women. I have watched him without watching him. I have seen Morongwa, unlike Vusi, take them with the single-minded honesty of a child. I have seen his eyes light when he falls into their arms and as they fall into his; his eyes light, like those of wolves and hyenas and jackals in the dark. They light and shine and laugh. Men are funny when they are face to face with women they love. They look mysterious, naughty, and like little boys. They even laugh like that. My men have taught me all this.

I listen to them talk about these women. They are different when they are with them. They have a different honesty. An honesty of hunters who know that if they are not careful, they will become the hunted. At times I become fearful, sad, despairing, even passionless, when I hear how much these women tell my men about their husbands. It is funny how affairs become sanctuaries where secrets are placed. It must be so, if affairs are of secrets; it must be so if being naked is to be exposed; it must be so if to be penetrated, and to penetrate is to express lust, passion and love, misplaced or not.

They lie. My men lie and lie and I fear they will burn in eternal hell. They lie to these women. One is a truck driver, the other is a train driver, and this explains their regular and at times long absence from the burning lust of these women who cheat their husbands. It is, I am sure, convenient for them too: let the drivers go, as long as they will come back. Then there will be no long and unexplained absence from their husbands.

I am so virgin with these matters! I have been amused and at times bewildered by their plans, which I know are masterminded by Vusi; he and Morongwa have forever thrown women into my lap. Over and over they find out, from the very women, that I thanked the women, and sent them away without touching them. Only Vusi dares to ask me. I give him only one answer – silence!

In our work, silence talks. I must come back to this one day. Who said silence is golden?

Aus

MIKE NICOL

Aus. When he first saw the site – nothing but a large compound with rows of white tents enclosed by a wire fence – William groaned. 'Bloody God, no!'

'Ja, but this is no cause for despair,' said a quiet voice from among the prisoners of war behind him. 'You should not worry, sergeant major. We can turn this into a most pleasant home. There is sand. There is water. Together they make mud. And from this we can build small houses.'

William turned round, dubious. The heat was pressing at his head. A small man stepped towards him and bowed: 'I am Oberst Heinrich von Trotha at your service, so, you must not be concerned. Let me create eine kleine Deutsche Phantasie here in the desert. Believe me a place like you have never seen.'

'Such as?' said William, squinting against the light. What crazy German madness was this man concocting?

'Perhaps this,' said von Trotha taking William by the arm. 'Please come with me, sergeant major, and I shall explain.' Together they walked about the compound. Using a stick von Trotha traced and measured out the plan of a village in the dirt and had men mark off the corners of each house he proposed with stones.

'There,' he said. 'What do you think? All that remains is for my men to build according to this scheme.'

William looked at the colonel disbelievingly. 'What for?' he said.

'For something to do in all these days while we wait for the war to end,' said von Trotha. 'You will soon see an interesting sight, sergeant major, on this matter you have my word.'

A week later there was still little more than this vision in the sand and the odd rectangle of mud bricks. Nothing that could be called progress. The station master loaned the prisoners of war some buckets but five fire buckets weren't enough to meet the demands of a building project designed to house more than a thousand men. At least not in a hurry. Despite a detachment trudging seven or eight times a day under armed guard to the spring, there was just never enough water. The mud hole was too small, the bucket-system ultimately ineffective as they could make only twenty bricks a day. At that rate William reckoned they might get four or five houses built before the really cold nights. Well, let them persevere. In the mean time they were blistered by the sun and no one had his heart in it. They were co-operating because Oberst von Trotha said they must.

'I think if we could have some barrels to fill with water it would make the building easier,' von Trotha eventually requested of William.

William shook his head. 'You're wasting your time, colonel. The men don't want to work.'

'Nein, nein, sergeant major, I cannot believe it is like that at all,' gesticulated von Trotha earnestly. 'We merely need some encouragement. Which is why I would ask you in your requisition for some other materials also.'

William raised his eyebrows: 'What sort of things?'

'Flat boards to make the doors and window shutters. Thick wood struts for the roof beans. Corrugated iron sheeting. Hammers, nails, hinges. Perhaps some cloth for curtaining.'

'Curtaining!'

'Why not? It will make the men happier. Their houses will feel more like home.'

'You're mad,' said William. 'What do you think the CO's going to say.'

'Nothing.' Von Trotha smiled. 'This is agreed with him already. He said you must just arrange the transportation.'

Two weeks later the consignment arrived. Everything down to the last trowel.

'Good,' said von Trotha to William as they supervised the unloading of the rail trucks. 'Now you will see a revolution in our progress, of this I promise.'

He was as good as his word. Building went ahead with rigour. The walls were daily higher, beginning to throw shadows at dusk and dawn across the forming streets. Men lounged around their half-completed houses in the evenings rolling Red Cross cigarettes, discussing the day's progress. Or joked about someone's crooked wall, or admired the sharp angles, the unwavering lines of the expert craftsmen. Yet it was still slow work. Slower than anyone wanted. Drawing water took time. The bricks often powdered. Walls collapsed.

William looked on, smirking at their frustrations. Crazy Germans, what were they hoping to achieve? Out in this heat day after day making no perceptible improvement, unless a wall raised a mere four inches after eight long hours could be termed development.

'What's taking you so long?' he sneered at von Trotha. 'Can't you get your men to put their backs into it!'

'No one can work any faster,' the oberst reassured him. 'Not in this heat.'

'Your men are slacking,' persisted William, 'You'd better talk to them, they're dragging their heels.'

'What's this dragging their heels?'

'Not pulling their weight.'

Von Trotha glanced at him: 'I do not understand.'

'There's nothing to understand. You can see for yourself some men are building slowly on purpose.'

'Ah, is this all,' laughed von Trotha. 'I thought it was a serious problem.'

'It is,' said William.

'Yes?'

'They're doing it deliberately. I would call that sedition. Sabotage of the Union's war effort.'

'No, mein gutte sergeant major,' laughed von Trotha. 'That is a good joke. But nein, nein, nein, no one is doing this.'

'I think so,' said William pointing to a group of men lolling on the ground. 'They're not even pretending to work for God's sake.'

'Ja, but surely they are waiting for more bricks.'

'They could get bricks,' said William, 'if they wanted them. The stockpile's hardly depleted. Uh, uh, colonel, those men are idling.'

'Ja, maybe taking a rest. Because who is able to work full time in this sun?'

'You must talk to them.'

Von Trotha didn't reply. He took out his silver cigarette case and opened it. With his thumb he eased up a cigarette and offered it to William.

'Please.'

William shrugged and accepted. Von Trotha took another and snapped the case closed. The men lit up separately, flicking their matches away in smoky parabolas.

'There is nothing I can say to these men,' the oberst said eventually. 'Everyone is doing this of their own free desire. They do not have to build these mud houses. The tents would be sufficient. We could sit here waiting for the war to end like it was a holiday. I think you will remember this conception was something that was suggested by myself. Which is always a point that we must not forget.'

'Of course,' said William. 'But now it's gone beyond a mere amusement. You've been supplied with building materials, your project's become an official army endeavour. Under the CO's orders. And must be completed as a matter of priority.' He exhaled three rings of smoke. 'Something we both have to oversee. As I am sure you understand.'

'Perfectly.' Von Trotha bowed, grim faced. 'I did not realise this before, although I should say it is very much like English trickery.'

'No,' said William, grinding out his cigarette. 'There's no trickery. Remember we wouldn't be here if your Kaiser hadn't started this war.'

'It is not my war. This is my single point.'

'You were caught fighting it,' said William.

'Doch . . .' spluttered von Trotha and walked off in disgust.

William now began – partly out of mischief, partly out of malice – cajoling the less able workers, those he considered slackers, by berating them for lagging behind. Although his words weren't understood, the tone was unmistakable. As were the gestures of disdain he showed at poor craftsmanship. However, for the most part those he singled out took his carping with tight-lipped for-bearance. They joked behind his back. Called him Herr Kohl. Said he was full of nonsense, tried not to let his pettinesses irk. Von Trotha watched William's quibbling with distaste and cautioned his men against responding. But inevitably William's continual irritations caused tempers to fray. Until a man snapped back at him.

'Warum quälen sie mich? Ich bin kein Maurer. Verstehen sie das doch! Ich tu mein Bestes.' He held up his hands. 'Gewöhnlich arbeiten diese hande mit Uhren. Und nicht mit Drek.'

'What?' William shouted. 'What? Are you threatening me? You little . . . you little . . .' He took a step forward and knocked over part of the wall. Pushing the bricks off the top.

'Nicht,' the man cried out. 'Horen sie auf. Tun sie das nicht. Bitte nicht.'

But William continued. One. Two. Three. Four. Five bricks smashed on the ground before the man could drag him away and others intervened to keep the two apart. Guards ran up.

William shook free of the scuffle: 'Arrest him,' he screamed. 'Arrest that bastard for attacking me.'

The man was in tears: 'Ich bin nicht schuld. Was habe ich nur falsch gemacht? Sehen sie was er getan hat. Jeden tag kompt er und verspottet mich. Immer das gleiche: Ich bin zu langsam. Ich bin ein quertreiber. Ich bin dumm. Meine arbeit ist slegt. Ich bin aber kein Maurer. Ich bin Uhrmacher.'

'What's he say?' demanded William. 'Tell me. You' – he looked at a man he knew spoke English.

The man hesitated, reluctant to translate.

'Go on. Tell me.'

'He says he is a watchmaker and not a house builder.'

'That's not all he said.'

'He says you must not think he is stupid or a saboteur. He is working in the best way he can.'

'He's lying,' responded William, glancing wildly about to see von Trotha clearing a passage through the knot of men. 'Here, colonel, this is exactly what I said was going on. This man's even assaulted me.'

The oberst glanced at the captive held firmly by a guard and at the florid William.

'Can I help with this problem, sergeant major?' he said.

'It's sorted out,' replied William. He jabbed a finger towards the watchmaker. 'He's under arrest.'

'I see,' said von Trotha. 'Good, then let us go and hear what his crime is.'

The hearing: took place ten minutes later before the camp commander.

'You say he is sabotaging the building programme by poor workmanship, sergeant major.'

'That's right, sir,' William confirmed.

'Then what we should do is put a good worker beside him, eh!'

'Yes, sir,' William admitted.

'Good,' said the camp commander. 'Then that's that.' He smiled up at the watchmaker. 'Auf wiedersehen.'

'Is there to be no punishment, sir?' asked a dumbfounded William.

'Whatever for, sergeant major? No, I don't think that's necessary at all.'

For a while afterwards William skulked morosely around the camp. He continued to make his twice daily tours of inspection and was no less convinced that the men weren't plotting deviously but he held his tongue. The watchmaker's house now went up more efficiently although William ignored the change. He knew men glanced at him with scorn when he passed and it rankled. But he realised his presence irked them and that gave reparation. He would not be cowed.

Fortunately, as a distraction, a consignment of wood arrived. Von Trotha called for carpenters and had them make doors and shutters. Others cut the roof joists. Within two weeks the first roof went on and others followed rapidly. Doors were hung, windows shuttered.

'You see, sergeant major,' glowed the oberst, 'I said this would become a German wonderland. What can you say now but this is a most impressive sight I do believe.'

'A bloody miracle,' retorted William biting at his lips.

Two days later the station master came to admire the progress, bringing with him some people riding in donkey carts.

'Basters,' he said in explanation. 'Swerfmense. It's good for their types to see how we do things.'

'No,' said the oberst, 'this is a bad idea. You should not have allowed it. I know these people. They have come to laugh at us.'

'These!' spluttered the station master. 'What on earth for? No, colonel. Look at the hotnots. They are drifters. Rubbish.'

An old man climbed from the leading cart and came towards them. The rest of the group stayed some way off, watching.

'This is Jan,' said the station master as the old man made a half salute. He beckoned: 'Kom Jan, come and see what the men have done.'

The group, with von Trotha – sternly, grimly – behind, passed in formal silence up and down the streets, the old man flanked by William and the station master. As they stood before the last house the old man turned to them and said he was a captain. One of Kaptein Witbooi's officers who'd fought a war against the Germans not so long ago. From his jacket he took a photograph that showed six men in wide-brimmed hats, two wearing military boots, one barefoot, the others in velskoens. They all carried guns and wore bandoliers of bullets. He pointed to the man seated in the middle. That was Kaptein Witbooi. He indicated a man to Witbooi's left. 'Ik,' he said. 'Mijn naam is Kaptein Swartbooi.' He was wearing boots and had his trousers tucked into them. The six stared gravely at the photographer. Kaptein Swartbooi handed the photograph to William who glanced at the cracked and faded print: why did they always look so bloody self-righteous? As if they hadn't caused the trouble in the first place. God almighty there was little to choose between these types and the German Südwesters. It was enough to curdle porridge in your gut. He held the picture towards von Trotha who wouldn't even look at it. The old man saw this and stretched out his hand and William gave him back the photograph.

'Ik ben tevreden,' he said. 'In de oorlog tegen ons is mijne familie door de Duitser geschlachten.' Without waiting for an answer, or not expecting one, feeling no response could be made, he went back to his people. He left the men speechless, gaping as he limped off.

'Damned kaffirs,' spat the station master.

'What did he say?' asked William eventually.

The donkey carts started away and a child waved.

'You see,' said von Trotha bitterly. 'It is what I have told you: they were here to gloat. And it is a lie: we did not kill their women and children in that war.'

Wet Area

SHAUN DE WAAL

Gerard says he's got an exercise machine at home now, so he only goes to the gym to cruise.

The best time is apparently in the evenings. Go on a weekend, from late afternoon on, and the whole of the wet area, as they call it, is a traffic jam of naked men moving between the sauna and the showers, the steamroom and the basins. At the basins, you can stand and pretend to be looking at yourself in the mirror while you're really looking at the man behind you, who's got his back to you but is looking at you in the mirror, at the endlessly repeated reflections of him and you, you and him, receding to infinity, looking at each other.

I wonder sometimes whether the straight men know about these things that happen in the gaps between them, whether they have any inkling of what goes on, this circulation of bodies, this watching and touching, not to mention mutual masturbation in the sauna. Experience tends to suggest that they don't have a clue, they don't even notice what's happening around them as they shave away blithely or steam themselves serenely, but who knows? Once their suspicions have been aroused, straight men begin to see moffies around every corner.

Then again, not all straight men are straight. Like the guy in the sauna the other day. I saw as I went in he was gazing at me with these big hangdog eyes. Settling my towel and myself on it, I couldn't help noticing the gold on his ring finger. Or the erection partly concealed by his little towel.

There was no one else in the sauna. I was sitting to his right. He was slightly plump, the gut spreading over his hips, but not too much. About my age. He had a nice face. The eyes kept swivelling up to me and then back down to his hard-on, which he clearly wanted me to see but also didn't seem to want to uncover entirely.

The sauna was getting too hot for me, or I was getting too hot, hot as in temperature, so I got up and left. I let my towel hang away from me, let my half-hard cock go past his eyes. I was sure they'd be straining in their sockets.

I left the shower door half-open, and, sure enough, a few minutes later he was standing in the cubicle opposite mine, his door also half-open. But he appeared undecided, or afraid. He wouldn't turn entirely towards me, as if he didn't want his groin to be seen, but he wanted to see. His head was twisted over his shoulder at what looked like an uncomfortable angle.

Now I'd've been quite happy to just watch him wank while he watched me wank. I had no desire to actually lay hands on him. But he wasn't interested in mutual voyeurism (or hadn't thought of it as an option). He left the shower, holding his little towel – barely bigger than a face cloth – over his crotch. I turned my shower off and headed for the basins. Might as well shave, I thought, and get out of there. My hard-on had dwindled. But he was standing outside the sauna and as soon as he saw me he gave me a meaningful look and stepped inside it.

Oh well, I thought, what the hell. I went into the sauna. He was in the same position as before, and I took up my previous seat on his right, at right angles to him, about a metre and a half away. He smiled nervously at me and said, 'Nice bod.'

I muttered something akin to 'thanks'. My first reaction was to say, 'Who, me?' I mean, here we are in a gym with any number of supermodel-type bodies or just young sporty still-slender bodies sweating away on shiny machines or groaning as they heave free weights. I know because I look for them and when I find them I look at them for as long as possible. There are broad shoulders and flat stomachs, arms that bulge out of tiny sleeveless T-shirts, legs that bunch and heap their muscles as they push, or lift, or hold.

By comparison with any of these (and now and again one has an epiphanic experience and catches one of these beauties naked in the 'wet area'), I'm staggeringly average. Not tall, not short, not thin, not fat. The expanding midriff is being kept in check, but not by much – I display no six-pack of ribbed abdominals. But now he was saying, 'What are you doing later?'

'Working,' I said, perhaps too quickly. But there was no way this nervy forlorn person was going to be spending much time with me, talking time or lying-down time. Is he asking for some kind of *date*? The whole point of anonymous sex is that it's anonymous. Casual sex is supposed to happen then and there. It's quick and then it's over and we go to work or go home or whatever, back to our solitude or to our spouses.

But I did have at least half a hard-on, and I wasn't hiding it. With another sheepish smile, his eyes pointing at what he was talking about, he said, 'I'd like to wrap my lips around that.'

Where did he get that line? Some old porn movie? It sounded borrowed, rehearsed.

I said, 'Toilets.' I didn't really want to talk to him; I prefer my casual sex silent.

'Too dangerous,' he said.

Well, I could have said, that's half the fun, isn't it? But I wasn't sure I wanted to touch him, anyway, or at least not much. Would he really give me a blowjob? I wouldn't give him one, not a casual cruise. In this day and age, it's strictly reciprocal onanism as far as I'm concerned. Or just watching.

I said nothing, but stroked my cock a little. Tentatively he reached out and touched it, and then quickly withdrew his hand. He was quivering, glowing sweatily.

'Not in here,' he said hoarsely. Beyond the sauna's glass door we could see an old man shambling towards us.

'Too hot, anyway,' I said. And it was: I was beginning to feel dehydrated, my head starting to throb. I got up and, leaning over him, gave his cock a quick tug. It was hard but not entirely so. I smiled down at him, seeing again that wedding ring, and said, 'I've got to go.'

The old man came stiffly into the sauna. I stood aside as he levered himself up on to the wooden platform. I went back to the shower. Again, I left the door half-open, but the man with the ring did not reappear in the opposite cubicle. I closed the shower door and jerked myself off.

I couldn't see him in the change-rooms. Just get out of here, I thought. He's a talker; who wants awkward conversation?

But I dressed too quickly. When I got to the car I realised I'd left my leather jacket behind in the locker. Shit, I thought, and went back at a trot. Things get stolen so easily in this place. There are warnings stuck on the lockers, and there's a legend newcomers get told about the man who emerged from the showers to find all his unpadlocked clothes gone, his gym stuff as well as his ordinary clothes. He had to phone his wife, they tell you, to bring him something to wear. I wondered what he'd have done if he were single.

I grabbed my jacket from the locker and headed back up the stairs, out the gym. But there, suddenly, he was beside me, coming up the steps with me. Had he been hiding somewhere all along? Lurking there waiting for me?

Oh, shit, I thought, but he said nothing. I glanced at him (a suit and a white shirt – work clothes?) and then away, not meeting his gaze. We left the gym. As we walked out into the carpark, into the twilight, he said, 'It's quite warm.'

'Mmm,' I said. I didn't look at him. It was almost dark anyway. 'And it's nearly winter.'

'Ja,' he said, with what sounded like a sigh. He stopped at what must have been his car, keys ready in his hand to unlock the boot.

'See you,' I said, and walked away.

Dammit, thinks K——, sitting at his PC. He has just written some fourteen hundred words about cruising at the gym. But that episode was meant to be a short introduction to or foreshadowing of a longer, hopefully funnier episode about cruising at the gym. It ran away with him. That is, he got carried away by detail – he should have harkened to the wisdom of Oscar Wilde, who warned that it was disastrous for the imaginative writer to fall into 'careless habits of accuracy'. The point of the episode which should have been shorter and tighter was that the man in the sauna is married, or at least has a gold ring on the third finger of his left hand. You would have thought that such a man, presumably a deeply closeted man, would remove the ring before heading for the sauna to (try to) pick up another man. But perhaps he didn't have a lock on his locker, and was afraid it'd be stolen. Or he just wasn't thinking. At any rate, K—— is annoyed with himself because now he isn't sure what to do about the episode which was supposed to form the

383

meat of the story. This episode would also be about cruising for sex at the gym, but with more confusion around the showers, sauna, steamroom, etc., trying to make contact, and it would end in frustration. The idea was to strike a note of anticlimax, of bathos. Why does he want to strike that note? He isn't sure, except that perhaps he feels it is a characteristic note of life, the falling short, the expectation denied. Perhaps it is just the characteristic note of cruising, where the chase is all, the excitement is in the pursuit, the dance of desire, and the sex itself – the orgasm itself – is something of an anticlimax. Or is he just feeling jaundiced today? Anyway, he can't write another episode too similar to this one; echoing is fine, foreshadowing is fine, but repetition (despite being another crucial element of cruising – of sex in general: repetition with variations) isn't. He goes back to what he's written and goes through it, taking out the words 'cock' (should he replace some with 'penis'?), 'erection', 'hard-on', wherever possible. He resaves the file as GYMNEW.TXT. He has already had complaints that there is too much sex in his work, that it detracts or distracts from its other qualities. Perhaps it turns off the average straight reader (it would almost be better to have only gay readers, at least for this kind of work) when presented in large quantities, or in its stranger manifestations. Certain sexual acts are of great interest to him, but he can understand the impulse to censor – he himself is disturbed by some kinds of gay sex. There are things (he does not want to name them) that bother him immensely. Yet sex is what he is most interested in at present, gay sex, with all its codes and protocols, sex between men, in all its various forms, even the forms he wants to censor, to erase. It seems to drive his writing at the moment. And maybe it will be in investigating the things that disgust or disturb him that he will do interesting work. But that's another story. The gym cruising one is what's in hand, so to speak (there was a power failure while he was busy with this story, and after waiting a bit in the dark for the light to come back, for the PC to ping to life again, he decided, being somewhat aroused by what he'd written, and for lack of anything better to do, to masturbate. When the electricity came back on and he returned to the computer, he found he'd lost some of what he'd written. Annoyed, he'd reconstructed it as best he could, but now wonders what he's left out, what he's forgotten in the half-hour since it went dark. It could be important, necessary. But it's gone). How to organise or reorganise the two cruising episodes? Should he discard the first altogether, or merge them into one? Perhaps he should put the other, as yet unwritten, episode elsewhere, insert it into another narrative, give it to another character, in a different text? And, instead of the rather cool, almost chatty style of the narrator in the wedding-ring episode, speaking directly to camera as it were (a style he over uses anyway), another mode of telling perhaps? Stream of consciousness? Present tense? *Style indirect libre?* Ah, give it to Gerard.

He leaves the shower door half open, wondering if someone will turn up in the opposite cubicle. He washes his armpits, his crotch, his bum-cleft. He is about to turn the shower off when a man enters the opposite cubicle – he is tall, slender, hairy but not too hairy. He looks about twenty-five, maybe thirty. He is fondling his cock, a reasonably sized cock, and glaring significantly at Gerard.

Not that a significant gaze is needed, under the circumstances. Gerard turns and displays himself, fondles his cock in turn. He'd be quite happy to stand here and engage this man in mutual voyeurism, for them to come in their separate cubicles, but the tall man wants more than just to watch, it seems. He turns off his shower and reaches for his towel, dabbing his face and holding the towel loosely in front of him to disguise his erection.

Gerard follows him, at a decent distance, to the steamroom. There is a third man in the grey-white gloom. They sit at opposite ends of the tiled shelf and wait for him to leave. Facing each other, their raised legs hiding hard-ons or half-hard-ons from any other observer, they caress themselves and watch each other hazily through the steam. The other man (lumpily silhouetted against the glass door) gets up and, panting slightly, leaves.

The tall man slides over to Gerard. Almost simultaneously they grab for each other's cocks. Then there is a light clang and the steamroom door opens again to admit someone. They leap apart, legs closing, turned away from each other. To an initiated eye – to a gay man – their postures would be an admission of guilt.

The other man picks up the hosepipe and turns on the tap. He sprays water across a section of shelf and then seats himself there. He sighs, leans back against the wall and closes his eyes. He is barely visible through the steam, which means that if Gerard and the other were to sit alongside each other and fondle each other's cocks, the third man would be unlikely to be able to see them. But they desist.

Their erections subside. Gerard gets up and leaves the steamroom. He heads for the showers. The other is soon in the cubicle opposite, but he wants more than to look. He wants to touch. He leaves the shower again, moving back towards the steamroom.

He is getting increasingly frustrated with the tale he is telling. Not that it isn't flowing (he almost wrote 'coming'), not that sentence isn't following sentence, but that the humour that he thought would emerge from the story isn't there. It's coming out dry, a bit jumpily, one damn thing after another, plod plod. And where's the stream of consciousness he thought of? Why can't more of this be taking place in Gerard's head? That would be more interesting – and more of a contrast to the earlier episode – than this bland third-person narration, Gerard did this, the tall man did that. Perhaps, he thinks, he's just tired; he's written too much today already. More than a thousand or fifteen hundred words and you're scraping, you're pushing. Sometimes that's when the best work happens, but not, apparently, today. It's gone: the story that he felt was in him, was waiting to be told, was sitting there in some comfortable mental compartment just biding its time until he got a chance to sit down at the PC and chuck it at the screen. But in that time it has gone dry, it has withered. The episode of the wedding-ring man has intervened, has replaced it, has drained most of its energy. The story feels like someone who's been sitting in the sauna for too long. Perhaps, he thinks, masturbating during the power failure was the mistake; that's what ruined it.

Into the steamroom, out of the steamroom. Into the sauna, and so on. Your fingertips are white and corrugated. They look like dead flesh, drowned. Showers, basins, where the tall man stands next to Gerard, allegedly drying himself but really displaying his erection once more (proud of his size, thinks Gerard. Exhibitionist). Trying to avoid the others, the straight men, the old men rheumily absorbed in their own ponderous movements, the gay men who know what you're doing, who might like to get in on the act.

386

There are usually a couple of moffies around to keep an eye on you – there's one hideosity who seems always to be there, to live in the wet area, peeking round his shower door, peering through the steam at you, even when nothing's going on. Gerard calls him the Ninety-Nine-Year-Old Lesbian Dwarf, the Nnyold for short (and still describes with relish how he once saw the Nnyold in Woolworths, shopping with what must have been his lover. The Nnyold caught sight of Gerard and hastily disappeared down the next aisle). In the wet area, you spend as much time avoiding the Nnyold as you do trying to catch someone's eye or to co-ordinate movements with someone who appears to be interested. But you get a small glimpse of the Nnyold's desperation when, one day, you watch two good-looking or at least good-bodied men going for each other, co-ordinating their movements, trailing each other just that telltale distance apart, carefully angling the shower door as they enter. You want to get between them, hijack their cruise, ask if you can watch. But you can't, and they're managing to avoid you.

Into the steam, out of the steam. Towel now soaked; you will never be dry. Getting hotter, redder. Getting muddled, losing the tall man; wandering back towards the steamroom (site of at least one delightful encounter – remember that short-haired young man? He can't have been more than twenty). But the tall man is coming the other way, an awkward manoeuvre in the passageway, two wet bodies less than a foot apart, but you can't embrace, not here, even if you wanted to embrace.

He heads for the showers, but there's no point in going back there. Stop at the basins, at the mirrors, wait for him to come out of the shower again. Will he head for the steamroom? Who else will be in there? If anyone were watching, were keeping track (you, the writer, are supposed to be watching, to be keeping track – *all the time*), they'd see the comedy of this ritualised dance, these strange circulating motions of bodies, conducted in silence.

Sometimes a jerk of the head or a wink will indicate where the other wants or intends to go; mostly, these movements are carried out with barely a glance at one another's faces once the initial contact has been made, once you're sure he's interested (don't let on – there seems to be some pressure to keep up appearances amid the straights. There is certainly some pressure from those who feel one shouldn't write about these things, shouldn't tell the straight people our secrets). Silence is best.

I hated it when one guy in the steamroom, who'd fondled me then watched and wanked as I wanked, kept saying idiotically, 'Come on, big boy.' Yet is was rather lovely when the short-haired youth, the delightful one, with whom I hadn't exchanged a single phoneme, whispered, 'I'm going to come,' and did.

In fact, I spent the rest of the day in a jaunty sort of state, basking in the afterglow of that encounter. I felt incredibly lucky to have been granted that experience with that beautiful person, that smooth, flat belly, that lovely tapering uncut cock. Afterwards, I wanted to follow him out into the carpark, to ask him his name, his phone number, his address, his everything, ask him if he wanted to live with me for the rest of my life. But I restrained myself. Pride is a great restrainer. And such things are not in the casual sex contract, are they?

Yet I felt quite differently after other encounters, after less pleasing ones with less pleasing people, like the thin guy with the beard who wanked vigorously while watching me wank, saw me come, and then stalked off with a disdainful air, as if he had suddenly found my – our – actions distasteful. Perhaps he had.

Gerard said to me that when he was cruising the gym and having these kinds of adventures while he was still with his boyfriend, who was much older than Gerard and demanded fidelity, he noted that he felt guilty after some of them, but not all. You feel much less guilty afterwards if the other man was really attractive.

As I see it, the episode of Gerard and the tall man can end in two ways. In the first ending, the two men lose track of each other in all the wandering back and forth, the steamroom occupied, the Nnyold refusing to leave the sauna (I hope he *shrinks*), and so on; back in his shower cubicle Gerard looks down at his half-engorged and tiring (up, down, up, down) cock and thinks, what the hell, and comes on the white tiles. He dries himself and leaves the wet area, and then notices, loitering – waiting, eyes expectant – near the toilets in his damp towel, the tall man. Anticlimax.

Or we could let the two of them finally connect. Gerard can't see the tall man, wonders if he's left the wet area; thinks he'll try the toilets, just in case. He dries himself, wraps the towel around his waist (clench that gut) and walks over to the row of toilets. The door of the last one in the row is ajar; it would look like an honest mistake if he were to push on it and find it occupied by someone genuinely defecating. But it contains the tall man, blowing his nose.

Gerard enters and locks the door behind him. The two men reach for each other's cocks and soon they are fully erect again; they rub and pull. The other man's cock is a good inch longer than Gerard's. A prize specimen, indeed. Gerard resists the urge to drop to his knees and suck. Danger zone. He thrusts a leg up between the other's thighs and the other grinds his perineum down against it.

The tall man's caresses are expert, and Gerard is coming, trying to catch it in his hand, seeing a drop land on the other's wrist, a gout of it plop to the floor. Should he wipe it up? To leave it for the cleaners or for another gym-goer to slip in seems wrong. He reaches for a length of toilet-roll. But the other is coming too, now, holding his cock up against his belly, letting the strings of semen stripe it there. For a moment he holds his cock like that, looking down at it, the semen gathering in his hand. With his other hand he reaches for toilet paper, first fastidiously dabbing his wrist, then scraping his own semen off himself.

No, he interrupts himself before he comes, to make that meticulous gesture, that tiny erasure, wiping his wrist, before going back to his cock and then coming on his belly.

He scrapes, dumps the wad in the toilet bowl, unlocks the door and is gone.

Gerard waits a while, wiping the floor, then flushes the toilet and heads back to the wet area, to the basins. After all, he must shave. His face is red, red like a boiled or steamed ham, as he lathers and razors; in the mirrors, waiting, watching, with yearning and hangdog eyes, he sees you, he sees me.

Maxi-jump

JANE FOX

They are in the barn. Maxi knows they are there because she can see the barn door open a crack and usually it is shut. She looks behind: two bicycles and the bottle store delivery van. She'll wait until the road is empty. She'll give them plenty of time. She'll stop to retie her shoelace. The satchel weighs very heavily on her shoulder because all her books are in it. They are not allowed to leave books in their desks this weekend because somebody is coming to repaint the classroom. If she puts them away under her bed as soon as she gets home, maybe Dad won't see them. Although she has got her long division right, at last.

Level, now, with the barn, and there's Karl's head sticking out round the door.

'Hey!' he calls. 'Come see!'

'What?' says Maxi. 'I've got to get home.'

'Ah, come on Maxi. Don't be like that. It's important.'

Maxi keeps on walking.

'You scared, or something?'

Maxi stops.

Norman's voice now, raised loud but muffled. 'Course she's scared. She's bang vir haar Pa.'

'No I'm bloody not, see.'

'Jeez, she swears, eh?'

They have come out of the barn by now and are standing looking at her. And behind them, there is Lennie. Lennie is older, in a higher standard at school. He has a very flat face with cheek bumps so near his eyes that they always look half shut. 'What other words

390

do you know? Come on, tell us.'

'Bugger off!' says Maxi.

They all laugh very loud, bending double and clapping their hands. Maxi grins back at them. 'I know a worse one.'

'What is it?'

'Come on Max, tell us.'

Maxi is silent, enjoying it.

'Bet it's the old F word.'

'No it's not.'

'Worse than that? Worse than fuck?'

'Much worse.'

Somehow the conversation has taken them to the barn door. Maxi takes a tighter grip on her satchel.

'Oh come on, Max, you're one of us. What's the word?'

'What's it start with?'

'I'm not saying.'

'She doesn't know. She's faking it.'

'Faking it, fucking it, faking it!' They go off into caterwauls and whoops of laughter, barging at each other and taking swipe s at each other's heads.

'She's only a kid,' says Lennie, 'not old enough to be in the gang really.'

Maxi drops her satchel. 'Yes I am then – it's CUNT.'

Dead silence. Slowly they all crouch down, watching her.

'Don't you believe me? It's a real word.'

'Yeah,' says Lennie, 'we believe you.'

'Cunt,' tries out Karl. 'What's it mean?'

'Tell you afterwards,' says Norman.

'How old are you?' says Lennie.

'I'm nine.'

'When's your birthday?'

'August the eleventh.'

Karl says: 'We had to wait till we were ten.'

'Yeah,' says Norman, 'but you're a real dikhead.'

'Fuck off,' says Karl.

'Shut up,' says Lennie. 'Who's your favourite pop star?'

Maxi hovers, and then says 'Michael Jackson.'

'He's really a floppy, you know that?'

'Shut up,' says Lennie again.

'Yeah,' says Norman. 'Shut up. Dikhead.'

'Listen guys,' says Lennie, 'come over here a minute.'

They go into a tight huddle, their backs to her. Lennie is showing them something he has in his pocket. They are whispering. Maxi looks around the barn. There's an old rusty tractor and some other stuff which she doesn't recognise. At the farther end are heaped up to the roof great bales of straw held together by wire. They are coming back. Their faces are grave.

Lennie says: 'See, Maxi, it's like this. We don't really want to make the gang any larger, but we kind of, well, we like you. You're not like a girl. But you gotta prove you're brave enough to join us, see? All the guys had to prove it. Even me.'

Maxi's heart has begun to thump. 'OK,' she says. 'OK. I'll prove it.'

His hand shoots towards her face. There is a wriggling and squeaking, and suddenly her neck is being scratched. 'What? What is it?' She plucks it away from her and looks at it. Warm white fur and pink eyes. A very big rat.

'It's an alien from outer space!' shouts Karl.

'I like rats,' she says. 'What's its name?'

'My sister only screams, hey,' says Norman.

Lennie takes it from her and stows it in his pocket. 'Hasn't got a name,' he says. 'It's just a rat. See the straw bales over there? What's the highest you can climb and jump off?'

'Easy,' says Maxi. 'Puddysticks.'

She scrambles up to the step which is about head height, the straw rustling and scraping her knees. It looks a lot further, suddenly, from up here, but she jumps, carefully, letting herself go limp as she lands. She still jars her ankles, though. She doesn't rub them.

'That's not so bad,' says Lennie, 'for a girl.'

He nods his head to the others and they begin scrambling up. But they don't stop where Maxi stopped. They go one, two bales higher. They drop like stones.

'*Ow!*' says Karl as he lands.

'Chicken!' jeers Norman.

Lennie is climbing in his turn. He goes one, two, three bales higher. As he stands there he raises his hands and touches the roof timbers.

'Wow, Lennie! No, man, you'll break your leg or something!'

'Shut up. Get back.'

He stands absolutely still for a moment and then launches himself. Maxi feels the wind of his fall on her face. He lands in a crouching position and for a moment he doesn't move. They watch him, and slowly he gets to his feet, steadying himself with his palms on the floor.

'Wow!' breathes Norman. 'Wow, Lennie! You all right?'

'Course I'm all right. What do you think?' But he's limping a bit, as he walks over to them.

Now they are all looking at her. First they look at her, and then they look up at the straw mountain, and then back at her.

She mustn't give herself time to think. She's there, scrambling up, scarcely feeling the pain in her knees, knowing only that she must do it quickly before she loses her nerve. Up to where she jumped the first time. She leans her stomach on the next step and swings her legs up. Grabs the next with her hands and straightens her elbows. Up to the ledge where Karl and Norman jumped. For a moment she looks down at their pale faces upturned and then goes on up to Lennie's ledge, her breath rasping in her throat. When she stands up and looks down they are far away, three pale discs in the shadowy light. She looks up, and there just above is the rusty ceiling with chinks of light where bolts have fallen out of the tin.

'Maxi,' says Lennie, 'come down a bit. You don't have to go right up there.'

'Shut up,' says Maxi.

'You'll hurt yourself.'

Easier, really, when you can't quite see the ground. The thing to do is to remember to go like a sack of mealies. All the way down. O Jeez. O Jeez. This is it. Only way out of this is to do it. There's a moment, on the brink, when her body just takes over and does it, while her mind is still screaming NO.

She doesn't bargain for the awful feeling in her stomach, for the speeding up of the fall so that she knows she must hurt herself. The floor hits her, hard. Much, much too hard. She must be dead because there's nothing, not even breath. This is what being dead is. Everything still and black and not moving. But her feet and legs are hurting now and when you're dead nothing's supposed to hurt, and how, for god's sake, does she start breathing again? Her chest is trying to heave in and out but nothing happens, she can't get it to go. Now she can hear the others yelling at her but she doesn't know what, and now the first piece of jagged air is at last going down into her middle and there it goes out again, and in and out. She rolls over and lies on her back, panting.

Their faces are staring down.

'Jeez, Maxi.'

'You OK?'

'Say something!'

'Maxi?'

'Maxi? You hurt or anything?'

'Why can't she talk?'

'Shut up.' This is Lennie. 'Leave her alone for a minute.'

He is down at her level, talking into her ear.

'Maxi? Can you hear me?'

Her tongue seems to be paralysed. 'Umm . . .' she gets out.

'That was a good jump, Maxi. Wanna join the gang?'

With great care, Maxi sits up and holds herself tight in, arms round her knees.

'Nope,' she says.

Song of the Locust

JOHNNY MASILELA

I

The laksman is a small bird with a tendency to flap its wings, and taking flight at the slightest provocation.

One Spring morning the small bird flew in circles around the dark green branches of a withaak, then landed and took position atop the tree.

Watching from a safe distance was Cousin Skoolpad, his hands trembling slightly as he held a catapult.

Slowly Cousin Skoolpad took a wobbly step forward, placing the foot of the deformed leg ahead of the other. His eyes were alive with anticipation. That the laksman was a very wild species made Cousin Skoolpad's heart beat fast.

He was taking aim and stretching his catapult when the laksman suddenly cringed at a passing lizard. But the bird did not take flight as he had feared. His hands damp with sweat, Cousin Skoolpad stretched the catapult once again, unleashed the little stone from the leather strap, which landed on the little bird's ear, sending the laksman to the ground with a light thud.

Cousin Skoolpad limped with quick steps to the dead bird. He stopped in front of the bird, took a piece of string from his pocket and tied the laksman's tiny legs, and then hung the string with the bird dangling from it, around his neck. He did the same with his catapult.

He then limped and joined me under the shade of the mopani, where we sat with our backs against the huge stem, looking after grandfather's cattle.

Cousin Skoolpad then produced the broken blade of an old hacksaw from his pocket, with which he started to chip his way around the two sticks of off-green reed, which I had brought along from the Soutpan Spruit.

Chip, chop! A hole here. Chip, chop! Another there. Cousin Skoolpad finally dusted off the curly splinters from his shorts, and studied the results of his craftsmanship with pride. The two sticks of reed had been transformed into a flute for each of us. Cousin Skoolpad handed one flute to me.

Drumming his long fingers into the holes of his flute, Cousin Skoolpad asked, 'What are we going to play?'

'What are we going to play!' I replied excitedly. 'Let me think. Hey! What did we play last time before the other flutes broke? Hey! I know what we are going to play. Let's play the song of the locust!'

Cousin Skoolpad pursed his lips, stuck the flute into his mouth and blew a few notes of the popular tune. He then led us in 'Tsie ke yeo', the lament of the coming of that destructive locust.

We played at regular intervals, taking turns in herding the cattle away from the maize and sorghum grain fields, which stretched like one endless grass mat against the backdrop of the grazing lands.

Because of the hoeing and cultivating and things, taking turns became an integral part of the lives of the people of our village. Like during schooldays, when one day I would attend classes while Cousin Skoolpad looked after the cattle, and the next day I would change my school uniform for the rags of the herdboys, while he went to school. This would continue until the time of the harvest.

Then suddenly, as we were half-way through the playing of the song of the locust, Cousin Skoolpad cried out excitedly: 'Listen! Listen!'

'Listen? Listen to what?' I was upset at his cutting short our play.

'Listen to the cow-bell.'

'What about the cow-bell?'

'Listen! Listen how the cow-bell combines with the song of the locust,' Cousin Skoolpad replied, flailing his hands in excitement.

'You listen! You listen!' And he again pursed his lips, stuck the flute in his mouth, then after the tinkle of the cow-bell, slowly he blew a section of the song of the locust in harmony with the sound of the silver bell around the neck of the troublesome bull, Witvoet.

The combination was sweeter than anything I ever heard at the grazing lands.

'Hey! Cousin Skoolpad, this melody we are going to keep as secret as the goings-on at circumcision school. No herdboy, villager, or even grandfather must know about it!'

I stuck my flute between my lips, and played alongside Cousin Skoolpad and the cow-bell. Ding! Wheeee! Dong! Wheeee! I went on like that for the whole day. Each time the cow-bell tinkled, we would follow up with a tune from the song of the locust. A melody we swore to keep as secret as the goings-on at mountain school.

Another day just before the harvest, I sat with Cousin Skoolpad under the shade of the mopani, keeping an eye on the grazing cattle. He was deep in thought.

'What are we going to play?' I asked him, in an attempt to break the silence.

It was after a while that he spoke: 'This thing of going to school one day, and the grazing lands the next day, is a waste of time.'

I did not understand.

'People of my age work in Pretoria,' Cousin Skoolpad continued. 'I'll go and work in Pretoria one of these days.'

A few harvests later, Cousin Skoolpad disappeared from the village, leaving the herding of the cattle to me and grandfather.

Cousin Skoolpad, we heard from those who worked in Pretoria, had found a job wheeling around bricks at a construction site. He lived in a backroom with other workers at his employer's home, at a place called Villieria.

II

One day as I sat under the shade of the mopani looking after grandfather's cattle, a laksman flew about chirping all sorts of summer songs. For the laksman can imitate the calls of other birds.

Suddenly the laksman nose-dived, seemingly rebounding on the ground and rose clutching a locust in its beak. The laksman then circled around the branches of a withaak. It landed on a branch, and used its beak to stick the struggling locust on to a sharp thorn. Village elders say by so doing the laksman was signalling the coming of someone from faraway places.

I then noticed, beyond the withaak, a troop of vervet monkeys, also watching in awe the movements of the laksman. After a while the monkeys suddenly broke into a run and disappeared into the bushveld.

They were running away from Cousin Skoolpad, walking with a limp along the footpath towards me! He was dressed in brand-new khaki shorts, a white vest, a brown hat with a band made of the hide of a wild animal, and big-nosed shoes with white stripes on the sides and studs underneath. He also carried a sling bag decorated with flowers on his shoulder.

'Hey! Cousin Skoolpad. How are you? How is Pretoria?' I asked of him.

Cousin Skoolpad spoke to me in our native Ndebele, but combined the language with words foreign to me.

'iPretoria ipragtig, man. iPretoria inwonderlik, juis.' He kept on muttering as we herded the cattle home.

During his short visit, Cousin Skoolpad looked rather troubled. He kept muttering he was tired of pushing around a wheelbarrow full of bricks. He wanted to play the penny whistle.

We later gathered from those working in Pretoria that Cousin Skoolpad had fallen in love with a washerwoman who worked for a white family in a Pretoria neighbourhood.

In an attempt to impress the washerwoman, we were told, Cousin Skoolpad bought himself a bicycle which he fitted with mirrors, lots of reflectors and a little FM.

Dressed in his favourite khaki shorts, white vest, brown hat and the shoes with the stripes and studs, Cousin Skoolpad visited the washerwoman to show off his colourful bicycle.

The washerwoman was shocked by all the mirrors and reflectors on the bicycle, and ended the affair.

A group of friends, we heard, had been assembled to approach the washerwoman and plead with her to give Cousin Skoolpad another chance. The washerwoman refused, saying she had fallen in love with someone who played guitar in a marabi band. She had no time for one who wheeled bricks at a building site, and cycled around on a bicycle with reflectors and mirrors.

That, we heard, was the reason why Cousin Skoolpad wanted to play the penny whistle so badly.

Grandfather was worried about Cousin Skoolpad's state of mind. He suggested Cousin Skoolpad consult Vilakazi, the village sangoma.

The next day grandfather, Cousin Skoolpad and I visited Vilakazi's homestead, and were led by one of his wives into one of the huts, in which she ordered us to go down our knees.

Bunches of sorghum grain, maize cobs and reptile skins hung from the hut's rafters. Some sour-smelling herbs were boiling in a drievoet pot on a fireplace. A flywhisk and patterns of beadwork were lined up on a grass mat spread neatly across the floor plastered with cow dung. There were also roots and dry plants piled up at one end of the hut.

'Vumani bo!' cried Vilakazi on entering the hut.

'Siyavuma!' we responded.

Vilakazi emptied his pouch of bones on to one side of the grass mat, studied them for a brief moment, and then declared that the three of us had come to consult with him on a serious problem, and what was the problem. Cousin Skoolpad related to the sangoma the story of the washerwoman, the bicycle, the guitar man and his own desire to play the penny whistle in a marabi band. And above all, his desire to win back the washerwoman.

The solution, Vilakazi advised, was for Cousin Skoolpad to save enough money to buy a beast, which he was to slaughter as a sacrifice to the ancestors. Following the spilling of the blood of the beast, Vilakazi explained, the ancestors would bless Cousin Skoolpad with the talent to play the penny whistle better than anything ever heard on FM.

With renewed confidence, Cousin Skoolpad returned to the job where he wheeled bricks, and worked hard to raise enough money to buy an ox from grandfather for the ancestral sacrifice.

But before the set day for the slaughtering of the beast, the white man who employed Cousin Skoolpad at the construction site told him he wasn't to work for him any more.

The white man overheard Cousin Skoolpad boasting to other workers he would leave his job to play the penny whistle in a marabi band. The white man could easily follow what Cousin Skoolpad was saying, because my cousin had this strange habit of harmonising his Ndebele with white man's language.

With a lump in his throat, Cousin Skoolpad returned to the village and joined me under the shade of the mopani, and together we played the lament of the coming of the locust, against the backdrop of the tinkling of the cow-bell.

Still Life

JOEL MATLOU

Living a still life, owning the world and doing everything in silence. Nowadays, this is the still life.

There was a young and beautiful black boy who lived like a bird. He was the twelve-year-old Tabogo. He lived with his parents in a two-roomed hut not far from the river bank.

His parents were old. His father was a preacher but Tabogo was not a churchgoer. His father, unlike him, had been a churchman since he was young.

Tabogo lived in the bushes. He did everything in silence. He was a clever boy. He did not want to meet visitors or make friends with other youths. When somebody wanted to meet him, he just spoke softly and left. For Tabogo this was living a still life.

At the bank of the river he moulded clay animals like cats, horses, cattle and dogs. When he showed the clay animals to his parents they praised him. But he destroyed the animals because they embarrassed him.

He was a barefooted boy hunting bird nests. He sang to the birds. He chopped wood and burnt fires for pleasure. He was hunting in stillness. Doing it alone as a young boy, he felt he was living a still life. Sleeping under the big tree, he never thought about the dangerous wild animals. He was living without thinking.

Climbing the trees, he thought his life would come to history. But all he was doing was raiding bird nests.

He played in the river. He got into the water and played with it. Playing with the roots of trees he never thought that he was risking his life. Hunting the Boreku tree, for its sugar, was living a still life.

One day while walking in the bushes he looked up and saw beautiful black smoke with a good shape. The smoke looked like the face of a smiling man. It interested him. He looked at a tree and in it he also saw the shape of a man. So he chopped wood and carved a man out of it without any carving instruments.

He thought of making a drawing and told his parents about this. They did not care even though he displayed a good deal of charm.

He, with his short black hair, freckled face, light brown eyes and slender body, was now an artist. His drawings, which he made in the bush, attracted many visitors. He, the bush lover, became the talk of the town. Although he was praised by many people like doctors, teachers, lawyers, priests, police, nurses and passers-by, he never attended school in his life. He could not read or write. But he painted, starting in the bush before going to his village and selling his work in town. His mission was art.

When he had to leave his village to work underground as a mine boy in a mine in Rustenburg, he made many paintings. His Xhosa induna gave him books for drawing. He lived in a one-roomed compound house shared with two Zulu men. They were good to him.

Later he moved from the compound and hired a one-roomed house in Tlhabane township. At night, he ate dry bread and chestnuts before going to sleep. When he had money, he spent it on art materials and models. He lived for four days on twenty-three cups of coffee. He lived without expenses.

His parents were happy about their successful son living in Tlhabane location. They lived in Ratsiepane. During his off day he went to Ratsiepane in Hammanskraal and sat under the big marula tree, doing nothing but folding his arms and thinking about his life. Passers-by thought he had gone mad, but Tabogo did not care.

In June 1969 he went to Johannesburg with the modest hope of selling his work. It all went well. When he went home to Ratsiepane he was visited by people with expensive cars, whites and blacks. It was a surprise to those who said that he, Tabogo had gone mad under the marula tree. For him it was living a still life with hope.

At the age of 27 he married the daughter of an inyanga from

Marokolong, also in Hammanskraal. Her name was Mmabatho. She was a beautiful woman with crossed eyes. To Tabogo this was another part of the still life.

They were visited by many people. His talents were highly praised. The house was full of his works which were sold in all corners of Pretoria and Brits and even as far as Pietersburg.

At the age of thirty-eight he became ill and was sent to Kalafong Hospital. At one o'clock, on the Tuesday after his admittance, he died.

When Mmabatho heard the news about her husband's death she sobbed pitifully without ceasing.

I wish I could go home to God and sleep, she said.

Before Tabogo died he wrote on his forehead: Mmabatho do not cry, I did it for the good of everybody.

He was buried in an expensive coffin draped in white with masses of flowers. His easel and folding stool, which he used when painting under the marula tree, were to be buried with him.

The people who gathered wept ceaselessly. His wife Mmabatho sobbed incessantly. The sun was ferociously hot. Hundreds of cars crawled to the cemetery at Stinkwater.

When he was lowered into his grave Mmabatho tried to stop the coffin. She wanted her husband close to her forever.

Sobbing, she thought about the stupid boy who was praised by famous people all over the country. It was then that she remembered how he, the beautiful black boy, sitting under the marula tree lived like a bird, doing everything in silence.

In her mind she saw him sitting in front of his easel. The leaves of the marula coloured the shadows green. Smiling, he was living a still life.

Our Mercedes-Benz

GLADYS THOMAS

The early blaze of a new day streamed through the small narrow window of the tin and timber structure. Here in a desert of sand, on the farthest side of the Cape Peninsula, is a so-called 'self-development' housing scheme named Lindeleni, Site Nine.

Encased in Shack No. 407, three hot sweaty occupants stirred in their beds as the sunrays played laser games across their sleepy faces. Rachel and Thabo, her common-law husband, felt their four-year-old son, Nozolo, moving as he lay entrapped between their bodies. Thabo moved the sleeping boy over so that he could lie in the middle and snuggle next to Rachel as he caressed her strong chocolate-coloured thighs. She felt his manliness hard against her and nudged him between the ribs giving him a 'stop-the-foolishness' look. As she searched between the bedding for her hair ornaments, she glanced at him and noticed his dejected look. She hated to see him hurt and playfully tickled him under his armpits.

They burst into laughter and frivolously kicked each other under the sheets. She suddenly sat up and tidied her long brown hair into place.

'What shall we do today?' she asked, rubbing her eyes.

'We must go to the rubbish dump. I need more building material for the children's playhouse,' he reminded her.

'Oh, no. Not the mop again! Thabo, I'm so tired of the long trek there and besides look at the sun. It's going to be hot today,' she complained.

'It's the only way to get the job completed. We have no money to buy timber and the children are waiting for their playhouse,' he told her.

Thousands of families were dumped here in this wasteland, without recreation facilities or playgrounds for the children. There was not a swing or even a crèche to be found. Because Thabo was an excellent craftsman, she had persuaded him, with the help of the other fathers, to build a playhouse next to their shack where she could care for the children while their mothers went out to work. She felt that she could put her high school education to use and prepare the children for school.

'Vuka! Vuka!' Thabo whispered loudly, tickling the sleeping boy behind the ears. The child stirred and kicked the bedding from him as he opened his eyes and looked at them.

'Where is our Mercedes-Benz?' he asked petulantly.

She embraced him because she could see that he had woken up moodily. 'I say, how about a good-morning for your Mama and Papa,' she teased.

'The Mercedes-Benz?' he repeated.

'Your Mercedes-Benz is parked outside,' they assured him.

Testing his awareness Rachel teased him. 'Tell me what is the registration number of the Mercedes?'

'CA 75347,' he told them proudly. They laughed and embraced him again. 'Jou ou slimkop,' she nestled him as she reached for her slippers under the bed.

Together they scrambled out of bed. Thabo went to the communal tap for water so that they could freshen up while Rachel made up the bed and tidied their tiny home. After breakfast Nozolo filled the bottles with drinking water. He took his father's axe and hammer from the toolbox and placed it at the front door in readiness for their journey to the rubbish dump. They drew the curtains and Thabo made sure the front door was secure.

Together they pushed the 'Mercedes-Benz' into the road. Excitedly, Nozolo jumped into the driver's seat. He 'started' the car with throaty sounds imitating a car's engine.

'Brrmm! Brrmm! Brrmm! Nozolo was ecstatic with this beautiful work of art that his father had created especially for him. He imagined that the car was real with its blue steering wheel and its bright yellow number-plate. He could also look at them in the rear-view mirror while his parents pushed the cart forward along the never-ending gravel road.

He manipulated the steering wheel wildly in all directions and every so often would look in the rear-view mirror and wave to them. They were having an intimate conversation. As he looked at his mother he realised how beautiful she looked in her wide-brimmed straw hat which was decorated with posies of flowers. His father looked like a warrior with the axe and hammer swinging from the leather belt around his waist. He reminded him of King Shaka.

He heard them talking about money. Thabo was a good provider and worked at many different homes as a handyman. They were never in want of food. Nozolo held the steering wheel tightly as he stared ahead. In the distance he spotted a troop of baboons scratching for roots in the ground.

'Imfene! Imfene!' Nozolo shouted excitedly to his parents. They stopped to watch the antics of these playful animals.

'Will they harm us, Tata?' Nozolo asked concernedly.

'Not unless you hurt or stone them. This is their habitat and we are intruding,' he told the boy.

They continued with their arduous journey. Pushing the 'Mercedes-Benz' uphill along that endless gravel road. Now and again a slight breeze would blow the red dust up into their faces. The midday sun, directly overhead, warmed their inner spirits and reflected latticed patterns through Rachel's sun-hat on to her face. They walked in silence, each engrossed in their own thoughts.

She remembered how it all began six years ago. It was a bright summer's day. They were enjoying a Sunday afternoon drive in the family car and had stopped at the wayside to buy firewood from a woodcutter. She had got out to open the boot of the car for him to pack the wood in while her father paid the woodcutter who had politely thanked them and returned to his pile of wood.

'Daddy, you wanted a boy to help you in the garden. He seems such a nice young man,' her mother told her father. Her mother had the most irritating habit of calling her father 'Daddy'. Her father reversed the car and soon he was in conversation with the woodcutter who took a pen from his pocket to write down their address.

'He tells me that he can walk to our township,' her father said when he returned to the car.

Monday morning she awoke to the sound of the two men in conversation. She heard her father laugh heartily and she could not remember the last time she had heard him laugh like that. Her father came into the kitchen and soon she heard the sound of the gardener's spade as he dug deep into the earth. She peeped through the curtains and noticed that his jeans were folded neatly under the fig tree. His muscles glistened with sweat.

He worked half-days and her father said he could come one day a week. After a few weeks their weedy garden looked neat and inviting. She also remembered the day she and her mother had had a dreadful argument because of the gardener. Her mother had ordered her to take his food outside to the yard and she had refused.

'Why must he eat outside?' she had asked angrily.

'What kind of question is this? Since when do we eat at the same table with our Bantu workers?' her mother demanded in no uncertain terms.

'Then you take the food yourself,' she had shouted back. Because of this loud altercation her father came rushing into the kitchen.

'What's all this shouting about?' he demanded.

'Ask Rachel,' her mother said. 'I will not have him at my table!'

'I hope he's not hearing all this,' her father said, stunned.

'I don't care. This is my house!' her mother barked back.

'And you go to church every Sunday? You also read your Bible every night!' he reminded her.

She dumped the dishcloth into the kitchen sink. They heard the bedroom door shut loudly.

Disturbed and angered by her mother's outburst, Rachel set the table and then went to the garden to call Thabo to lunch. Very politely he stood at the kitchen door holding his hat in his hand.

'Come and have something to eat before you leave,' her father invited him inside.

While he poured the tea she made sandwiches and took her tea to her room and left the men to enjoy their lunch but she eavesdropped and heard the two deep in conversation. They spoke in general, discussing political issues and the coming elections.

'At long last we will have our long-awaited liberation. We had to free ourselves of this evil apartheid regime,' said her father with anger.

'It will not happen overnight, not after three hundred years of exploitation,' Thabo explained.

She listened intently from her room. It was clear that her father needed someone to talk to. Her mother was afflicted with menopause moodiness and spent her days cleaning and dusting the same ornaments day after day while she grieved about her disappointments and her husband's failures, not to mention that their only daughter had her matriculation certificate but no job. Rachel knew that the argument during lunch would have her mother sulking in her room for days to come, and that they would have to tread lightly until she had recovered from her self-inflicted depression.

The old man sat with his hands folded on the table and looked at Thabo and talked about his past.

'There was a time years ago when I was very involved with the United Democratic Front. I remember especially in 1987 when we spent almost the whole year marching into Cape Town to protest against the apartheid laws of the Botha regime. The Nationalists were getting away with murder! What with Group Areas laws that had uprooted thousands of families, and every winter they would move into Crossroads with the police burning down the people's shacks, especially in 1986, leaving women and children out in the rain. And all because of their racist laws. We were forced to take action and marched on Parliament. We were never scared for we were a united people. And we were led by our leaders, the priests and the lawyers. They used teargas and set their dogs upon us but our slogan, "Forward We Will March To A People's Government", carried us forward.

'I remember during one of our protest marches outside St George's Cathedral, when a policeman grappled with me and forced me into the back of the police truck. He went to look for more victims and I saw my chance and jumped out of the truck and disappeared into the crowd quickly. Why be a martyr?' he asked, looking at us listening to him in silence.

'I'm too old to march now. I will look to the young ones like you,' he told Thabo.

'The happiest day of my life was that hot Sunday in 1990 when Nelson Mandela was freed from Victor Verster and came to talk to the thousands of supporters on the Grand Parade. Rachel and I went into town. I remember Rachel lost a shoe in the crowd and came home barefooted. She was ever so angry,' he laughed heartily. 'And what about yourself?' he asked Thabo.

'My parents worked the farmlands belonging to Oubaas Jan

van Niekerk, near the valley under Chapman's Peak. Many families lived on the farmland hired to them by the farmer on which they built their own shacks. We were a large community. We were very content. That's where I grew up until 1986. The farmer and the whites in the area decided to move us. They wanted the land for a drive-in cinema, or for irrigation, I'm not sure. So they told the people to move but we protested because there was no alternative. We held meetings but nothing helped.

'One morning at dawn, they brought in the police and while our mothers and children were still asleep they began to demolish our homes. When the men returned from the fields they found their homes flattened. They could not rebuild the shacks as the farmer had given orders that all the building material had to be taken away from the site. We had no place to go and then the men decided to move their families to the mountainside near the golf course.

'After a few weeks they even used a helicopter to hunt us. We were too terrified to make a fire for fear of being discovered. At that time we were always running, trying to stay ahead of the law. After my parents died I went to live in the caves near Kalk Bay, going out daily to work in the people's gardens. But now I'm happy. We are settled at last and running no more. I have a good home in Lindeleni Township and we will never need to move again!' he told my father defiantly.

'We have all been to hell and back under the apartheid regime. It's only sad that our freedom took so long for now I'm too old to reap the fruit of my efforts. But there is a good future for all you young ones,' my father said with a twinge of bitterness in his voice.

They sat thinking in silence when suddenly Mother's throat had become dry and she slunk into the kitchen, her face still flushed with anger as she stared at the men. Without saying a word she poured herself a cool-drink. Thabo felt awkward, picked up his hat, thanked the old man for his kindness, and left for home.

It was a very hot day when Rachel returned from the beach. She went out to the backyard to hang her towel and swimsuit on the washline. Thabo observed her while he was busy fixing the fence.

'Did you have a good swim?' he enquired.

This surprised her as he had never spoken to her before. 'It was enjoyable. The water was just right,' she answered with a smile.

He continued speaking to her, enquiring about her day.

'On good days I go down to the rocks to dive for crayfish which I sell in the white areas. I make good money,' he told her.

'Can I go with you next time? I was always interested in diving. Will you teach me?' she asked him excitedly.

'Sure, you can go but I must warn you that it can be very dangerous. These creatures hide between the crevices of the rocks. Some time back a friend of mine got his hand caught under a rock. He could not surface in time for air, and we lost him. You must never dive alone,' he warned her earnestly.

'I'm sorry about your friend but I want to go with you,' she insisted.

He laughed and in his friendly manner agreed.

'Fine, you just tell me when you're free.'

She smiled and went inside the house.

On their free days they would go down to the rocks. There he taught her to dive amongst the rocks. He taught her how to find the elusive crayfish. Sometimes they would just swim around, fascinated by the beauty of the underwater world. Or they would sit on the sand dunes and talk. Sometimes about the political situation and the end of apartheid.

She found him to be a good conversationalist and admired his knowledge of so many topics. She simply enjoyed being with him. Some days he would give her his catch to take home to her family. His community did not care for the seafood. They referred to it as 'spiders'.

After many of these secret trips, her mother became curious.

'Who taught you to dive?' she asked.

'An old school friend of mine,' she lied.

'I don't like you going down there to Long Beach. It is too deserted,' her mother said.

These rendezvous on the beach resulted in the inevitable. She became aware of the changes within her body. For months she kept her secret until she could not hide it any longer. When her mother realised what was happening to her only daughter she cursed and became hysterical.

'What will the people say? Thabo is the blackest kaffir I have ever seen! You did this deliberately to destroy our family!' she accused Rachel. 'You encouraged this shameful disgrace,' she screamed at the old man.

'Stop! Stop! Don't blame our Rachel. These things happen all the time. Love knows no colour. You've been brainwashed by the system,' he told his wife sternly.

From that day on her mother built a wall around her. Rachel spent all her time in her room and whenever she looked through the garden and saw the flowers in bloom she thought of Thabo. How painstakingly he had tended the plants. Now her mother had forbidden him to come near the house. She felt that she was going crazy with her continued restricted existence and decided to move in with Thabo at Shack No. 407, Lindeleni Township, Site Nine.

Making friends with the other women came easily to Rachel. Many mornings the mothers would come over to ask her to care for their children while they went out to work. They would share many interests when they returned from work to collect their children. She still missed her parents, but felt happy in her new surroundings. Except for Mandla, a young man who lived at the bottom of their road. He drove a red taxi and never returned her greetings or stopped for her to use his taxi. His attitude instilled a feeling of rejection in her. When she discussed her fears with Thabo, he advised her to ignore the matter and accused Mandla of racism.

The shrill shrieks of the seagulls overhead made her realise that they were near the rubbish dump. They found the usual people scavenging in the garbage. Nozolo jumped out of his cart and ran around wildly kicking in the dirt, hoping to find something useful. Thabo walked around nonchalantly poking amongst the dirt.

'We are lucky today! Some builders have left a pile of wood over there,' said Thabo, pointing towards the pile.

They helped to carry the wood to the 'Mercedes-Benz'. Nozolo's special job was to search for nails which he stuffed into his pockets. They rummaged around for a long while, collecting timber of various lengths and thicknesses, before taking the long road home.

The following week, after Thabo had discussed the plan for building a playhouse with Rachel, he started work. The men who passed by came over to see what he was doing.

'Ndigakunceda?' they enquired and soon everyone joined in the building of the playhouse. Every Saturday one could hear the chatter and laughter of the men while they hammered away, resting now and again to enjoy a glass of beer. Soon the construction was completed. Thabo brought out the paint-brushes and they all began to paint.

When they had finished, Thabo called Rachel to come and see their work. She stood in the pathway and felt so proud. There stood the children's playhouse painted a beautiful bright red. When he saw her smiling face he said: 'Uselenzile, enkosi,' as he thanked all the men. They packed their tools and went home.

Rachel realised how well her plan had worked for now she had more space. Every morning the mothers brought their children before going to work. All she asked was that the mothers bring their own food. She could not afford to feed them all.

For a while Rachel was at peace within herself. They received a message from her father inviting them to visit over the weekend. She took special care with her appearance. All week she wore her old worn tackies. Now she chose her new black pumps and a bright floral dress for the sake of her mother. When they were all dressed up and ready to leave, Nozolo could not wait to jump into his 'Mercedes'.

Their journey was along the hot tar highway to the Coloured township on the other side of the mountain. Thabo took the opportunity to sell firewood. He piled the 'Mercedes' around the smiling little driver at the wheel. His customers would walk around the cart and read the number-plate and discuss the workmanship with proud Thabo. As they paid for their wood they would also hand Nozolo some money for they all said he looked so cute driving this wonderful work of art. One kind motorist gave the boy a small plastic flag, its many colours representing the new South Africa.

Proudly Nozolo and his father tied the little flag to the 'Mercedes' while Rachel looked on. Thabo noticed a change in her manner.

'What could upset you so suddenly? Are you worried about the visit to your parents?' he enquired tenderly.

'I don't want Nozolo to take their hand-outs. Why must they give our child money? It teaches him to take money from strangers,' she complained.

'Next time we will teach him to refuse politely,' he nodded in agreement.

When they stopped outside her parents' home she noticed her

mother peeping through the lace curtains. She felt strange knocking on the familiar front door. Her father opened it and embraced his daughter warmly. He picked up Nozolo and held him tightly and had a warm smile for Thabo. Before going inside they all went out to admire the 'Mercedes-Benz'.

Her mother just took one look at the cart.

'A real contraption. Why all the decorations?' she asked, unimpressed. Rachel went inside and felt hurt and furious at her mother's coldness. As the afternoon passed her father and Thabo had a lot of talk to catch up with after such a long absence. Their son played outside with the children. They took turns to ride in his colourful cart.

Rachel felt uneasy. It appeared that the estrangement from her Mother had increased to the point of no return. The two women had nothing to say to each other and Rachel was happy when they finally said their farewells.

'Why do you have to go home so early?' her father asked, disappointed.

'We must leave before dark,' she lied.

'I can drive you home,' he offered.

'And what about my Mercedes-Benz?' they heard the small voice of clever Nozolo.

His grandfather laughed heartily while the grandmother did not see the funny side of it.

'We enjoy the walk,' Thabo said. They did not want to hurt the old man.

'Please don't stay away so long,' her mother said unconvincingly at the gate.

'We shall see you soon, Mother,' Rachel replied, hugging her with respect. But she was happy to be back on the road as they started the long journey to their own township.

Nozolo fell asleep at the steering wheel and they laid him down on the foam mattress in the go-cart. They pushed him along and soon they were home. She made coffee while Thabo lit the candles. A warm glow soon filled the shack and they decided to have an early night. Thabo went outside to make sure that the playhouse was properly locked because the children's stationery, toys and games were inside. After checking that all was well, he returned to bed and as he slipped in next to her he placed his arms around her and held her tightly.

It was quite late one night when they heard a loud thud. It woke them from their deep slumber. They hurried from their bed. Thabo could not find time to light the candle. They groped in the pitch-dark, peering out the window and searching for the cause of the crash. To their horror they saw that their neighbour, Mandla, had crashed his red taxi into the children's playhouse. As they rushed out to confront him, he reversed his taxi causing the building to collapse completely.

'I'll get him for this!' Thabo cursed. He pulled on his pants and ran from the house in a rage, but the red taxi was nowhere to be found. Rachel felt that she was having a nightmare until she became aware that some of the mothers had also left their beds to come and support her. After a while they all returned to their shacks and Rachel went inside. She knew that they would work out some alternative for the care of the children.

She stood at the window looking out into the dark night waiting for Thabo to return from his search for Mandla. She was worried that he might do something which he would later regret, but then she saw him coming towards their home. When he came inside he was still quite angry.

'Come let's get back to bed before Nozolo wakes up,' he told her.

'I'm glad that the 'Mercedes' is not damaged,' she sighed. 'He could've driven that taxi right into our shack and killed us all!'

'I will confront him tomorrow. He had better have a good reason,' Thabo said angrily. 'Let's get back to sleep. We can rebuild the playhouse,' he promised.

'That means that we must trek back to that rubbish dump again,' she reminded him.

He looked at her and had a better idea. 'Do you remember that white man that I worked for, Mr Green? I will go to him and ask him for all his leftover building materials,' he caressed her back and they fell asleep.

The next morning Nozolo opened his eyes, got out of bed and dressed himself.

'Why are you in such a rush, little one?' his mother asked.

'I want to go to our playhouse,' the child replied.

Rachel and Thabo glanced at each other. Nozolo went to look out the window and saw that the playhouse had been flattened.

He began to cry.

'Don't cry. Your Tata will build a new playhouse. There was an unfortunate accident last night,' she comforted the tearful boy.

The destruction of the playhouse caused great inconvenience. Many mothers had to stay at home from work to care for their children. An angry Thabo went many times over to Mandla's home to confront him but he was always told that Mandla was at the taxi rank. It was clear that the culprit was avoiding him.

'Maybe Mandla lost control of the steering wheel. We do not know what really happened. Don't hound him any longer. We must forgive him,' Rachel urged.

One evening, Rachel and Thabo were listening to the radio. They heard a soft knock on the front door. She went to open it.

To her surprise there stood Mandla, his hand outstretched in greeting. They shook hands. He asked for Thabo. Rachel invited him in. Thabo entered when he heard Mandla's voice. The two men exchanged greetings and went into the bedroom. Rachel overheard Mandla apologising profusely. He had lost control of the taxi and was very sorry for the distress he had caused.

'You have put all the mothers in a difficult situation. And my Rachel is very upset,' Thabo told him.

'I'll come on Saturday to help you rebuild the little house,' Mandla promised.

'That will be fine,' replied Thabo.

When Mandla left he came into the kitchen to say goodnight to Rachel. 'All is well. We are brothers once more,' he told her as he left the house.

Thabo went down to the valley to see Mr Green and told him why he needed wood. Without hesitation, the man agreed. They loaded his bakkie high. Then Mr Green drove to Lindeleni Township. When they arrived all the children came to help unload the wood. They were delighted that the playhouse was going to be rebuilt. Thabo shook Mr Green's hand and thanked him. Mr Green promised to come and help them the following Saturday. The children waved and ran after the bakkie as he drove away.

The following Saturday some of the men got together with Thabo and worked on the new building. Mr Green had kept his promise and came to assist them. With him was his small son Peter, who played with Nozolo and his friends. The happy laughter of children filled the air. They pushed each other along the road in the 'Mercedes', followed by their dogs. Mr Green remarked that it seemed that Peter was having the time of his life, since he had no friends in their area. The men were hard at work hammering away and Mandla could be seen high on the rooftop. With so many hands the work went at a great speed.

The children were excited and at regular intervals they would come over to see how the building was progressing.

'Don't hold up the men. You kids go back to your playing,' Thabo told them.

The afternoon was hot but the men worked hard and before sundown the new playhouse was completed. The children clapped their hands in delight. Nozolo stood hanging on to his mother's hand and smiling proudly. Some of the mothers came from their nearby shacks to admire the playhouse. Now they felt that their children would be safe and off the streets while they were working.

'Wensa kakuhle! Wenza kakuhle!' they said as they shook hands with all the helpers.

'Well done! Well done!' echoed Mr Green.

'Now all that remains is that the outside must be painted,' added Thabo.

'Any bright colours will make the children happy,' offered Rachel.

Soon the paints were mixed and everyone painted his particular colour. Mandla decided to paint the roof a bright red. The little front door was painted green and many other colours were used. When the painting was completed, Rachel said that it was a magnificent sight. Passers-by stopped to admire it while the children shouted with joy.

'The children are the colours of this rainbow. It is very beautiful,' remarked Mr Green, moved by the attention they were getting.

They packed away the tools and Thabo and Rachel invited the helpers into their shack for a little relaxation and beer. The children continued playing outside tirelessly, pushing each other up and down the road in the 'Mercedes-Benz'. Mr Green had followed the other men into the shack and stood around talking animatedly. He felt that this was the best Saturday he had had in a very long time and had decided that he was going to enjoy it by sharing a beer with the men.

INTERVIEWS ON A WRITING LIFE

All's Unfair in Love and War

ANDRÉ BRINK

We meet, this time, Nadine Gordimer and I, in an office that could also be a lounge, with polished wooden surfaces, books, leather upholstery, paintings, photographs, a tray with tea and coffee. The French doors are opened to a green garden with birds and trees, and the city has receded to a distant hum. We might be in the chambers of a senior counsel, like Harald and Claudia Lindgard in Gordimer's new novel, *The House Gun*; except that for them violence – 'Something terrible has happened' runs like a refrain through the book – has insinuated itself into the fibres of their most private existence, whereas for us, here, now, in this well-appointed room, it appears almost unreal, rumours from a distant and unlikely war zone. Although we both know, through the years in which we have been shaped and marked by it, that the unreality pertains more to this room than to the violence.

She talks about a documentary film she has just completed in collaboration with her son, set in Johannesburg and Berlin, 'two cities in which a wall has come down' – with the difference, she is quick to point out, that in Berlin the wall lasted for thirty-odd years, while in South Africa it existed for centuries. Her film features, among others, Günter Grass and Christa Wolf, but also a young author, in his twenties, born just off the Alexanderplatz, who vividly remembers the excitement of a youth spent among the ruins and bombed-out alleys of East Berlin; and I am reminded of a friend who grew up in Dresden just after the War, and tells animated tales of playing hide and seek among the rubble, and of burrowings that unearthed old abandoned fridges or stoves, the discarded limbs of toys, and all manner of treasures the grown-ups had no

419

conception of. All these images from The Other Side, and the way in which they impinge on our own South African consciousness where most whites still have little or no conception of how The Others lived, or continue to live. It is the breakdown of *this* wall which makes living in the New South African so exciting, so challenging, to the writer as much as to any individual, black or white, prepared to open a mind's eye to it.

It is also this breakdown which informs the anguish of Claudia and Harald in the novel, when their son Duncan is accused of murder and, like the Smales family in *July's People* some fifteen years ago, they suddenly find themselves depending for their moral survival and sanity, and for the redefinition of meaning and of values in their lives, on the black man Hamilton Motsamai – a man from what used to be The Other Side – as guide and mentor, as the Virgil who accompanies them through the circles of their hell.

'When I started writing this book I thought only of Harald and Claudia, and of Duncan. The fact of the *climate* of violence only came to me as I was writing,' she remarks. 'And when I look back on it I know it was right, because as a writer you start with the centre, unlike the way people think you start with the set and then place the characters in it.' Which illuminates the intensity of urgency with which in *The House Gun*, intended from the outset to be a 'spare novel', she explored the deepest recesses of the private mind, the private anguish, when faced with a public world that suddenly implodes into it.

But where are the roots of this violence? Even though she insists that her concern is 'not just *our* cities, not just Johannesburg or Cape Town, but the whole atmosphere you find in almost every city in the world', she is only too profoundly aware of a kind of climate that still sets South Africa apart. It was driven home with particular force when, last November, she was in Ghana for an African writers' conference, and discovered that one could drive about in Accra at any hour of the night without having to turn the windows up or feel threatened in any way. 'Where does the difference come in? I used to think violence is directly related to social misery, to a lack of jobs, to poverty. But in Accra, beyond the city centre which has changed dramatically, you find the same slums and hovels, the lack of sanitation we have here – and the violence is absent. What is the explanation? I think at least part of it must be that Ghana had no struggle for liberation to compare with ours. There was never the level of state violence, sustained for so long, we had to contend with. And this is how apartheid continues to be with us.'

'So you wouldn't agree with people who keep on asking us, "What are you going to write about now that apartheid is over?" '

'I find it the most vexing of questions. Who are these journalists to ask us what we're going to write about next? Have *they* run out of things to write about?'

'Still, there are readers who say they're sick and tired of reading about apartheid.'

'If you read a book like Achmat Dangor's *Kafka's Curse* – terrible title, but a wonderful book – you have all the answer you need.'

'And Zakes Mda's *Ways of Dying*?'

'Absolutely,' she says. 'Those are the two I'm always quoting when people say, "What are you on about . . .?" '

'What do you think of the suggestion by an American critic that the end of apartheid has "liberated" our imagination? To me it seemed he completely missed the point: our imagination may be working in a different way now, but . . .'

'I don't even think it works in a different way,' she cuts in, with a characteristic intensity which yet blends in seamlessly with the easy manner of someone completely at peace with herself while at war with the world. 'The point is that in South Africa *people* have changed. What we absorb from people has changed. The structure of their lives and ours has changed. I mean, nothing happens in a vacuum . . .'

It is this awareness, and this process, of *contextualisation* which has always informed the tense interaction between private and public in all her work, and which also shapes the complexities of *The House Gun*. The two spaces seem to strike an amazing balance in novels like The *Conservationist*, *Burger's Daughter*, veering perhaps slightly more towards the intensely personal in *July's People* and *My Son's Story*, but nowhere quite as acutely as in *The House Gun*. I couldn't help thinking, while I read it, of the Léon Bloy motto Graham Greene used in *The End of the Affair*: 'Man has places in his heart which do not yet exist, and into them enters suffering in order that they may have existence . . .'

There have been 'issues' at the heart of most Gordimer novels in the past, ranging from the core problematic of land (*Six Feet of the Country*, *The Conservationist*, or *None to Accompany Me*), to 'love across the colour bar' (*An Occasion for Loving*, *My Son's Story*), detention without trial (*The Late Bourgeois World*), the possibility of a race war (*July's People*) . . .: but Gordimer's real concern has always gone far beyond 'issues', and nowhere as movingly and impressively as in the new novel. Some critics, especially abroad, have reduced the whole novel to an exploration of issues like gun control, or the death penalty, or even gay liberation – and of course these are important to the unfolding of the story, but its ultimate concern is to test the limits of human relationships, and of language. ('Are you conscious of wanting to say the unsayable?' I asked her point-blank. 'I am,' she said, 'but aren't we all? Every time you think you've gone to the edge of something, thematically or otherwise, you think you've got nothing more to say about it – and then you realise there's a whole other way of approaching it.')

When Harald and Claudia – he a successful businessman with a penchant for religion and literature, she a physician, both of them politically apathetic liberals – are forced to face the fact that their son Duncan has killed the man he caught making love to his own lover (complicated by the fact that this man once seduced Duncan himself into a gay relationship), they land in a kind of moral *in extremis*, sometimes reminiscent of Dostoevsky, where none of their old props and remedies work any more. Their difficulties in coming to terms with the fact that they must now rely on a black man to salvage the life of their son, parallel the much more subtle and profound struggle to redefine themselves in a shattered world, to rediscover both what keeps them together and what constitutes their individuality. Just as their son stumbled on the sight of his lover and his ex-lover in a sexual clinch, Harald and Claudia are now forced to discover the most intimate of experiences in the life of their son, and in their own lives. Their minds are stripped as bare as once the bodies of the lovers were.

There are so few 'facts' to go on, and these are but the flotsam and jetsam on the turbulent current of their lives. The reader who considers only these 'facts' may be partly enthralled by the tense courtroom drama in which all the different versions and possibilities of the story (that is, the configuration of available 'facts') are played out, and even partly bored by the seeming endless rehashing of 'what happened' in order to try to make sense of it. But the reader intent on following the more submerged quest of the novel – the urge to make sense of self and other, to test the limits of the possible, even of the sayable – embarks on an adventure of story-telling even Gordimer herself has seldom matched.

It is, indeed, as she confirms, a 'spare' novel, concerning only the Lindgard couple – 'two creatures caught in the headlights of catastrophe' – and their son (and even the restricted space allowed to Duncan as he himself tries to grapple with 'what happened', appears to disturb the almost unbearable focus on his parents). Even the intriguing young woman, Natalie James, who may be regarded as 'responsible' for the murder, isn't allowed to speak for herself. Natalie, I suggested to Nadine, is worthy of a whole novel in her own right. ('Now why didn't I go more deeply into her?' she responded. 'I think in a way she represents the kind of person who frightens me . . . They are always immensely attractive in every way, but they are very dangerous, they are such a danger to themselves . . . They resent being looked after, yet they *need* to be totally looked after. There's nothing you can do for them, yet the guilt remains . . .') Gordimer's achievement is that what little the story does reflect of Natalie James, suggests all the weight and complexity of a life lived below the surface of the words; and the same goes for Duncan's black friend Khulu, who voices one of the central questions of the book, 'Who of us can say what it means to love?'

Has this been the central concern of all Gordimer's work? – love in its infinite manifestations, between lovers (male or female, black or white), between parents and children, between siblings, between friends, between man and earth. ('The *responsibility* of love,' says Nadine when the subject comes up. 'You still have to take up that burden, no matter how that person has disappointed or betrayed you.')

Gordimer's novel is indeed about 'something terrible (that) has happened.' But this 'something terrible' is not only a murder which might never have been committed had there not been a 'house gun' lying about. It concerns many other territories of the terrible: the loss of understanding (between husband and wife, between parents and child, between friends, between lovers, between individuals and groups within society, between past and present, and the web of relations that holds all these together), the loss of a grip on the world, the loss of a grasp of the self ('How could they know, any of them, what they have a word for'). There are, indeed, 'dangers within existence itself'.

And it is only 'the terrible genius of literature' that can bring some insight into the turmoil presented in *The House Gun*: a turmoil which is a legacy of the apartheid past, but which has acquired a life and a shape of its own in the new country we live in; a turmoil of the mind, disturbed out of its habitual complacency by the awareness of 'something out there' we have put off dealing with, but which has a way of coming back to haunt us.

There is an ultimate mystery that can never be explained or probed (otherwise why would it be a mystery?): the mystery of *being human*. No court case can ever really reveal why one person has killed another, even if the story has been told from all possible angles, and by all concerned, including the perpetrator. Even the narrative 'tricks' Gordimer employs contribute to this: the gliding from present tense to past, the fusion of one character's point of view with another's, the absence of markers of dialogue so that direct and indirect speech often become indistinguishable. All of this serves to keep the characters at a distance, even in their most intimate moments, while maintaining a sense of the unknowable. Yet there is something deeply rewarding in the experience too, however disturbing it may be: it resides in the discovery that one's very *attempt* at understanding or confronting the mystery opens up spaces of awareness one has not suspected before.

This goes far beyond 'issues', however important these may have been in the gloom of apartheid, or still are in the mottled light of the present. 'I'm wary of talking about the "function" or "obligation" of writers,' says Nadine when our conversation inevitably moves in that direction, 'because it's a big danger if one becomes a functionary of one's own beliefs. But if we do have a function it seems to me to reside in something Goethe said on behalf of all of us: Wherever you put your hand down into life, you bring up something.' This, she points out, was what we did under apartheid; it is what we still do. We cannot *not* do it.

If Gordimer's novel reveals, or confirms, one thing it is the need this country has of literature to continue explaining it to itself; the relevance of literature to the disturbingly – and exhilaratingly – changing world we live in; and the quite remarkable way in which post-apartheid writing can appear to use the same shapes and strategies as before, and yet be totally new and different. Through the consummate skill with which she unmasks 'the catastrophe that lies at the crashed limit of all morality' Gordimer jolts the reader into a rediscovery of the place we live in, and the responsibility we owe both it and ourselves.

An Interview with
Nadine Gordimer

KAREN RUTH LAZAR

T his interview took place nine months after South Africa's first democratic elections in 1994. The interview covers a range of different areas, including the question of Gordimer's political involvements since the early eighties and her understanding and evaluation of recent South African history; some discussion on feminism and female sexuality; some aspects of her 1994 novel, None to Accompany Me, *and some thoughts on immigration and Jewishness.*

Karen Lazar: Nadine, I have some questions to ask you about your involvements as a citizen during the eighties and early nineties, and then a few questions about your more recent work.

In the early eighties, what stirred you to become involved in political organisations? (It seems you had had a reluctance to do so before that point.) Which groups were you specifically involved in? I know about ACAG (Anti-Censorship Action Group), but wondered about your other organisational commitments at that time?

Nadine Gordimer: What spurred me was a new opportunity to be involved. In the seventies, we had the separatist movement, Black Consciousness, which I understood and sympathised with. Many whites were incensed by it. It was, of course, hurtful for all whites because, for instance, even the writers' organisations, PEN, at that time black-led (in fact under the leadership of Mothobi Mutloase but with a non-racial national executive) broke up because of the

BC movement. It didn't break up acrimoniously, though it was seized upon by the popular press as having entailed a terrible row. This wasn't so at all. We just decided that we wouldn't carry on as an organisation. The black members had had some pressure brought to bear upon them: that this was not the time for small gatherings of like-minded people of this nature, it was rather the time for the consolidation of blacks.

Then, of course, in the eighties, the position changed very much. I, like many others, had been in the position where there was no organisation with a public profile that you could belong to, unless you wanted to belong to the Progressive Party, as it was at the time, or the Progressive Federal Party, as it became. So there were liberal organisations that you could belong to, but nothing to the left of that, if you were left-inclined. So I was homeless, so to speak, as a social being. I had, of course, my attachments to the African National Congress (ANC) which I'd had all along, but it was underground, so these things were also underground. But then, in the eighties, with the formation of the United Democratic Front (UDF) in 1983 – it was non-racial, anyone could be a member – you could openly avow yourself. So I think that was a great encouragement. Here was some sort of organisation to which I could attach myself, which I did, and I met and worked with some wonderful people.

KL: And COSAW (The Congress of South African Writers) formed later in the eighties?

NG: Yes, COSAW formed later. But COSAW too became possible out of the new climate, the feeling that apartheid wasn't totally granite, that it was crumbling, that there was some kind of attrition from within – the UDF surviving without being banned being proof of that. And there was a more confident mood among blacks that it wasn't necessary to maintain this total separatism. And so we were able to form COSAW. It was preceded, importantly I think, by a little thing called The Writers' Forum, a small organisation in Johannesburg greatly concerned with links with the African Arts Fund, whereby young people, mainly blacks but some others, got scholarships to go and study abroad in the arts – drama, film, and so on. But they did not have bridging money – in other words, they were given money for tuition fees, but they wouldn't be given money for the airfare. So we saw to that, promoted study in this way, and we had various readings and got small groups of writers together. And out of that came the idea that the time was right to start a national writers' organisation, so we called together all cultural groups concerned with writing and aspects of writing, including theatre, and had a meeting. Out of that came the Congress of South African Writers.

So that is really how my involvement moved. Running parallel with that I was also becoming more and more involved, especially with the culture side of the ANC. I was one of the people who went to Botswana to the Culture and Resistance festival, as many of us did. Somehow things were really beginning to move. I also had quite frequent contact with Wally Serote overseas, when he was running the cultural desk of the ANC from London.

KL: During the eighties, were there any particular and decisive political events, trials, funerals, assassinations and so on, which might have shaped your decisions as a writer? I'm thinking, for instance, of your portrayal of Whaila's assassination in *A Sport of Nature* and of the graveside scenes in *My Son's Story* – those kind of cruxes in your work.

NG: Well, the graveside scenes came out of my own several experiences of funerals, one in particular when I experienced teargas for the first time. So that came out of what was going on at the time and my own personal experience of it. What had made me think of Whaila's murder is the assassination of David Sibeko. I had known him virtually as a kid, an adolescent, when he was on the telephone exchange at *Drum* magazine; he first worked there. Then he became active in the Pan Africanist Congress (PAC). He was extremely bright and very charming, and he rose steadily in the hierarchy of the PAC. He was one of the people assassinated abroad in the seventies, so that was somehow at the back of my mind. It's interesting how these assassinations first of all took place outside the country – it's a mystery why during that period they were not taking place inside. Now political assassinations in the last few years have taken place inside the country.

KL: I wondered what had been decisive for you, because for me,

Eastern Cape leader Matthew Goniwe's murder in 1985 had been a totally decisive event. Perhaps one is ripe at a certain point for a consciousness shift.

NG: It's true, and that event can haunt you. Other events start becoming part of a general category after that.

KL: Moving to the censorship side of things: a Johannesburg advocate, Gilbert Marcus, mentioned to me that you frequently took part in representations to the Publications Appeal Board on behalf of other writers during the eighties. Which literary texts did you appeal on, and on what grounds?

NG: I can't remember the details, but there were quite a large number of texts we appealed on. I think I was there as a member of the Anti-Censorship Action Group, and ACAG would naturally have chosen a writer if it were fiction in question rather than choosing a journalist who'd be more appropriate for a particular banned edition of a newspaper, or something. So it's quite true that I was called upon, and went, a number of times.

KL: What were your impressions of the Appeal Board, especially coming out of your experience of the banning of *Burger's Daughter*?

NG: Well, that was really very interesting. They were unbelievably polite and positively smarmy. One of the accusations I had made again and again, was not only the whole principle – I always started with the principle – but also to point out the incredible lack of qualification of these people to decide. Members of the Appeal Board would sit facing us, and there was an old retired schoolmaster from Witbank or somewhere, and a retired dentist at one point, I remember, making decisions like this.

I think one of the texts we appealed on was probably Don Mattera's *Azanian Love Song*, a book of poetry, and there were many others.

KL: In the records of the mammoth Delmas Treason Trial of 1986-9, your testimony points to the peaceful and legitimate nature of the UDF – as I understand it that's why you were called in (**NG**: yes), and then in your testimony your support for the still exiled ANC and your understanding of why the organisation was forced into violence comes through.

NG: That was the real purpose of my testimony. It wasn't so much the UDF because these were really ANC people, most of them on trial. I suppose we can talk about it now. I had been involved in that trial because Terror (Patrick) Lekota was writing a book in the form of letters to his daughter. So bits of it I was smuggling out with the help of the lawyers and then with a friend going over it and she did a wonderful job of typing it out. I knew the trialists well, particularly Terror and Popo (Molefe).

KL: Did Terror's book ever come to light?

NG: The book did come to light. It was published by, I am not sure but I think it was the small publishing house Taurus . . . It's a pity. It sank like a stone. The interesting thing about it: the idea that came to Terror, I would have thought was inspired by the letters to Indira Gandhi by her father. But he'd never heard of them. It just came to him out of his situation. There were problems because he wasn't near a library and couldn't look up and research dates and the names he couldn't remember he couldn't verify. So we did our best with that but it wasn't strong on fact. But it was interesting because it was one of the attempts to write from the people, to see history from the personal point of view rather than from the historian's point of view.

That was my initial access point to the trial. And then, it is customary, I didn't know this, for the accused to give the names of people they would like to speak for them in mitigation. And I was one of the people that they asked for. And I was then very nastily questioned by the prosecutor. I was not used to this. He asked . . . quite bluntly, was Nelson Mandela my leader and then he said is Umkhonto we Sizwe your Umkhonto we Sizwe? And I said yes. So I suppose in a way that was a watershed in my political development.

KL: Have you, yourself, written anything about the Delmas trial?

NG: No, nothing. Actually it's interesting. I've been to a lot of political trials over my lifetime but I don't think there's a trial in any of my books. Trials are just natural good theatre, aren't they?

KL: If they aren't very tedious!

NG: They can be, yes. But they can make good theatre if you know something about them.

KL: Nadine, when did you actually join the ANC?

NG: Oh, the moment it was legal. You couldn't join before. What you did meant you were with it or not with it. The moment it became possible to do so, it was very nice because a friend and I went down to JISWA which was the Johannesburg Indian Welfare Association (at that time run by a friend of mine Cas Saloojee and his wife Khadija) because we were told that this was one of the first places where you could get your ANC membership card. So we went down there and he is a good friend, Cas Saloojee, and we were his first two members. That was the end of February 1990.

KL: A few more questions about your perceptions of left politics in the 1980s. In *My Son's Story*, Sonny gets marginalised by his comrades in 'the movement' for reasons which are not made entirely clear. When did you become aware of splits in the Congress Left, and what splits were you aware of? Is Sonny's 'movement' to be associated unequivocally with a UDF/ANC alignment?

NG: Oh, I think so, in response to the latter. It was clear from the kind of things he was doing. The tensions, the splits, these are there in every political formation and it doesn't require any great feat of imagination to concoct something with these things. And I'd already done it before on a different scale in *A Guest of Honour*.

KL: At that stage in the late eighties, or in the time that *My Son's Story* was being written, did you ever believe that any *other* liberation sectors might come to centrality within South African politics?

NG: Such as?

KL: I don't know, perhaps worker sectors, PAC, alliances of other kinds? The reason that I ask is that I've noticed the pervasive way in which you use the definite article in that novel, *'the* movement', suggesting that there is no other.

NG: I used the definite article because, to me, the movement did encompass others. I specially didn't want to make it specific. Of course there was certainly the SACP and the ANC and the rising Trade Union movement that were already allied, even if there was not official recognition of this, but they were working together. A very significant development for me in the eighties was the recognition of black trade unions. I can't imagine that, to use a cliché, without the worker power we would have moved as we did. When I think of my youth in that mining town, Springs, and those miners who were even kept out of the towns ... they were so completely cut off from any normal kind of concourse with people in the town (I'm talking about black people too). And then in the eighties I would go down to Braamfontein to the post office or the bank and out of National Union of Mineworkers' offices there would come these young men in their T-shirts striding down the pavement. It was to me such a graphic illustration of a huge change. So the Trade Union movement opening up was also important to my thinking. That was clearly encompassed under 'the movement'.

I think that somehow, the underlying conflict seems to be between UDF and the movement: the more direct political forces, ANC, PAC, SACP and so on. The kind of thing that happened when the ANC exiles came back between them and the UDF people, I anticipated that in my book *My Son's Story*. It hadn't happened yet because people hadn't come back. But when they did come back it did happen. One saw people who had done such wonderful work who were somehow set aside or got minor positions.

KL: Did you have any direct contact with FEDSAW (Federation of South African Women), FEDTRAW (Federation of Transvaal Women) or other women's organisations during the eighties, or with the documents and speeches emanating from these organisations?

NG: I always received the documents and quite often went to various functions but I was not an active member at all.

KL: Many feminist reviewers and interviewers, including myself, have attempted to draw you out on your opinions of feminism in recent years. Your description of feminism as 'piffling' in the early eighties was followed by your recognition that there are some 'harder, more thinking' kinds of feminism in the later eighties. What is your opinion, now, of the role that a political feminism may have in our current moment of governmental and constitutional change?

NG: My views have changed and they've changed because the situation has changed. It's interesting. I can't see any vestiges of that trivial feminism that I was talking about so disparagingly because I think it deserved to be disparaged in the early times. Because of the tremendous division that arose in the mid-seventies, around about '76, between the concerns of white women and the concerns of black. I'll never forget the attempts of Women for Peace which was a good idea although it came out of a White Lady Bountiful thing. They did have some meetings and some sort of contact with black women. It was based on the idea, you see it again and again, that we all have children and what happened in '76 was a threat to children.

But what happened then was, come November, all these white adolescents are preparing for the matric dance and what was happening in Soweto or Gugulethu all over the place ... So that black women who were running behind their kids with bowls of water and *lappies* to wash the teargas out of their eyes. There was really no meeting point for these women unless the white women had directly challenged the government, which they were not prepared to do. You can't change a regime on the basis of compassion. There's got to be something harder. I'm not saying that compassion is not necessary in our lives but you can't change a regime that way. I think that's one of the faults of a worthy liberal organisation like that. At least you could say that the women had moved along that far but I couldn't see how there could be any common feminism unless white women had truly thrown in their lot as some of the people in FEDTRAW did.

KL: And now?

NG: And now, I think the proof is there. We've got quite a lot of women in Parliament. We have got in place of a white male Afrikaner (which we've had for generations) a black person as Speaker, and she's also a woman and significantly, a South African Indian which is also for me a sign of solidarity, and a true demonstration of non-racism. Nobody said she isn't black enough or if they have, I haven't heard it. And I don't think they have said it. I think she is recognised for what she is. And then you have other people like Baleka Kgotsisile and Cheryl Carolus who has just got a high position now (as deputy secretary general of the ANC) and she is a remarkable person. And there are a number of others, Barbara Masekela is now going to be our ambassador in Paris, and as you talk about it you can think of other names. So they are all evidence of a very important kind of feminism from my point of view.

Another thing I'd like to say is that in the interim Constitution, the strong emphasis on no discrimination on grounds of gender – they've brought that up on a level with discrimination on grounds of colour or race – is a very important step of the right kind now.

KL: And you think there's the will to enact that?

NG: I think so, certainly among younger black women and some white women.

KL: Nadine, a few questions on your work. When one looks at some of your portrayals of left-wing or activist women, one can see a kind of physical type coming across. I'm thinking of Joy in 'Something Out There' and Hannah in *My Son's Story*, both of whom are depicted as sloppy dressers and sexual improbables when compared with your more conventional beauties such as Hillela and Aila. Is your depiction of this 'alternative' female aesthetic (the Hannah/Joy kind) based on something you've observed in left-wing circles over the years, or could you suggest where it might come from?

NG: Oh, of course. These are things that come from observation. I think we all fall into some kind of uniform. I remember years ago arriving in America – I was going to some meeting at Columbia – and I was put up in a sort of complex, where we were all writers and painters and artists. And it was a year when if you were a writer or painter, you wore black trousers and a black polo-neck sweater and you wore a certain kind of ear-ring and you would not wear another kind. And one day I looked at myself and thought, you're wearing the uniform. So I think this observation comes from simply living among people. Just like the sweater-and-pearls aesthetic: it isn't true of everyone, but it does define a certain kind of woman, doesn't it?

KL: Some critics have commented that your latest novel, *None to Accompany Me*, is surprisingly sombre in mood, given the largely triumphant political period from which it emerges. Could you comment on this?

NG: Well, I think there's a certain solemnity when, after a long, long time, extraordinary good things happen, when things open up. Sometimes in the last year, I think we've all had what one might call a sense of awe. And I think this probably comes out in that book.

KL: Your portrait of the consequences of violence, as in Oupa's death in the latest book, seems to me to be more sustained – you took more time over it – than in any such portraits in earlier works.

NG: Yes, because such events became so terrible in view of the fact that we were coming to the end of this struggle against the apartheid regime. You know it's rather like, in war, soldiers being killed while the armistice is being signed somewhere else. It pointed to the tremendous waste that took place over years and years and years, and also to the mindless and criminal violence that has come about in this country as a result of poverty and the conditions of apartheid. So in a way, the prolonged attention to Oupa's death, the whole process of his dying, really encompasses many deaths.

KL: Your protagonist in this novel, Vera Stark, moves towards a recognition of the fundamental solitude of the self as she grows older. At the same time, she withdraws further and further away from sexuality, such that her relationship with her final male companion, Zeph, is a celibate one (even though he is still sexually active – with younger women). Could you perhaps comment on why Vera's eventual life choices are coterminous with a sexual removal from the world? And what might that say about the ageing process for women in our society? Does it exert different stresses on women than it does on men?

NG: There's a different attitude to women's sexuality than there is to men's. It's still not recognised in the way that men's is.

KL: By whom?

NG: By everybody. By other women too, by conventional women. Vera is a strange woman because in some ways she is conventional. She attacks her daily work; even though it is unconventional work she goes about it in this rather strict, direct way, rather authoritarian. She doesn't seem to belong to any women's movement. She's a women's movement in herself, I think. And she bluntly asserts her sexuality. She even quotes Renoir at one point – 'I paint with my prick'. But she has her fill of sexuality, she works her way through it. She's had a very active kind of sensual life, she hasn't cared too much about the morality of it.

KL: So you don't see any loss when she moves away from sexuality?

NG: No, it's a conscious decision. You've said something that many other people miss because they say how lonely she is, but you've said she recognises the ultimate solitude of self. If you're going to make a journey towards that, towards accepting that, then you are shedding some things along the way. She sees the baggage of her life as something which she took on and wanted and wouldn't have been without, but that she doesn't want it dragging around with her forever.

KL: And sexuality might have been part of that baggage?

NG: Yes. And of course, who can say? People's sexuality dies down at different ages. Some people seem to be finished with sex in their mid-forties, or fifties. Terrible! Others take on lovers, both male and female, at seventy. It's a matter of the glands, I suppose. Vera genuinely doesn't want another sexual relationship and doesn't resent the fact that Zeph has his little pleasures on the side.

KL: I notice some of your work (stories and sections from novels) have been published over the years in the glossy women's press, such as in *Cosmopolitan*, *Femina* and *Fair Lady*. What is your impression of these magazines?

NG: Well, I've always had very mixed feelings. Quite frankly I don't read them, though I see them around. But I notice, through the kind of contents thing they splash on the covers, that they have changed quite a lot and also you see – talking about local ones now – black faces on the cover these days. Admittedly, they're usually beauty queens. I haven't seen any of our black women writers or actresses on these covers. But, you know, that is the women's magazine culture: to be a beauty queen is the ultimate ambition. It's rather interesting that women have to be very consciously feminist in order to reject the whole beauty queen thing. I suppose quite a lot of young women do get quite independent through modelling, though, it's a financial thing.

KL: Incidentally, what do you make of the ANC coming out in support of something like the 'Miss South Africa' contest?

NG: I suppose this is the kind of thing that political parties do, and the ANC is now a political party. If people say, look, this is part of the emancipation of blacks, it's a little thing, and I have no objection to it. I'm much more worried about us becoming nice big arms dealers.

KL: Nadine, are you a television watcher, and were you watching South African TV during the eighties?

NG: No, I never watch it. I'm a newspaper reader.

KL: What newspapers and journals did you subscribe to or read during the eighties, and are you still reading those papers?

NG: During the eighties, the usual local English-language ones (I'm afraid my Afrikaans isn't up to much), and of course the alternative press: *Weekly Mail*, *New Nation* etc. And then, literary journals such as *New York Review of Books* and so on. For a long time I used to get *The Observer* and then *The Independent*, and then it just got too much. In recent years, once *The Weekly Mail* started printing pages from *The Guardian*, I thought that will do.

As for local cultural journals, *Contrast* comes here and *Staffrider* of course (I was involved in that in COSAW) and now and then, *The Southern African Review*.

KL: Finally, the mandatory question! Nine months after South Africa's first democratic election, what are your impressions: of the pace of change, of the receptiveness of South Africans to this change?

NG: I've been pleased, I should say surprised, by the receptiveness of South Africans. I think the crisis of expectation which absolutely obsesses people overseas – I can't tell you how many times in America I got questioned about this – is much exaggerated. I think what people want – in my experience, my small experience of talking to grassroots people, and from what I gather from those who do have a big experience of it – what they want is truly basic. I think this has been recognised now in the ANC. It's not recognised by the press, it's not recognised by people who saw April 27 this year as the beginning of the millennium. People are not asking for Mercedes-Benzes and big houses. You know what they're asking for: a roof over their heads, electricity, education, jobs.

KL: But that is a tall order for a new government.

NG: It is a very tall order, of course. As for how much has been done, of course it seems too little, but one can't say a start hasn't been made. I think the question of how much can be done how quickly should be explained to the black majority in a different way from the way that it is being explained. When dissatisfaction comes up, as it has, for instance, in the prelude to the ANC Congress now, along the lines that the ANC has bent over backwards to placate whites and done nothing for blacks . . . I think Mandela answered that very well, but he didn't go into it enough, from my point of view, when he said the placating of whites has cost nothing, no money has been spent on it. What money there was has been spent

438

on providing electricity, water where it's been possible . . . This is great. To me it's progress. It's not spectacular, but it's progress.

What should be explained much more fully, and is not, to the black majority is the reason why whites have to be soothed and kept in place: because the government, ANC-led, does not want any abandonment of our very complicated economic infrastructure here, such as you saw in other parts of Africa, while there is still insufficient skill to take over such things. So if there are too many concessions to whites, in terms of tax or keeping them in a certain measure of control of various boards . . . if it could be explained that this is only because you cannot move towards greater prosperity and development without using them. In other words, whites are being used, and they should accept it; we should all accept it. Whites have got things that blacks never had, and they are now being used to help provide these things. Of course there's also the question of investment from overseas. And this is not put clearly enough to blacks. If you look at material concessions to whites, what have they been? Nothing, except that white life has been left intact. People tend to ignore the quiet, slow – much too slow, of course – integration of schools. As far as I know, from friends white and black, the kids are now going to school together and there's no problem.

So my feeling is of realistic optimism. Of course, new hitches arise all the time. I turned on the radio at lunchtime, and now the farmers on the borders of Lesotho whose cattle are been rustled by people coming over the border from Lesotho, have made counter-attacks and burned down cattle kraals where they say their stolen cattle have been housed. I heard one of the farmers say that, unless this whole thing is stopped, this rustling over the border, there's going to be bloodshed. Also, a year ago, who would have thought that we would have the problem of illegal immigration which we now have – that we'd have Koreans selling watches in the streets, Zaireans talking French in the streets. Who would have thought this? It's something we couldn't possibly have imagined.

KL: Why do you think this has happened? Is it that we are seen as a place of extreme bounty relative to these other countries?

NG: Oh absolutely, but we can't afford this. We must think of our own people first, and somehow this has got to be stopped. Of course, this ill becomes somebody like myself who comes from immigrant stock. All of us who are whites here originally do. So who are we to say that the Koreans must be kicked out?

KL: But most whites come from immigrant stock a long way back.

NG: Precisely, but do you think that really makes such a difference?

KL: I notice that some critics writing for Jewish journals and papers, claim that you have denied or suppressed your Jewish origins and your family's immigrant history.

NG: Well, I think it's truly based on nothing. I have never denied that I'm Jewish and I've no desire to deny it. For me, being Jewish is like being black: you simply are. To want to deny it is disgusting. It's a denial of humanity. There's no shame in being black and there's no shame in being Jewish. But I'm not religious, I haven't had a religious upbringing, and whether I'm an unbeliever in terms of Jehovah or Jesus Christ to me is the same thing.

KL: Being black in our society surely amounts to a more politically disadvantaged state than being Jewish, for most people anyway?

NG: Yes, of course, much more. I wonder how these Jewish critics feel about Joe, Joe Slovo and others, who've put something else first. I've never seen any criticism of them. I'm not sure why it's happened to me! Perhaps writers are always easy targets. In America I'm asked, do you think your Jewish background has influenced you politically? I've thought about it a lot, and I think not. I would hate to think that you have to be Jewish in order to understand racism, just as I would hate to think you have to be black to understand it. It should be something absolutely repugnant and quite impossible for anybody who is a real human being. So, to say I'm not Jewish so I don't care about the Holocaust or I'm not black so I don't care about Sharpeville or all the other Sharpevilles that followed . . . that's appalling.

There are strange little ethnic loyalties, I suppose, that come up. I can't help being pleased, and have been pleased over the years, to think that in South Africa, in the liberation movements and in progressive circles, there have been – given the smallness of the Jewish population – a really disproportionate number of Jews. I'm rather proud of this. Though of course you may then get the accusation, as you do in America, that Jews dominate progressive thinking and the press, and so on. So it can be used as a stick to beat you with as well . . .

Because I Marvel:
Interview with Nadine Gordimer

MAUREEN ISAACSON

Nothing goes unnoticed. Not the way I decline the 'rather nice' biscuits Nadine Gordimer offers me with tea during my interview with her, nor the pendant I wear around my neck. Not the latest truth commission report, that the severed hand of ANC activist Stanza Bopape was preserved in formalin, nor the shooting of security guards in downtown Johannesburg. Gordimer retains everything.

In July this year, 1998, when her Goodwill Ambassadorship for the United Nations Development Programme was announced, and Gordimer was briefed to further the eradication of poverty, worldwide, her willingness was mentioned. Willingness is the right word, I thought. Like all good literature, this author yields many levels. I have always been taken aback by her compliance, at gatherings of the Congress of South African Writers, of which she is a patron and when *The Sunday Independent*, the newspaper I work for, has published her work.

The interview, for *The Sunday Independent*, is conducted in March this year. The occasion is the publication of her twelfth novel, *The House Gun*. She emerges from the depths of her study, in her cool, double-storey house in Parktown, Johannesburg. She has temporarily abandoned her proof reading and her search for the precise French translation of the word 'dread'. It is dread that fills Harald and Claudia Lindgard, the parents of Duncan, who has committed a murder in the novel.

The interview continues as an informal dialogue. I remember

442

Gordimer's rage about the fate of the Nigerian writer and activist, Ken Saro-Wiwa. I recall her standing outside the Nigerian consulate in Rosebank, Johannesburg, 1995, presenting a petition demanding Saro-Wiwa's release. She was wearing a hat and holding a banner, looking fierce, yet somehow contained in her anger. Some months later she returned. Saro-Wiwa had been hanged by the Nigerian military. Flanked by Archbishop Desmond Tutu and ANC MP Carl Niehaus, she called for sanctions, her fist raised. She says exactly what she thinks and she speaks as quickly, with candour.

In 1996, I saw her ire raised at the Windybrow Theatre in Johannesburg, when the African American writer Amiri Baraka visited South Africa. Insensitive to the plight of writers here, he advocated that they abandon trade unions and publish their own work.

She is often seen at the Windybrow Theatre, attending plays and book launches, organising readings, listening to the music of Vusi Mahlasela.

She is also seen at the Electric Workshop, in Johannesburg's Newtown, listening to Linton Kwesi Johnson's rap songs and at Gallagher Estate, a guest at President Mandela's birthday party.

Despite her public profile, she is protected by a determined privacy. At home, personal interviews are rare. Even today, she prefers to talk about the nature of her fictional characters than her own. Her friend of forty-six years, the writer Anthony Sampson, says she does not make close friends easily and when she does, they usually endure for life. 'There is no dirt on her,' he says. Still, it takes some digging to get through to Gordimer, despite her gift of articulation. She also speaks much as she writes, crisply and with meticulous detail. When she describes a wooden sculpture she bought in a Rosebank street, its half-human, half-animal figures come to life.

The idea of South Africa's Nobel Laureate for Literature taking her inspiration from the streets of Johannesburg is in turn inspiring. Johannesburg is the home to which she returns after her frequent travels. Although aware that 'freedom has its discontents . . . to paraphrase Freud,' this is where she wants to live. 'Cape Town is a beautiful place for a holiday. Johannesburg is home.'

Johannesburg appears in many of her stories, it weaves through the body of her work like a character. It is here she set her 1958 novel, *A World of Strangers*. It features in later novels, such as *Occasion for Loving* (1963), *The Late Bourgeois World* (1966),

Burger's Daughter (1979) and *My Son's Story* (1990). Her first post-apartheid novel, *None to Accompany Me* (1994), is set in Johannesburg. Johannesburg also occurs in several short stories, such as *Good Climate, Friendly Inhabitants,* where the protagonist with the bleached hair says, 'it's not only because it is not safe to walk about alone at night because of the natives, this whole town is full of people you can't trust.' The razor-wired suburbs of Johannesburg become truly nightmarish in the more recent story, *Once Upon a Time.*

Johannesburg has also nourished *The House Gun.* The impact of the crime on parents is universal, but Gordimer stresses that this does not take place in a vacuum. 'This could have happened anywhere but it happened here, in a particular way, in our country, in our city, Johannesburg, at our time. It happens with all the consequences of apartheid around us, that is the structure of the novel.' This ability to make universal the specific, so that we are able to see the world as we look at ourselves in the mirror she holds, is another gift.

She wants to know: 'How much are we influenced in our lives by the social, political and moral atmosphere in which we live?'

In *The House Gun*, Gordimer returns to an earlier theme: the change in dependency. Like Bam and Maureen Smales, the protagonists of the 1980 novel, *July's People,* Harald and Claudia Lindgard relinquish their independence to a black man, the advocate Hamilton Motsamai, who steers them through the consequences of their son's actions.

Gordimer's depictions of the complexities of power have not lessened with the recent shifts. 'The Smales are dependent on their servant, July, who is taking care of them in a civil war situation from which they are all refugees. But Motsamai belongs to the ruling class, he is a distinguished professional. So now the dependency has moved again.'

The House Gun also continues her exploration of familial relationships. 'It is largely about love . . . it is about the extent to which one will go for the other. I am looking at these themes *vis à vis* the parents and Duncan and *vis à vis* Duncan and the girl. She is one of those fatal people who is attractive but really self-destructive.' She talks about the characters as if they are people we both know intimately. Harald and Claudia are lonely with each other. She warms to Harald who, like herself, is an avid reader.

'How far do you go in changing your own life and taking on responsibility for the other – can you run away from it? Could Harald and Claudia have said that what their son has done is so terrible that we will cut ourselves off from him? Could he, and why did he not, get rid of the girl instead of getting into the entanglement that he did? These questions are connected with the responsibilities of life – what it means, how far you will go – for me that is central to the book.'

In her only autobiographical novel, *The Lying Days,* Helen Shaw, aged seventeen, declared 'Nobody told me love was warm.' This début novel was written in 1949 when Gordimer was twenty-six.

Love runs like a current beneath the steely intellect, through the exterior some experience as aloof. It is in her relationship to the world and her keen desire to put right at least some of its wrongs. Her husband, Reinhold Cassirer, who calls her 'darling', laughs when she spills the tea. She heaves an armchair bigger than herself to the centre of the room for a guest. When she serves drinks with fat olives and crackers, she wants you to feel right at home. She has a daughter from a brief first marriage, a son from her second marriage of forty-four years and she is the grandmother of four.

Through the country's 'realistic problems' and what she calls 'the morning after' the 1994 euphoria, she is thrilled by the fact that black and white children are integrated at an early age. The present reality accentuates the distance she has travelled from her East Rand mining-town childhood in Springs.

Gordimer's father was a watchmaker, who left Latvia at thirteen and whose solitary journey to South Africa she has imagined in the moving short story, *My Father Leaves Home.* This story was inspired by a visit to a Hungarian *shtetl,* which seemed similar to the one she assumes he came from. She has not seen his home. She has, however, visited Goldhurst Terrace in Hampstead where her mother lived in London before she came to live in South Africa as a child.

In the 1963 essay, 'The Bolter and the Invisible Summer', she recalls the beginnings of her writing career and how she 'bolted' from kindergarten and school. She describes herself as a rather unkind mimic, a bossy and quite wilful girl. However, she says she wasn't really spoiled, 'but I was my father and mother's baby'.

The younger of two daughters, Gordimer saw her mother as over-protective. Yet this cocooned life nurtured her remarkable talent. She borrowed books from the local library. 'For birthdays I would say, this is the book I want for my birthday, it was a great thing, to have a book of your own, so I was building up my little library. My mother was very understanding about that but I don't think she ever bought a book for herself, she just assumed there was a library. She read a lot.'

At nine Gordimer had written her first poem – about Paul Kruger – and by fifteen, her first short story, *Come Again Tomorrow*, was published in *Forum*, a liberal weekly. It is about the plight of an old man who is taken in to his daughter-in-law's house. Gordimer defends the right of the writer to take imaginative leaps and cross gender and racial barriers. And she is clear that she does not want to be marked as woman's writer. Earlier this year she insisted *The House Gun* be withdrawn from the short list of the Orange Prize, a British literary prize for women.

Much has been made of the fact that during the struggle Gordimer declared feminism 'a piffling issue' in the light of more pressing matters. Now her attitude has changed. 'The rape in South Africa is appalling. I ask myself if it was always there and we just didn't know about it. Of course the law dealt with it in such a manner that if a woman was raped people didn't believe her. This isn't feminism to me, I would hope that if I were a man I would feel the same.' But with regard to women being paid the same as men, 'when they do the same job and having opportunities to do the same job then I am certainly all for it – I am a feminist.'

I wonder if being a woman has ever stood in her way? 'I have been very fortunate. But of course you never know – with our biological role sometimes you think it's a privilege – sometimes you think it's a drag.'

Certainly her gender has not hampered her creativity. At seventy-five, she is robust. 'Seventy-five! It's three-quarters of a century!' Men decades younger than her say they find her attractive.

One of the world's foremost post-colonial novelists, she embraces modernity in her work. *The House Gun* is surprising in its immediacy and its style, which sometimes seems experimental.

'To me style is the way you tell the story. Before I begin to

446

write, I have to hear the "voice" in which it is going to be told. I am telling it to myself and hearing whether it is the right voice. What was right for *None to Accompany Me* is not the right way of telling this story.

'I don't think you find your style – I think if you do it is dangerous, because you tend to repeat everything in the same voice, you tend to be too much in one book so you are not letting your characters and their way of life speak. I am intrigued in this book as I don't think I have been before. There's a chapter that begins with, "Why is Duncan not in the story?" This is something the writer is asking herself and brings the reader into it. Let's ask ourselves instead of myself why he is not in the story, then of course it is up to the writer and Duncan to answer this.'

Gordimer ranks *The House Gun* with her Booker prize-winning novel, *The Conservationist*, published in 1974, of which she says, 'I achieved what I wanted to.' In *The Conservationist*, she took bold stylistic strides and she first dropped the use of 'he's' and 'she's'.

'So many people have taken as my comment the remark, "This is not a detective story". This means they have not read the sentence after this. Because this is Harald saying, Oh God this is not a detective story, but in the next sentence, apparently murders when they are described in the court record, really are like a detective story – in other words the detective story is true. But because I don't use "he said" and "she thought" and "he contemplated", they seem to be unable to read this into it for themselves.'

Like the great French novelist, Balzac, Gordimer has chronicled what she has referred to as the country's 'psychological history' in her novels and volumes of short stories. Looking back on the volumes, she seems amazed at the enormity of her output. She has been published in thirty-one languages, as well as in English. At home and abroad, she has received the highest literary awards for her novels and has been awarded fifteen honorary doctorates.

When asked by *The Observer* to name the book she wished she had written, she realised she was very happy to have authored her own books. She would, however, have liked to have written poetry.

Earlier in her career she said that her truth was to be found in her fiction, but it is also apparent in her journalistic and critical work, in the photographic books she has collaborated on with David Goldblatt.

Her South African publisher, David Philip, says many South Africans have a resistance to reading about the situation we live with. Could the fact that her work has met with reluctance by some South African readers have anything to do with the way she reveals her countrymen, particularly white liberals such as Harald and Claudia Lindgard?

This refusal to engage with the acute prose of her fiction, the sometimes surprisingly explicit sexual scenes, the unrivalled descriptions of her native landscape and the consistent logic of her essays is often born of ignorance. Her critics sometimes assume, inaccurately, a predictability.

The stories that do not revolve around what she calls 'the big theme' and deal with old women travelling by train, such as Mrs Clara Hansen in *Enemies* and Franz Kafka's father, in *Letter From His Father*, are not often mentioned.

It is also possible that with Gordimer, as with her friend, Seamus Heaney, the 1995 Irish Nobel Laureate, the reaction to international success in one's country is accompanied by envy.

Why have her books been more prominently displayed in bookstores in New York and Rio de Janeiro than in her home-town? Philip says that within two weeks of the announcement that she had won the Nobel Prize, her German publisher, Fischer Verlag, reprinted all of her novels in German. Fischer Verlag held a banquet for her in Frankfurt, which was attended by all of her publishers, worldwide. Philip recalls queues of thousands, waiting to get Gordimer to sign their books.

In South Africa, there was no such reaction. The then president F W de Klerk sent no word. However, she recalls the 'overwhelming reception' when, at the airport, Bishop Tutu joined her young black comrades, who dressed up and blew horns when she returned from accepting the prize. Sales of *Jump and Other Stories*, published earlier that year, leapt. I think of Gordimer, all five feet of her, jumping to open the latch on the top of her front door when it is time for me to leave her house. Always there is an energy that precedes her and leaves its footprints where she has been.

Her critics are often irked by the commitment that has shaped her life and she has been accused, variously, of being not political enough, 'too political' and politically correct. But for Gordimer, commitment means 'commitment to all kinds of integrity – in other words, one shouldn't distort it even for a cause which one believes in passionately.' She says that even though she was involved from early on with the ANC, she couldn't make her ANC revolutionary characters angels, 'because I knew they weren't – nobody is. The first duty of a writer to his or her society, if we are looking at the arts from that point of view – is to try and tell the truth as far as he or she sees it – warts and all.'

This truth is also apparent in the documentary film scripts she has collaborated on with her son Hugo Cassirer and in the screenplays she has written from her short story collection, *Six Feet in the Country*. The title story of this collection is about the land; another preoccupying theme. 'Who owns the land? The white man who bought it and has a piece of paper saying it is his or the people who owned it long before he came?' She reminds me that she wrote about this in *The Conservationist*. Also, the central character of *None to Accompany Me* is on the land commission.

There seems to be not a false note in her entire range. Her uncompromising stance was learned the hard way, by banning and gagging under the apartheid regime, yet, considering the sacrifices made by Ruth First, Bettie du Toit and Bram Fischer, she feels that she has not been brave enough. People close to her testify to acts of generosity and loyalty.

Mongane Wally Serote, a poet and Parliamentary Arts and Culture portfolio committee chairman, says Gordimer 'demystified' whites. Together with the *Drum* writer, Nat Nakasa, in the fifties, Gordimer founded *The Classic*, a literary magazine that gave voice to the many writers whom Serote says she nurtured. When Nakasa committed suicide in the United States, where he had gone to take up a Nieman fellowship on an exit permit, she wrote sadly that he had left his hope behind and, hopefully, that there would be others to take it up. She has kept an eye on those who have done so.

The writer and critic, Lewis Nkosi, who worked on *Drum* with Es'kia Mphahlele, Bloke Modisane, Can Themba and Todd Matshikiza, remembers that in the fifties Gordimer was 'extremely beautiful'. He recalls that her clothes were 'not showy, they were

449

like her prose, elegant and precise and her hair was done up in the same way.' She wears her cotton trousers and shirts with ease; she favours orange and red. Her shoes are always flat-heeled, comfortable. Her house is similarly tasteful and unadorned.

Sampson, on his visits from London, has stayed here with her and Reinhold since the fifties. He says almost nothing is changed in her home, with its sweep of green lawn, its deep wooden floors, tall ceilings, its paintings and sculptures, its African masks. The kitchen still has its original fittings. The house reflects her lack of sentimentality, her efficiency. A 'house cat' is always ready to be petted, always told by her to leave the guests alone.

Sampson, who was editing *Drum* in 1952 when he met Gordimer, says she was 'an extraordinary discovery. I think I in a sense helped to introduce her to the black writers at *Drum*. Her ability to see private relationships came through in her early novels and stories – I felt ashamed to be unable to see what she could do in that world.' Nkosi recalls Gordimer at his 1960 farewell party, 'leaning against the jamb of the door, not saying anything, just observing . . .'

Above all an African writer, she has said that twentieth-century Africa is her time and place and she looks set to take things further. 'I always have a few stories.' On a small table in the lounge, next to the chair where she sits, is a small radio, a copy of the *Mail & Guardian*, the *New Yorker*, the *Los Angeles Times*.

If in Africa, the elders are the 'libraries' in the eyes of the young, Gordimer is well placed. She enjoyed Don de Lillo's *Underworld*. Reading Hermione Lee's biography of Virginia Woolf, she was irked by Woolf's egocentricity, surprised that she had read all her work when there were people such as Thomas Mann to be read. She believes writers of the southern hemisphere have much in common and is interested in the ground shared with writers such as the Colombian Gabriel García Márquez and the Chilean exile, Ariel Dorfman. Gordimer was saddened by the death this year of the Mexican Nobel Laureate for Literature, Octavio Paz. She admires Carlos Fuentes, Günther Grass, Naguib Mahfouz, Amos Oz and Chinua Achebe.

'He (Chinua Achebe) is studied at universities all over the world but he is not read by people who read. With a few exceptions,

African writers are not known – although this does not mean that many of the writers who are meaningful to us would be known to a wider public.'

She is fascinated to know what local literature will yield in the future. Perhaps satire, such as local theatre has produced. Perhaps something such as the young German novelist Thomas Brussig's satirical look at the Stasi in the post-unification novel, *Heroes Like Us*. So much of our past has not been touched, and she looks forward to seeing it written in 'a lyrical or symbolic way'. Gordimer is also tuned in to the present.

For Gordimer, illiteracy is 'intellectual poverty'. It is responsible for the fact that South African writers have such a small public. Without libraries in townships and the publication of more books in indigenous languages, there can be no progress. 'Some people learn to read and write at school, they can read a comic book, or poster, they can make out an official form, but they cannot read a book, even in their own language. I have had this confirmed by Es'kia Mphahlele and others.'

Although irony is a keen feature of her work ('it is something I like very much'), and her stories lend themselves to various inter-pretations, in person she is direct. Of Jewish origin, she is an atheist. She wants to know if I believe in God and she listens to my answer entirely without judgement. She inspires confidences because you trust that she will understand. She wrote, in her 1975 introduction to her *Selected Stories*, that 'emotions are events, too, of the spirit'. Through her remarkable composure and tough-mindedness are flares of vulnerability. She is too sensitive to probe.

Hers is not 'a wry look at the world ... I suppose I have a streak of pantheism – if there were to be a god it's in nature. The nearest I have to religion in my life and I have had that since a child is a sense of wonder – I marvel and sometimes I am horrified and that is because I marvel. But where one's moral ideas come from, I don't know – I mean why do you and I feel that we will never kill anybody? Why? It is because we get it from religion? Where does it come from?'

I suggest it is within our natures but ask if perhaps we would kill if we were forced to. 'I don't think so. No. Perhaps involuntarily in self-defence – but what Duncan did, I can't see that. I couldn't do it. No. Maybe I am old now and I know if I was going to do it I would have (she laughs). It is different with you.'

'That I might kill someone?'

'No, but you are still young enough for these situations to arise.' More laughter.

'We all say sometimes, "I could just kill her or I could kill him", but we find other ways of doing it.' Duncan saw no options – he had 'a brainstorm', which was rooted in the attack on his sexual emotions and on his love emotions. Seeing his two lovers together on the sofa, 'seemed to be a terrible kind of revenge on him. As the psychiatrist said, he was emasculated by it – they both rejected him.'

Harald reads Simone Weil, as Gordimer did when she was thirty-one. He prays that his son did not commit the murder but this has no effect on the fact that he did. 'Yes, of course I can understand Harald because I know a lot of people who are religious and they have a worthwhile framework for their life. It gives them a moral structure in which they live. It is also something to turn to in times of trouble though with him it seems it doesn't quite work, it brings doubts.'

I wonder if being an atheist means that she has no spiritual framework at all?

'Well, an atheist is a humanist as well. I suppose you could call me a humanist but some humanists are also believers or perhaps being a believer implies that you are a humanist. But one wouldn't think so when one thinks of some of the things that are done in the name of the Lord. I don't believe that there is a god up there. I wish there were but there seems to be proof every day, alas, that there isn't. I think of the terrible problems in the world, where does this come from?'

If death puts a final end to life, with no promise of the afterlife, where is the continuity?

'I think continuity is in generation to generation and perhaps in the case of people who write or paint or compose music, in what they leave behind. There's the only continuity that I can see.'

Of course she will not describe herself: 'No, I don't think so. No.' As in *The House Gun*, there is no resolution on offer.

PLACES OF A WRITING LIFE

Home for Intimacy

NJABULO S NDEBELE

After some twenty years of absence I returned home with a family in 1991. On the first Saturday of our return, I took them on a drive to see the house in which I was born at 923 John Mohohlo Street, Western Native Township. I could not identify it. When Africans were removed to make way for 'Coloureds', it seems the township was redesigned so that it could be made more spacious, more comfortable, more liveable, in the thinking of apartheid's planners. My home may not have survived the demolition. And so it was, that a historic event was to translate into a personal failure to demonstrate to my children that my life began somewhere.

Returning home, I did not find my home. But then again, I have returned home. Yet, it is true that I am still looking for a home to stay. (Where in this vast country will I finally live?) These contradictions force home the question: what is a home? Surely it is not merely a house. Is it a place associated with long memories? Somewhere to dig up roots? If so, is it still possible for me at forty-seven, and those of my generation, to sink in roots to dig up later? When is later? What experiences will add up to 'later'? Perhaps home for us can only be some concept of belonging to some historic process; some sense of historic justice assuming, on the day of liberation, the physical space of a country.

Where so many homes have been demolished, people moved to strange places, home temporarily becomes the shared experience of homelessness, the fellow-feeling of loss and the desperate need to regain something. It is this sense of home as homelessness that began to take a different shape on April 27, 1994. Home became the experience of the reality of national boundaries, the setting up of new institutions of governance, and yes, the building of private homes. It is this meaning of April 27, 1994 that will stretch far into the years ahead.

One of my abiding memories of the old South Africa is my experience of space and the sense of distance and time through travel. In travelling from point A to point B, I remember not so much the pleasure of movement and anticipation; the pleasure of reflecting at the end of the journey, why the journey was undertaken. What I do remember, is that the intervening physical space between A and B was something to endure because of the fear of being stopped and having my existence questioned by those who enforced oppression. No journey was undertaken with the certainty that the destination would be reached. Thus, the journey was experienced not as distance to be traversed, but as a series of anxieties to be endured. Time was not distance and speed, but the intensity of anxiety. The longer the distance the more intense was the anxiety. Nothing else existed between A and B but mental and emotional trauma.

In this situation, the concept of tourism is impossible. Tourism was something white people did. They could drag their caravans at a leisurely pace; stop along the way to view endless vistas of physical beauty; eat leisurely at a roadside café while I searched for a small window to buy food to eat in the car in motion. The distance between A and B in my world, was not filled with trees and mountains, and rivers. It was psychological time without space. I had to endure the absence of space; to endure the possibility of a challenge to my existence, a challenge that could come at any time and take any form.

How different the situation is now! There is something exhilarating about being able to stop at any time and enjoy the physical beauty of my country. I can adjust the speed of travel according to my needs. I can take as long as I like to traverse the shortest distance. This is my newly found home; not a building with rooms, but a country full of people, trees, mountains, rivers, houses, factories, farms, mines, roads, the coastline, parliament, schools and universities, military bases, the museum, the art gallery, theatres, the research foundations, the observatory, the stock exchange, the airline . . . everything!

But I needn't have left South Africa to feel this way. Millions of people had to endure long years of internal exile. There must be relatively few South Africans who can still point to a home that they associate with rootedness. At some point in their lives what makes for memories stops, and traumatic fresh beginnings had to be made and endured. The growth of the imagination both for individuals and communities, became a series of interrupted experiences. Is that why I have resorted, in the last two years, to a feeling for the country in place of homes and individual communities?

South Africans have an intriguing capacity to be disarmingly kind and hospitable at the same time as they were capable of the most horrifying cruelty. We have continued in the last two years in fits of violence, to wipe out our families and whole communities; we have abandoned patients to their death in hospitals because we are on strike; we hold university officials hostage, trash campuses, block highways; we burn people suspected of being witches; we abuse our children and rape our women; we engage in brutal taxi wars in which if passengers miraculously escape being killed, they will surely die once the mini buses of death, in a display of recklessness, charge down the highway in a frenzy of speed. All this while we celebrate democracy, human rights, victories in sport. We have abolished the death sentence, are working on the best constitution in the world, have declared free medical care for pregnant women, and continue to receive and welcome guests into our houses with the most moving hospitality.

Has this got anything to do with the dislocating traumas of 'interrupted experiences'? How is the growth of the imagination or the nurturing of human sensibility affected by the dramatic oscillation of individuals and communities between comfort and discomfort, between home and homelessness, between love and hate, between hope and despair, between knowledge and ignorance, between progress and regression, between fame and ignominy, between heroism and roguery, between honour and dishonour, between marriage and divorce, between sophistication and crudeness, between life and death? Has this dislocation become part of the structure of thinking and feeling that characterise our society? How long can we continue to use past traumas as an excuse to justify forms of political action which may have the effect of trivialising, rather than strengthening, democracy? A nation of extremes!

If my home is the whole of this land, because I have rediscovered the physical space between A and B, and that this discovery has become some basis for reconstituting my imagination, for reconciling extremes, I have also become uncomfortably aware that I may no longer have the keen and vital sense or feeling for home as a specific place and a house with so many rooms, so many brothers and sisters and relatives, with family and community experiences stretching many years back. That kind of home for now has been a mere convenience for me to live in from day to day. This thought has frightened me as I have begun to wonder about the fate of intimacy. Can there be any society without private lives; without homes wherein individuals can flourish through histories of intimacy?

Intimacy! A dangerous word which has the capacity to imply banality or profundity. Yet when we gave up the AK-47 for the discourse of negotiation, we opted for intimacy. In the choice between negotiation and revolutionary violence we opted for feelings and the intellect. We committed ourselves to posing questions and researching them for solutions. We opted for complexity, ambiguity, and nuance. It is here that we will develop new political meanings and values. It is here that we will find new homes. It is here that we come to terms with the disturbing truth that both friends and enemies of yesterday can no longer be taken for granted. The heroes of the revolution may reveal distressing flaws, while the devils of repression may become disturbingly lovable.

Enter the Truth and Reconciliation Commission. Through it, we seek to understand the particular nature of our state and how the fluid boundaries between state induced behaviour and personal volition so destroyed the sense of both personal and public morality that there was nothing left in the end by self-perpetuating violence without transcendent goals. The Truth Commission is really not about truth, but about the revelation of hidden facts leading to knowledge and interpretation in the public domain. It is about enriching ethical consciousness in the public domain. It is not so much about judgement, but about the process of formulating judgement. It is about reconstituting the public domain through social insight.

And so it is that the rebuilding of homes and communities is something far more than the political act of meeting the needs of 'the constituency'. There is something more fundamental at play. The rebuilding of homes and communities may have become the most compelling factor in enabling us to sustain our nationhood. That way we may yet prevent our democracy from being an event in which extremes of behaviour can dangerously ossify into spectacles of superficiality, where verbal assertion becomes coincident with reality.

I dream that my children can build homes of the kind that eluded me; homes that can never be demolished by the state in order to make memories impossible; homes that can sustain public life because they infuse into it the values of honour, integrity, compassion, intelligence and creativity. Public intimacies do need private intimacies. This is the discovery of personal and social meaning through the pains and joys of belonging, participating, trusting, and, just feeling at home.

And what have we regained since we voted? Certainly our voices. Our speech. We have yet to regain our homes, our neighbourhoods. We have yet to feel at home.

459

The Meaning of an Island

STEPHEN WATSON

Since the end of the last Ice Age, 12 000 years ago, and the subsequent rise in the level of the sea, Robben Island has remained a place apart, cut off from mainland South Africa by roughly ten kilometres of icy south Atlantic. Every successive role which the Island has taken on in recorded history – whether it be as penal colony, a place of exile for princes from the East, as a British military prison, a leper colony and lunatic asylum, and most recently a high security penitentiary for political prisoners – has only served to further separate this island from the mainland, making its apartness something more symbolic than geographical.

No doubt many people have some inkling that Robben Island is one of those patches of earth invested with significance literally unfathomable because it is the actual site of a human suffering that the mind cannot compass. But unlike Germany's Dachau or Tasmania's Port Arthur, long visited by thousands of people annually, relatively few South Africans, let alone foreigners, have ever visited Robben Island. Paradoxically, South Africa's most famous island, so easily visible from Cape Town, has been more thoroughly exiled from the knowledge of most South Africans than any comparable piece of land. Until a matter of months ago, it has persisted as a place apart, cognitively as much as geographically. The fatal void which the Island was to become for so many lives is also the void in our own memories.

This was something underlined, both wittingly and unwittingly, by one of the most important cultural exhibitions yet to be held in this country. At the Esiquthini-Robben Island Exhibition, mounted

460

at the South African Museum in Cape Town in 1993, there was to be found more information about the Island than had ever before been gathered together. Yet at the same time this exhibition demonstrated, in spite of the efforts of its joint organisers, the Mayibuye Centre at UWC and the Museum's own staff, just how little was known about the Island's history, particularly before the twentieth century. In fact, it was the very gaps in this exhibition's documentation which suggested that Robben Island harbours a deeper, more difficult, and indeed haunting significance, than the obvious political one so often claimed for it.

Not surprisingly, the Robben Island Exhibition gave most weight to the period between 1960-1991 when the Island was a high-security prison for opponents of apartheid, its name virtually synonymous with those of Nelson Mandela, Robert Sobukwe and others. It was from this recent period that most of the exhibits were collected. Thus we found displayed a pair of shoes that a prisoner had lined with fur for the winters on the Island; a jersey handknitted by another; someone's metal bowl, mug, fork and spoon – but no knife. There were faded jotters with notes on dialectical materialism, personal notebooks of aphorisms carefully transcribed, books ranging from Aeschylus to *Lady Chatterley's Lover*, all of them emphasising the extent to which the prisoners, in this period, were able to turn the Island into a virtual university. In addition, there were handmade sports trophies and certificates presented to the prisoner athletes at the Island's annual 'Summer Games', all indicating the degree to which the inmates were able to take their highly abnormal situation and domesticate it.

And there were small items that spoke volumes, such as Ahmed Kathrada's prisoner's ID card, against whose pre-printed 'Vonnis/ Sentence' a single Afrikaans word had been typewritten: LEWENSLANK. The eye was no less arrested by a prisoner's letter sent in the early seventies to the Commanding Officer of the Island prison, humbly requesting permission to purchase sweets worth R16,17 as prizes for the winners of a soccer match. Although this precise sum had been donated by the prisoners themselves, there was scrawled across the letter in official red ballpoint: 'nie goedgekeur nie'.

Such examples of bureaucratic cruelty also suggest, if only by inference, the resilient humanity of the inmates themselves. Many a political prisoner, in his own writing about the Island, has repeatedly stressed the refusal of the prisoners to be brutalised by all that which sought to debase and break them. Thus Neville Alexander, himself incarcerated there for ten years, has spoken of that 'dignity' and 'nobility' which he now associates with the Island before all else. Similarly, Ahmed Kathrada has been concerned to stress that Robben Island should be regarded, above all, as a monument to 'the triumph of the human spirit against the forces of evil – a triumph of freedom and dignity over repression and humiliation'. In fact, this was the chief meaning, the ultimate symbolic significance that something like the Robben Island Exhibition sought to attribute to the Island's history as a whole.

Ironically, it was this selfsame exhibition that revealed why this was only a partial meaning, a half-truth at best. For this was an exhibition which also spoke eloquently of that about which it had far less to say – those much earlier periods in the Island's history for which the surviving documentation is either imperfect or non-existent. Long before Robben Island became a symbol of resistance to apartheid, 'an icon of the struggle', it was South Africa's first dumping-ground, a literal black hole or vanishing-point for lives that society had declared criminal or otherwise deviant. Over the last three centuries it has also been a place of hard labour for British military convicts, of exile for princes from the East Indies, of banishment for Xhosa and other chiefs during the frontier wars, and, not least, a place of confinement for lepers, prostitutes, lunatics (as they were called in the nineteenth century) and human beings otherwise deemed, in the extraordinary phrase of that time, 'the sick poor'. It is because Robben Island has been all these things that it possesses a more far-reaching significance than any it might have gained most recently by becoming one of the world's notorious political prisons.

More than two centuries before Nelson Mandela's imprisonment there, Robben Island was also the place where Rijkhaart Jacobz of Rotterdam and the Khoikhoi prisoner Claas Blink were convicted of sodomy and, on 19 August 1735, with weights tied to their live bodies, were thrown into the sea to drown somewhere between the Island and the mainland. But we simply do not know whether, or in what sense, lives like these might be called, in Kathrada's words, 'a triumph of the human spirit against the forces of evil'.

In 1751, the Island saw an abortive revolt by a number of 'Indiaanen bandieten', after which six men were broken on the cross and three hanged. Here, too, we have no way of knowing if there was a liberatory meaning in the fate of these condemned men. We know only that they must have suffered appallingly: first in the manner of their lives; and then in the manner of their deaths. By the same token, only an illegitimate act of imagination could attribute a triumphalist political meaning to the words of Katyi, the sick wife of the Xhosa chief Maqoma, both confined to the Island in the late 1850s, and who is reported to have refused medicine with the words: 'No, my heart is sore, I want to die.'

On relatively or absolutely unknown lives like these – about whom we know little more than that they were socially unacceptable in the deepest possible sense of that word – the Robben Island Exhibition had almost nothing to say. This was, of course, through no fault of its curators. But it is precisely because there is this relative absence of knowledge and documentation about the Island in the seventeenth, eighteenth, and nineteenth centuries, that one's mind is impelled towards these periods. Even when viewing that exhibition, one wanted to know some of the actual names of the hundreds of lepers confined there between the 1850s and the early 1930s. These were people whose lives were not dignified by their association with a political cause; who were forgotten in a way no political prisoner in the last three decades has been; who found themselves doubly outcast by the mistaken belief of the time which held that their disease was both incurable and highly contagious. What became of the fifteen women suffering from venereal disease and sentenced to banishment on the Island in 1815? Who was Elizabeth Fielding, daughter of a British officer at Fort Murray, commited by her own father to the Island's lunatic asylum in the mid-nineteenth century and who, as the medical records of the time reveal, manifested her insanity in 'a harmless frivolity and indifference to her present situation' on the Island?

By now there are any number of published books which, in the prisoners' own voices, give us some idea of the kinds of homesickness that afflicted them during their sentences. Of the much earlier Koranna prisoner, Jacobus Africaner, however, we know only from a note in the Island's chaplain's diary that he was driven insane by the emotional pressures of his exile there, having to be secured temporarily in the male lunatic asylum in 1882 and once again in 1886. Otherwise, over all such lives, black and white, there hangs the spectre of indefiniteness. Learning the little or next to nothing that there is to be known about them, we cannot be certain whether the sufferings of people like these were redeemed (or not) by a sense of purpose and meaning that reached beyond the predicament of their individual lives.

No doubt an ignorance such as this only adds to the kinds of difficulty which two of the Island's finest historians, Nigel Penn and Harriet Deacon, have already noted in their attempts to piece together its past. But it also points to the further weight of meaning which, I believe, Robben Island has always carried – and ought to carry. Having been, for the greater part of its recorded history, a place of punishment where innumerable lives were sentenced not only to hard labour but to anonymity, the Island remains a natural memorial to the nameless; and, not least, to a suffering no less extreme for having been overwhelmingly anonymous and now largely unremembered.

A few years ago, a Cabinet decision ensured that Robben Island would not be turned into that ultimate triumph of bad taste and bad faith, a playground for tourists, with a casino and other money-spinning attractions. (It is worth mentioning, though, that the present government's decision to turn it into a museum was celebrated by a Cape Town newspaper with the headline that this promised a 'R400-million annual tourism boost' for the city.) But nor should the Island be preserved exclusively as a kind of radically alternative Voortrekker Monument, a place made sacred above all by being the site of Nelson Mandela's cell. For the mostly unavoidable gaps or absences in the Island's history make it clear that this, too, would be a skewing of the truth.

If this entire history is held in mind, the Island cannot but be seen as a place whose meaning lies in the nameless as well as the named, in the superfluous lives of the chronically sick confined there in the nineteenth century as much as in the destinies of more recent, famous political prisoners. Robben Island is separated from mainland South Africa, and should remain so, because it is there, in horribly concentrated form, that types of suffering have taken place which have as often gone unrecorded as they have been preserved in the memory of men and women. As such, one might say that this island represents more completely than any other patch of South African earth that which has been unspeakable (in both senses of the word) in the last three centuries and more of this country's history.

This is not to turn it into a pretext for an exercise in morbidity, but rather a subject for contemplation. South African history, like all history doubtless, consists as much of oblivion as it does of heroes and martyrs. If only for this reason, Robben Island should not afford present and future generations of visitors the luxury, the easy meanings, of a triumphalist political fable. Although it is rightly a memorial to all those who refused to be brutalised by the brutality imposed on them, particularly in the apartheid era, it also brings us up against something even less acceptable than apartheid itself.

It confronts us with the unacknowledged stories of those like Katyi, who may not have triumphed in their struggles with inhuman power; with the almost illegible traces of lunatics who, for all we know, may have died demoralised and confused – scarcely aware that their lives were testimony to a power they perhaps could not comprehend, or even to the calamity that power as such has always been for those condemned to suffer it. This is something that cannot easily be appropriated by any political party or contemporary interest group. But if such things are held in mind, then perhaps the deeper, unassimilable, and indeed haunting meaning of Robben Island may not be forgotten.

The Phone Call

HUGH LEWIN

The Prison Regulations said No News. Politicals can have No News of Outside. They must not know what's happening Outside, they must not know of any political event Outside. They must be totally isolated. In the interests of the State and its Security.

The politicals worked in the Carpentry Shop. This was a relatively small workshop accessible only from the inside yard and thus isolated completely from the outside, beyond the high wall round the yard, beyond the catwalk on top of the wall, guarded always by the man with a rifle. Inside the Carpentry Shop was space enough for four work benches, each with its own tool cabinet, with a listed inventory of the tools in each cupboard. The list was checked at the beginning of each work session and at the end of each day to ensure that all tools stayed permanently inside the Carpentry Shop.

In the far corner of the Carpentry Shop was a door leading into a smaller room, which was the Office of the Carpentry Shop Officer. He was a large man with huge hands and a strangely pleasant smile, who checked the tools at the beginning of each session, and again at the end of each session, and then locked the tools safely away in their cabinets at the end of each working day. The rest of the time he spent in his office in the inside corner of the workshop, studying his huge hands and cleaning his fingernails with a large chisel.

On some occasions he was seen to be sitting quite still, his chin resting on his fists, staring endlessly at the opposite wall. Once the unexpected arrival of another warder disturbed his apparent reverie and revealed that the Officer had, tucked into his hand, a very small radio that he was listening to – which, in a Carpentry Shop for Politicals, who had to be totally isolated, was strictly forbidden,

466

even for the Officer. Sometimes he would study the pages of a newspaper on his desk, quickly stuffing the pages into a drawer if any other warder visited the workshop. The prisoners, barred from news, were not allowed into his office: they stood at the door, asking aimless questions while they stretched their necks to get an upside-down view of the news page, which was invariably long out of date or contained only sports news and comics, over which the Carpentry Officer would chuckle for long hours.

No great events rocked the inner sanctum of the Carpentry Shop nor disturbed its secure isolation from the rest of the prison and the rest of the world. But the Carpentry Officer did have, on the shining smoothness of the desktop in his inner office, one temptingly fascinating object of attention for the politicals: a telephone. A telephone that worked, an aggravatingly tempting symbol of broken barriers, instant link with the great world of events and news outside.

The telephone didn't function much. It would occasionally ring to warn the Officer that some Important Visitors were about to descend on the workshop, whereupon he would scurry out of his office to ensure that all was well, hustling and shining and busy in the Carpentry Shop. Sometimes the Carpentry Officer would appear to make internal calls, lifting the receiver and speaking to someone presumably within the prison because the call involved no dialling. Very occasionally he could be seen actually dialling a number himself: then he would settle back into his chair with the receiver tucked under his chin into his shoulder, a contented look about him. On these occasions, he would lean across his desk and push the door of his office so that it became partially closed to the inquisitive eyes (and ears) of the prisoners.

Every afternoon, having checked the tools in each of the tool cabinets and locked them, the Officer would return to his office and methodically place a lock on the dial of his phone, then lock the key to the lock in a drawer, then carefully lock the door of his office, then lock the door of the Carpentry Shop. Once only, the prisoners noted (for they watched these things), did the Officer forget to lock the dial of his phone before he locked his office and locked the workshop, and on that occasion later in the evening, after lock-up when the cells were all already sealed for the night and just before the night-man with his fearsome dog appeared in the yard, the Officer was spotted hurrying back to the Carpentry

467

Shop, presumably to fix the forgotten phone lock.

So, for the prisoners, ill-content in their isolation and perpetually seeking ways to bridge the walls of silence, the Officer's phone in the Office of the Carpentry Shop was thought of as an unlikely source of smuggled enlightenment. Greater potential seemed to lie in the chance that the Officer would one day bring to work more than just the comics and sports section of his newspaper, or that – a true prize – he would neglect to return to his pocket the mini-radio and that there would be some chance of lifting it. The telephone remained firmly in the realm of Outside, beyond reach.

Until the day of the Big Visit. Nobody seemed to know who was coming, nor precisely when, but quite early one morning a young warder came running breathlessly into the Carpentry Shop and shouted that the prisoners had to line up IMMEDIATELY outside in the yard with their coats on and that the Officer must come now, now, NOW because the Chief was there and wanted to see him now-now-QUICK, and he shouted at the prisoners to Hurry-Hurry as he skidded out again and ran dementedly toward the Chief's office on the other side of the yard. The Carpentry Officer was, for once, considerably roused by this display of official energy and bustled around the prisoners as they downed tools ('Leave them where they are!') and fell into line outside the Carpentry door, ready for whatever High Dignitary might be looming.

At first the Carpentry Officer stood firmly beside his line of prisoners, his bulky hands clasped behind his back and scowling for silence as everybody peered across the yard toward the Chief's office, waiting for signs of the visitation. The young warder with the Urgent Message was hopping from foot to foot outside the office, but there was no further sign of any cause for panic, and the Carpentry Officer, hands clasped still behind his back, began slowly to move across the yard towards the office, occasionally glancing behind him at the prisoners to ensure that they stayed silent and in line. By the time he reached the hopping youngster, the Carpentry Officer was all of thirty metres away from his workshop, able still to keep an eye on the line of prisoners standing outside it.

At which point the prisoner standing immediately in front of the door of the Carpentry Shop was able to slip out of line and back into the workshop itself, temporarily out of sight of the Officer and the other guards. Inside the shop the Officer's office door stood open. The prisoner urgently whispered to his fellow prisoners nearest the door to knock loudly if someone returned from across the yard, then he nipped into the office, going straight to the Officer's desk. There were only three drawers: the top one was locked and there were no keys in sight on top of the desk; the second drawer was open and cluttered with scraps of paper, but no newspaper; and the third had only an empty lunch box in it. No newspapers, no radio. Not even a morsel of contraband.

But on the shining top of the desk, sitting neatly next to a Prisons Department blotter full of doodles, was the telephone. The telephone, with no lock on the dial. The prisoner quickly ran, bent double beneath the window line, back to the outer door and repeated the instruction to warn him with knocks if anybody should return. Then he scuttled back to the unguarded phone and sat down opposite it in the Officer's chair. What to do? He was now four years into his sentence and, after four years of isolation, he found suddenly that he could remember no phone numbers. No, one: the number of his original home, at the village outside Pretoria, going back fifteen years: 65119. He could remember with absolute distinctness how his father, now ten years dead, used to lift the old black handset and say: 'Hello, this is six five one one nine.' Or his mother's more frequent 'Six five double-one nine.' But the rest, gone, blank. And the special dialling code between Pretoria and his home town, Johannesburg, unused and unthought-of for the four years – gone.

It was madness. Here was a phone, unguarded, a godsend, but no numbers. The prisoner delved frantically back into the second drawer of the desk and found, among the papers, a tattered copy of a phone directory, for Pretoria only, without covers, but with lovely long lists of numbers. Whom to phone? Daytime, normal working hours of a weekday, and in Pretoria, where there had been so few friends. Whom to phone, and how to contact Johannesburg, where there were so many friends and wives of fellow inmates? He found the name of a friend, once quite a close and sympathetic friend, but they had not been in touch for several years and certainly not during the trauma of the trial. Not sure even that he was still business manager at his father's firm. But here was the same name, and the telephone number of the firm.

Was that a knock? The prisoner jumped from the chair and ran to the office door, but all still seemed calm, the warders standing in a chattering hustle across the yard.

Rush back to the desk but ... how to get a line? Would the phone connect to the office across the yard or to a switchboard in the main section of the prison? Would they recognise that it wasn't the Carpentry Officer on the line? The prisoner lifted the receiver, holding it carefully, strangely, and coughed to clear his throat. A woman's voice sounded: 'Ja?'

He coughed again and said gruffly, thickening the accent as much as possible: 'Lyn, asseblief. Line, please.' Silence. She said nothing. Had she suspected? He held on, his fingers straining on the handset, beginning to sweat. Then suddenly there was that old familiar click and the burr of a dialling tone. Just like that, Burrrrrrr. The prisoner laughed aloud, then hurried to find the number again in the directory. He dialled, dialled a simple telephone number again, so simple and automatic, after four years. It was ringing – again, the old sound, unchanged, almost welcoming and another woman's voice answered, sounding younger, less guttural than the Prison woman's voice: 'Knowles Brothers, hello.'

The prisoner stuttered. 'Is James there, please?'

'Mr James?'

'Yes, please.' Mr James now, indeed. His hand still sweating, still no warning knocks from the outside door. And the less-guttural woman (what did she look like?) politely asked him – 'Sir' – to wait. (Sir! Four years of abuse and being sworn at, and she called his voice Sir!)

'Mr Knowles' office,' said another, even sweeter voice. (What did SHE look like?) 'Can I help you?'

'Is James Knowles there, please?' he stammered, unsure. Perhaps he was intruding.

'Who's calling, please, Sir?' So sweet, but some frigidity there.

'Tell him' – perhaps all the lines were tapped – 'tell him it's an old friend, and it's urgent.'

'Please hold on, Sir.' Traces still of ice. Protective. But – 'I'm putting you through now, Sir.'

'Knowles here.' The same voice, slightly high-pitched and with a touch of gruffness, yet instantly recognisable and slightly apprehensive. (Wonder if he's gone greyer?)

'Hello, James, it's me' – and the prisoner chuckled. He could

470

almost feel the gulp and distant awkwardness from his friend. 'Don't worry, James. It's only me and I'm still Inside and I don't want anything. Just had the chance to phone and say hello.' The prisoner, secure in his imprisoned isolation, comforted his Outside friend, surrounded by the complicated insecurities of un-imprison-ment. 'It's only me, James.'

'Yes, yes. What do you want? I mean, how are you?'

The prisoner laughed again. 'Sorry to bother you, and how are you? It's been a long time.'

'Yes, yes, indeed,' – recovering – 'but where ARE you? I hear you've had a rough time, yes?'

'No sweat. It's good to hear you. I'm Inside. But, please' – the sudden recollection of the Officer's office and the line of fellow prisoners outside the door and the warders across the yard – 'tell me what's been happening? Quickly, I've not much time. What's new?'

'Oh, nothing much really. We're all well. Oh, Dad died. Last year and I'm now in charge here, with Raymond. You remember? No, nothing's happening really, nothing . . .'

'James, quickly, what's the news? I've not seen a newspaper for four years. What's the NEWS, man, the news?'

'Oh dear, yes, well, I see what you mean. Hmm, yes, the news. Well, there's really not much happening, you know. Are you sure this is all right?'

'Yes, it's all right. But the news, James, what are today's headlines then, just the headlines? Read me the headlines.'

But James couldn't find the morning paper, nor remember anything of importance from it, apart from a car crash, and the rugby team had lost.

'Internationally? The Sino-Soviet dispute? Middle East? America? Vietnam? Europe? What's been HAPPENING? What's happening in the townships? Anything happening HERE?'

'It's really rather difficult, you know. And such a surprise to hear your voice again, nice surprise. You sound so completely unchanged. Marvellous to think you're all right, well, getting through it all, all right, are you?'

'Yes, all right, James, thanks.' The prisoner shrugged and tried to comfort his Outside friend: it didn't matter, really, and everything would be all right, but could he please look up a number in the Johannesburg directory, quickly please: the Stewarts in Melrose,

Malcolm Stewart, probably somewhere like Melrose Drive, Melrose, if he remembered right. Yes, that sounded right, many thanks. And he scribbled the number on the back of a piece of sandpaper lying on the Officer's desk and – 'Thanks, James, goodbye then. See you sometime' – putting the receiver back, clammy.

Outside the office, the line of prisoners stood as before, watching the cluster of warders across the yard. No apparent change, and still no sign of the impending visit. So the prisoner ran back into the office and, almost before getting to the Officer's chair again, lifted the receiver and confidently asked for 'Lyn, asseblief' and, again, there it was. Burr-burr.

The prisoner reached for the piece of sandpaper and then stopped: he had the Johannesburg number, but how to dial there? He had forgotten to ask James for the code. Was it perhaps 19? He paused, tried that, and got what could only have been an engaged sound. Slowly he replaced the receiver and wondered. Could he dare? Was there time? (Hurried check at the door – all well.) So he tried again, easily now adding a greeting: 'Môre, mevrou. Morning. Lyn, asseblief' – and again she gave him one and, with smiling care, he redialled the Pretoria number. 'I've just been talking to Mr James. Could I please speak to him again briefly? Thank you so much.' And straight through: 'Hello again, James. No panic. Just what's the dialling code to Jo'burg? Thanks. 'Bye now.'

Surely she would start to suspect something. Did the Officer ever make so many outside calls, so soon after each other? Maybe it was a big switchboard with several guttural ladies. Unlikely. What would she do, would she really care? What could they do, anyway? Worth the risk: 'Nog 'n lyn, asseblief. Another line, please.' This time she said nothing: burr, just like that. Easy. With extra care, the prisoner dialled first the code, then the new number, and it began to ring. This would be better, he thought: these friends were in fairly close touch with his family and knew his conditions, and were more interested in world events than James – and now he could ask the right sort of questions, quickly, straight away, feeling better prepared and more confident.

'Hello,' said a strange voice, young but not Lydia's. A new maid, perhaps.

'Mrs Stewart, please,' said the prisoner.

'Not here, master.' Oh, my God – master. Four years into a

sentence for actions against apartheid and – *master*. 'Madam's not here, no, master. No, the master's not here either, master. Phone back this afternoon, please, master.'

Yes, all right, thank you – but how could he begin to explain the problems of phoning back this afternoon, any afternoon, and no, he's sorry he can't easily be reached if he left the number, which he doesn't actually know because it's not written here on the Officer's phone? But, thank you, and are you well all the way over there in Johannesburg?

The Officer's phone . . . The prisoner suddenly realised there was something of a commotion outside the office. He hurriedly replaced the receiver and just had time to reach the door of the office when the urgent young warder burst through the line of prisoners and rushed into the empty workshop, his eyes wide, almost tearful, meeting the prisoner inside the workshop. 'Wat *doen* jy hier? What are you *doing* here?' – it was more of a choked scream than a question and the warder at first ignored the prisoner and ran straight into the Officer's office, looking around everywhere, pulling open the drawers and, finally, lifting the handset of the phone and staring at it. 'Were you here?' the warder shouted, still holding the handset and raging at the prisoner. 'Were you *here*, I say!' – reaching again to a scream.

The prisoner shrugged and stared back, gaining insolent confidence in the face of the young warder's hysterical discomfort. 'Miskien, ja. Perhaps, yes.' He turned his back and began walking out of the workshop. The warder stuttered after him: 'Ek sal jou *charge*. I'll charge you!' The prisoner looked back over his shoulder and shrugged again. He was in time to slip back unnoticed into the line of prisoners just as the Commanding Officer and his deputy, with the Carpentry Officer and the several visiting Dignitaries, emerged into the yard and stepped formally towards them. It was an Official Visit from several Important People who, as they reached the Carpentry Shop, were greeted with a snappy salute from the young warder now standing alongside the line of political prisoners. The warder looked flustered but lifted his chin and shouted: 'All's PRESENT and CORRECT, SIR!' The Commanding Officer, with the Carpentry Officer beside him, nodded contentedly, happy to see that the State's interests remained sound and secure, at all times. All under control. No chink in the armour.

A PLAY FOR A WRITING LIFE

Thabo for Thabo

MIKE VAN GRAAN

This version of the playscript was first performed in October 1997
at the Playhouse Theatre in Durban with
Ashley Donds and Mzwandile Kamang in the roles of the two
characters

Spotlight on Vusi, seated by himself at a table, talking into a tape-recorder.

Vusi: I'm sorry you didn't make it to the funeral, Debbie. But I'm sure he would've understood. Australia's far away, and you were here only eight months ago. You can't keep coming back every time there's a family funeral. I should've known Debs. I should have known from our last conversation. I should've done something ...

Fade to blackout. Lights up on a new scene, the scene of the 'last conversation'. Steve, a human rights lawyer by practice, is seated, looking somewhat unkempt having spent a few days in a police cell. Vusi is excellently groomed as a suave human rights lawyer, a colleague of Steve.

Steve: Fourteen years ago, Vusi. 1982. That's when we first met. Right here, in this very cell. Bizarre, isn't it? I remember you being led in by Captain van Jaarsveld. Your right eye was completely closed and the other was only half open. You had a massive bruise on your forehead. And there was dry blood all

477

around your nose. You looked like 'Dead man walking'. I'll never forget Van Jaarsveld's words. 'Look, Rambo's been fighting with the AZAPO detainees again. But they really *moered* him this time!' Did he *really* expect me to believe that? I wonder what he's doing now. Probably farming with an early retirement package.

Vusi: Did I ever tell you?

Steve: What?

Vusi: That I bumped into him at the World Cup Rugby Final.

Steve: No!

Vusi: He was with his two sons. About twelve and fourteen, but both already had fully developed policeman ears (*cups his hands behind his ears, to make them stand out more*)

Steve: I could never think of those guys as having children or wives or dogs.

Vusi: They were all carrying new South African flags.

Steve: What!

Vusi: That's exactly what *I* thought. I said to him, 'Hey Captain, it's nice to see we're on the same side at last.'

Steve: What did *he* say?

Vusi: He didn't recognise me at first. So I said, 'Captain, it's me, Rambo.' And he said 'Which one?' Eventually he made the connection. Then it was like we were old buddies. He told me how he had been following my career in the papers, how proud he was that he knew this famous lawyer. I was one of his boys. Like we were now all rich and famous for having passed through his correctional school.

Steve: The bastard.

Vusi: Then I said, 'I don't suppose you'll be supporting a team called the "All Blacks", Captain'. He told me that we'd *always* been on the same side. And that he'd *never* supported apartheid.

Steve: (*ironically*) Of course.

Vusi: He was just doing his job as a security policeman. I said 'Ja, Captain. I still have the scars to show just how well you did your job.'

Steve: I wonder if he's applied for amnesty.

Vusi: I don't know. And you know what? I don't particularly care.

Steve: (*surprised*) Really? If I hadn't got you out on a legal technicality, he'd have *killed* you. Like he killed Khumalo, Maponyane, Dixie . . .

Vusi: I've had to put all of that behind me, Steve. I don't know what it would do to me to have to remember all of that again. To talk about it. Publicly. I used to fantasise about what I would do to Van Jaarsveld if I ever met him in the street. Like push him in front of a bus. Or throttle him with my bare hands. Maybe I would throw a petrol bomb into his car. What if I kidnapped his children. And tortured them. Like he tortured so many parents' sons. (*laughs at the thought*) It became an obsession. And it got to me. I became this post-detention cliché, swinging from irrational anger to pathetic self-pity. I was afraid to sleep because of the nightmares. When I *did* sleep, I used to wake up weeping. I spent a lot of time in counselling. You know. You arranged it. And paid for a lot of it.

Steve: And now you can talk with him. Joke with him.

Vusi: Twelve, fourteen years – that's a long bridge. A lot of water has passed in that time. And anyway, isn't this the new South

Africa? It's reconciliation time!

Steve: I think I'll nominate you for the Nelson-Mandela-Over-the-Top-Reconciliation award.

Vusi: (*laughs*) Sure.

Steve: I don't know how you can do it, Vusi.

Vusi: Because of you, Steve.

Steve: Me?

Vusi: *You* got me out after months in detention. *You* convinced me not to leave the country. To take up arms. *You* persuaded me not to become like them. That violence was not the answer. *You* got me a scholarship to study law in Britain. And who got me a job at his law firm when it wasn't yet cool to do so? *You!*

Steve: And look where you are today.

Vusi: And look where *you* are today.

Steve: Ja. History certainly has a sense of humour.

Vusi: (*pause*) Are you comfortable?

Steve: It's not exactly *The Holiday Inn*.

Vusi: We're working on getting you out on bail. We're offering to put up R500 000.

Steve: (*incredulously*) What!?

Vusi: Remember Themba Mogau?

Steve: The Black Lawyers Association heavy?

Vusi: Exactly. He was appointed recently as a senior prosecutor.

Part of the Justice Department's fast tracking programme. Anyway, he's handling your case. And he thinks that he can make his reputation with this one.

Steve: Good for him.

Vusi: He's been watching too much OJ Simpson, if you ask me. He's been seduced by all the media coverage you've been getting. And he'd like to bask in some of that.

Steve: Why 500 000?

Vusi: Mogau's arguing that you killed two people, and badly wounded a third. And that it's likely that you'll go after the third to finish him off, since he's the one who allegedly pulled the trigger. So we're offering R500 000 as bail. We think he'll bite if you also agree to some other bail conditions like ... some form of house arrest, surrendering your passport ... Also, the law firm will stand surety for you to show that *we* believe that you'll be a good guy once you're out on bail.

Steve: And *do* you believe that?

Vusi: The whole truth?

Steve: Nothing but ...!

Vusi: We don't know ... I don't know. We're all still in a state of shock. This is like out of the movies. It's not supposed to happen to us.

Steve: I'm sorry.

Vusi: For what?

Steve: For letting it happen to you.

Vusi: You sorry for what you've done?

Steve: Why don't you just walk away?

Vusi: Do you have *any* remorse, Steve?

Steve: Vusi, you don't have to do this.

Vusi: No, no. I want to do this. But I want to know . . .

Steve: What?

Vusi: If you've got rid of your demons.

Steve: What's that supposed to mean?

Vusi: If we get you out on bail . . .

Steve: . . . will I be a nice guy?

Vusi: Yeah.

Steve: I don't know.

Vusi: You don't know?

Steve: No.

Vusi: So where does that leave us?

Steve: Why are you doing this, Vusi?

Vusi: Because I want to.

Steve: It's an open and shut case. I shot three guys. Two of them dead. I'm guilty. You shouldn't be wasting your time with this.

Vusi: I'm not doing this as a lawyer. I'm doing this as a friend.

Steve: As a friend, I'm saying you shouldn't be wasting your time with this.

Vusi: That's for me to decide.

Steve: Fine. But if I were you, I'd walk away from this.

Vusi: No, you wouldn't.

Steve: So what is this? Payback time? Because I once helped you . . .? You don't have to, Vusi. I appreciate it. Really. But you don't have to.

Vusi: Look. Let's cut the crap. I'm your lawyer whether you like it or not. And I'm your friend. OK? Not for this or that reason. I'm your friend. Period. Just accept that. And I'm going to handle this, OK?

Steve: OK.

Vusi: So, will you be a good guy if we get you out on bail?

Steve: You asking as my lawyer, or as my friend?

Vusi: Both.

Steve: As my lawyer, take whatever answer you think you need. As my friend, don't put up any of the 500 grand yourself. I can't guarantee the investment.

Vusi: (*sighs*) Where'd you get the gun?

Steve: I bought it.

Vusi: When?

Steve: One, two years ago . . .

Vusi: It's been licensed in your name for two and a half years. I checked.

Steve: (*shrugs*) That long.

Vusi: You signed the office petition for a society free of guns.

Steve: Yeah. Sure.

Vusi: And you've been a closet gun-carrier for two and a half years?

Steve: Disappointed?

Vusi: Confused.

Steve: You remember the first time they broke into our house? Renee and I laughed it off as our contribution to contemporary dinner talk. The second time, when they wiped us out for just about everything we had, again we looked on the bright side. We got the insurance money, went on an overseas holiday, and redecorated our house. But the third time . . . when they broke in while we were asleep, and this after we put up high walls and everything, that really got to us. We were scared, Vusi. Very scared. We sold at a great loss, and moved into a safer neighbourhood. And that's when I bought the gun. When Renee fell pregnant, she wanted us to move to Cape Town. We thought it would be safer. But I couldn't go. I'd just become a senior partner . . .

Vusi: Do you regret it?

Steve: Of course. If we had moved to Cape Town, none of this would have happened.

Vusi: I meant the shootings.

Steve: The shootings? Do I regret the shootings?

Vusi: Yes.

Steve: (*gets increasingly excited*) Do I regret shooting those bastards? Are you kidding?

Vusi: You don't feel *any* remorse?

Steve: You already asked me that.

Vusi: And you didn't answer.

Steve: Will they reduce my sentence if I did? Is that it?

Vusi: I just want to know.

Steve: You want me to act like I'm sorry?

Vusi: Only if you are . . .

Steve: You want me to put on a song and dance? To impress the judge? To make him feel sorry for me? I'll show remorse, Vusi. I'll weep! I'll cry! I'll drown the judge in tears if you want. But it won't be for those bastards. Cos you know what, Vusi? I don't feeling a fucking thing!

Vusi: Don't become like them, Vusi!

Steve: Is that what I used to tell you?

Vusi: Don't let them take away your heart . . .

Steve: Sure. I remember saying that.

Vusi: When they take your heart . . .

Steve: . . . they take your soul . . .

Vusi: And so you too . . . become nothing more than a beast.

Steve: So I was wrong! So I lied to you! So I didn't know what the fuck I was talking about back then. Maybe you should have gone and joined MK. And come back, and pumped Van Jaarsveld full of bullets. Till he bled like a sieve . . .

Vusi: And then?

Steve: I don't know . . . You would have felt better.

Vusi: I feel fine. I feel especially good for not having killed anybody.

Steve: Oh bullshit, Vusi! You would have come back. Like all the ANC cadres who came back after years of planting bombs. Killing policemen. Taking out informers. And you'd have been a hero. You would be in parliament, or a diplomat in some foreign embassy. Not exactly un-adjusted!

Vusi: Maybe. Or maybe I could have come back like one of the kids you shot. Drafted into the new army. Downsized. Retrenched. Unskilled. And all I knew . . . was how to use a gun.

Steve: (*shrugs his shoulders*) My heart bleeds, Vusi.

Vusi: You shot them in cold blood.

Steve: (*ironically*) Yes, your honour . . .

Vusi: And you feel nothing.

Steve: No, your honour . . .

Vusi: It leaves you cold . . .

Steve: No, Vusi! I know what you're trying to do. It's not the same thing! It's not a Jimmy Kruger-Biko thing.

Vusi: They were human beings . . .

Steve: They were murderers!

Vusi: So it's OK to go around shooting murderers.

Steve: I'm not saying what I did was right . . .

Vusi: You've set us back, Steve. Three years. Maybe more. We're trying to build respect for the rule of law. Respect for human rights. Respect for life. And then you go . . . and betray us.

Steve: Betray?

Vusi: I'll bet that every Dick, Tom and Sipho is saying to himself, if a top human rights lawyer can do this, why should we restrain ourselves?

Steve: You want to know what betrayal is?

Vusi: All vigilantes have now found themselves a patron saint. Steve Charles Bronson Andrews!

Steve: Think about it, Vusi! Is this what we were struggling for? To be held hostage by thugs? Rapists? Murderers? Out of apartheid's frying pan, into crime's fire! What does it take to feel safe nowadays? Become a cabinet minister, with legions of body-guards? Maybe Dick, Tom and Sipho *are* the betrayed. Betrayed by politicians! By incompetent police! By the law!

Vusi: I don't believe I'm hearing this!

Steve: Yes, I know . . .

Vusi: You sat on the technical committee . . .

Steve: . . . that helped to redraft our bail and other laws in terms of our Bill of Rights. I know. But I now also know what it's like to be a victim of a criminal let out on bail. I know what it means to grieve for a loved one, killed in cold blood! Senselessly!

Vusi: So what are you suggesting? That all victims go out and arm themselves? And hunt down all criminals and kill them? Feed the anarchy?

Steve: I am suggesting nothing!

Vusi: But you already have. You've sent out a signal. You shot three guys. And where? In a courtroom!

Steve: They were standing in the dock . . .

Vusi: And you shot them.

Steve: One minute, they were waving and smiling at their families . . .

Vusi: And the next minute, you shot them!

Steve: I resented them. Like they had no cares in the world . . .

Vusi: Then, bang! Bang! Bang!

Steve: All rise in court, the orderly said.

Vusi: And before the judge could make his appearance, you shot them!

Steve: Yes, I shot them.

Vusi: In cold blood.

Steve: Yes!

Vusi: At point blank!

Steve: Yes!

Vusi: Their brains on the wall!

Steve: Yes!

Vusi: Their blood on your face, your hands, your clothes . . .

Steve: Yes! Yes! Yes!

Vusi: And you felt nothing!

Steve: Yes! No! I felt nothing!

Vusi: Ten seconds.

Steve: That's all it took . . .

Vusi: Ten seconds to end two lives, and nearly a third.

Steve: That about makes it square.

Vusi: Arsehole! You're such an arsehole!

Steve: I know. But I've never felt this good.

Vusi: I've been having these screaming matches with you. In my head. Nothing as polite as this.

Steve: So, take the gloves off.

Vusi: (*ironically*) Of course. You're the tough guy.

Steve: Don't feel sorry for me.

Vusi: Right! You don't need sympathy. Not mine or anyone else's.

Steve: Say what you want to say, Vusi . . .

Vusi: Sure! You can handle it. (*Pause. He bangs his fist into a wall*) I am so pissed off with you . . . Why, Steve? Why? Why didn't you say something to me? To anyone? Why didn't you let us know what was on your mind? What you were thinking! Feeling! No! You're Mr Do-it-yourself! And what happens? You fuck up everything! Everything! Your career! Your life! Friendships! Not to mention the human rights agenda! This wasn't spur-of-the-moment stuff! This was premeditated, cold-blooded murder! Were you afraid we might talk you out of it? Damn right we would have! I would have strapped you to your bed if I had to! I've been there, Steve! I've been on the brink! If anybody knows about anger, about hate, about revenge, it's me! I've been there, man! And you helped to pull me back. Why didn't you give me the same chance!

Steve: (*his attitude changes as a result of the last speech, now engaging Vusi*) I don't know. Because . . .

Vusi: Because what?

Steve: Because . . . because I had to do it.

Vusi: You *had* to shoot those three guys!

Steve: Yes.

Vusi: What? Was it in your horoscope that morning? 'You will shoot three guys today.' What happened to Steve, the pacifist I once knew?

Steve: He doesn't exist any more.

Vusi: Really? Since when?

Steve: Since . . . (*changes his mind, goes off on another tack*) I'm scared, Vusi. I'm more scared of living than of dying. I've never felt so helpless. Never. So out of control of my life. Everytime I see a black person, I think, 'Is he a hijacker, a mugger? Does he have a gun?' It wasn't like that. I've become a racist. *After* apartheid! Funny, isn't it? I see it happening to me! And it angers me! It angers me that I cannot do anything about it! What kind of life is this? The pacifist? He's dead. The non-racist? He's dying. The human rights lawyer? He's just fucked up! Badly!

Vusi: Listen to yourself, Steve.

Steve: What do you hear?

Vusi: You've become this pathetic little victim. Like all those victims of 'the system' who think life owes them something.

Steve: (*Pause*) I hope you never have to do it, Vusi.

Vusi: Do what?

Steve: Bury your wife and unborn child.

(*Moment of silence as neither says anything*)

Vusi: Oh God!

Steve: I know what I did was wrong. I know it contradicts everything I ever stood for. Everything I believe in. But I had to do something. For eight months, I've been plagued by guilt, tortured by how things might have been different if only we had moved to Cape Town, if only we had done this or that! Then, when they arrested those bastards, I felt that justice would be done, and somehow, this great burden would be lifted. But then Vusi, they all got out on bail of R500. Five months later, all three of them are back in court, charged with another hijacking. I couldn't let them get away with it, Vusi. I couldn't. This wasn't about some nameless statistics. This was about my wife. My son. My daughter.

Vusi: I don't know what to say.

Steve: You know what the coroner said? The foetus had been shot through the neck. It wasn't even just a foetus any more. It was a six-month-old, living creature! They *must* have seen that she was pregnant. But it didn't matter to them! They shot her in the stomach area, twice, and once in the chest. Why? Why Vusi? Why? For a BMW convertible? What did she do? Did she plead with them not to shoot her? I can't imagine that she tried to resist. I go over and over it in my mind. She's about to pull into the driveway, waiting for the automatic gates to open. These three guys appear from nowhere, with guns. Did she scream? Did they panic? Did they just callously blow her away? I'll never know. All I know is that she's dead. She's dead, Vusi. And the child we were looking so forward to having . . . If he was a boy, we were going to call him Thabo, a gift of life.

Vusi: Thabo. As in Thabo Makhanye.

Steve: Thabo Makhanye?

Vusi: He's the one who's still struggling for his life under police guard in hospital.

Steve: (*softly*) A Thabo for a Thabo . . .

Vusi: Steve . . .

Steve: I campaigned for the abolition of the death penalty. So I know I'm supposed to feel guilty about having taken human life. I know that two wrongs don't make a right. I know that even murderers are human beings, and that they have a right to a fair trial. I know all that! So I've tried over and over to replay the shootings in my mind. To see if they would conjure up any emotion. But there's just a numbness. I try . . . I try hard to feel something. But all I see are their three faces distorted with absolute terror as I'm about to shoot them. I keep waiting for remorse to hit me. For regret and shame to swallow me up like quicksand. But nothing. Nothing. Just calm. The last two nights are the first in eight months that I've been able to sleep through without medication.

Vusi: You just talk, OK?

Steve: (*teasingly*) So now you're my shrink.

Vusi: No. Still just your friend.

Steve: Good. So no more lawyer questions.

Vusi: Not today.

Steve: Renee fell pregnant soon after we were married. Totally unplanned. It was a shock for both of us. It came at such a bad time, especially for Renee whose career was just beginning to take off. I was quite keen that we have the child, but Renee wasn't. She had an abortion in London. Hey, I'm a human rights lawyer, right? It was her decision, as a woman. Three years later, we both felt ready for kids. And I was looking forward to catching up on having the child I could have had three years earlier. Yet all the time in the back of my mind, I had this thought that maybe there was this moral universe, and that all these aborted foetuses would get together and exact revenge on us by sending a kid with twelve fingers, or with no head or with some other deformity. I never for one moment thought that their revenge would be this wretched.

Vusi: You should've gone for professional help, Steve.

Steve: I know.

Vusi: You bottled it all up inside, till it exploded.

Steve: You're right. (*Pause*) I don't know how you did it, Vusi.

Vusi: What?

Steve: How you got rid of your demons after what they did to you.

Vusi: Time and distance, Steve. Time and distance. Life goes on.

Steve: Yeah.

Vusi: Oh, I nearly forgot. We've received all these faxes for you.

Steve: For me?

Vusi: People out there think you're a hero. (*reaches into his briefcase and pulls out faxes, hands these to Steve*)

Steve: Oh God!

Vusi: Have you seen the newspapers?

Steve: No.

Vusi: You've made headlines in all of them. Even the Nats are sympathising with you . . .

Steve: (*he has been looking through the faxes while Vusi has been speaking*) This is bizarre. Here are faxes from The Campaign for the Death Penalty, from PAGAD . . . (*having glanced through more faxes*) Can you believe this?

Vusi: What?

Steve: There are two marriage proposals!

Vusi: Yes, I saw those.

Steve: (*reflectively*) I miss her Vusi. God, I miss her . . . You still religious?

Vusi: You know what they say. Once a Catholic . . .

Steve: Will you pray for her? And for our Thabo? Will you pray for me?

Lights fade to black. Spotlight comes up on Vusi as in opening scene, talking into a tape.

Vusi: I should have known that he might do something like that, Debbie. I should have known. The waste of it all. The sheer waste! They took away his belt and his shoelaces. But he stuffed his nostrils with the faxes which I had brought. Then he rolled what was left into a ball, and jammed it into his mouth. He lay on his bed, folded his arms, and suffocated himself to death. The waste, Debbie, the sheer waste of it all . . .

Lights fade to black.

Chronology

1923 Nadine Gordimer was born on 20 November in Springs, near Johannesburg. Her father, Isidore Gordimer, a Lithuanian emigrant at thirteen, was a watchmaker and jeweller by trade. Her mother, Nan Myers Gordimer, emigrated to South Africa from England with her parents when she was six. Gordimer was educated at the Convent of Our Lady of Mercy in Springs until the age of eleven after which she received private tuition until she was fifteen or sixteen.

1937 First published story, 'The Quest for Seen Gold', appeared in the Children's Section of the *Sunday Express*, 13 June.

1939 First adult fiction, 'Come Again Tomorrow', published in *The Forum* (Johannesburg).

1945 Attended the University of the Witwatersrand, but left after one year.

1949 Married Dr Gerald Gavron. Publication of *Face to Face: Short Stories*.

1950 Daughter, Oriane, born on 6 June.

1952 Publication of *The Soft Voice of the Serpent and Other Stories*. Divorced from Dr Gavron.

1953 Publication of *The Lying Days*.

1954 Married Reinhold Cassirer, an art dealer originally from Heidelberg, Germany.

1955 Son, Hugo, born on 28 March.

1956 Publication of *Six Feet of the Country*.

1958 Publication of *A World of Strangers*, banned in South Africa till 1970.

1960 Publication of *Friday's Footprint and Other Stories*.

1961 Awarded the W H Smith Literary Award for *Friday's Footprint* (1960) and the Ford Foundation Fellowship to the United States as Visiting Lecturer at the Institute of Contemporary Arts, Washington, DC.

1963 Publication of *Occasion for Loving*.

1965 Publication of *Not for Publication and Other Stories*.

1966 Publication of *The Late Bourgeois World*, banned till 1976.

1967 Edited *South African Writing Today* with Lionel Abrahams.

1969 Granted Thomas Pringle Award for creative writing in English in South African magazine (South Africa). Visiting Lecturer, Harvard University (Cambridge, Massachusetts) and Northwestern University, Illinois.

1970 Publication of *A Guest of Honour*. Visiting Lecturer at the University of Michigan (Ann Arbor).

1971 Publication of *Livingstone's Companions*. Appointed Adjunct Professor of Writing, Columbia University (New York).

1972 Awarded James Tait Black Memorial Prize (England) for *A Guest of Honour*.

1973 Publication of *The Black Interpreters: Notes on African Writing* and *On the Mines* (with David Goldblatt).

1974 Publication of *The Conservationist*. Awarded CNA Prize (South Africa) for *A Guest of Honour* and joint winner of the Booker Prize (England) for *The Conservationist*.

1975 Publication of *Selected Stories*. Awarded CNA Prize for *The Conservationist* and Grand Aigle d'Or Prize (France). Visiting Gildersleeve Professor at Barnard College (New York).

1976 Publication of *Some Monday for Sure*.

1978 Publication of *No Place Like: Selected Stories*.

1979 Publication of *Burger's Daughter*, banned 11 July and reinstated in August. Appointed Honorary Member of the American Academy and Institute of Arts and Letters.

1980 Awarded CNA Prize for *Burger's Daughter*. Publication of *A Soldier's Embrace*, *Town and Country Lovers*, and *What Happened to Burger's Daughter or How South African Censorship Works*. Appointed Honorary Member of the American Academy of Arts and Sciences.

1981 Publication of *July's People* and broadcasting of 'A Terrible Chemistry' – Writers and Places Television Series, England. Scripted screenplays for four of the seven television dramas collectively entitled 'The Gordimer Stories' 1981-1982 ('Country Lovers', 'A Chip of Glass Ruby', 'Praise', and 'Oral History'). Awarded Scottish Arts Council Neil M Gunn Fellowship, the Common Wealth Award for Distinguished Service in Literature (USA) and the CNA Prize for *July's People*. Honorary Doctorate of Literature conferred by the University of Leuven, Belgium.

1982 Granted Modern Language Association Award (USA).

1983 Co-scripted and co-produced 'Choosing for Justice: Allan Boesak' with Hugo Cassirer.

1984 Publication of *Something Out There*. Awarded Honorary Doctorate of Literature by the University of the Witwatersrand.

1985 Awarded the Premio Malaparte (Italy) for her contribution to literature. Honorary Doctorates of Literature conferred by Smith College (Northampton, Massachusetts) and Mount Holyoke College (South Hadley, Massachusetts). Awarded Honorary Doctorate of Humane Letters, City College of New York.

1986 Publication of *Lifetimes: Under Apartheid*. Awarded Nelly Sachs Prize (West Germany), Officier de l'Ordre des Arts et des Lettres (France), and Brockport Writers Forum International Award (State University of New York, Brockport). Honorary Doctorates of Literature conferred by Harvard University (Cambridge, Massachusetts), Yale University (New Haven, Connecticut) and University of Cape Town (South Africa). Assisted in organising the Anti-Censorship Action Group (ACAG).

1986 Elected Vice-President of PEN.

1987 Publication of *A Sport of Nature*. Awarded Honorary Doctorates of Literature by Columbia University (New York), the New School for Social Research (New York City) and York University (England). Elected Patron and Regional Representative, Congress of South African Writers (COSAW).

1988 Publication of *The Essential Gesture: Writing, Politics and Places*.

1989 Scripted and narrated a documentary in BBC series 'Frontiers: Gold and the Gun' concerning the South Africa-Mozambique frontier. Broadcast 6 June on BBC1 Television.

1990 Publication of *My Son's Story*.

1991 Elected Publicity Secretary of COSAW. Awarded the CNA Prize for *My Son's Story*. Publication of *Jump and Other Stories* and *Crimes of Conscience*. Awarded the Nobel Prize for Literature, October. Granted the highest French Art and Literature decoration, the Commandeur dans l'Ordre des Arts et Lettres, November.

1992 Elected COSAW Vice-President. Participated in the Mayibuye Community Arts Academy held in Port Elizabeth from 15-20 December concerning the role of the arts in the transformation of South Africa. Honorary Doctorates of Literature conferred by the University of Durban-Westville and from Cambridge University (England). Participated in the Grahamstown Festival Winter School Lectures, 5 July. Publication of *Why Haven't You Written? Selected Stories – 1950-1972*.

1993 Elected member of a board of trustees charged with the responsibility of overseeing a proposed Foundation for Arts and Culture concerned with the process of transformation and cultural reconstruction in South Africa, under the wing of the ANC's Department of Arts and Culture.

1994 Publication of *None to Accompany Me*.

1995 Publication of the Charles Norton Lectures *Writing and Being*.

1996 Appointed as trustee of the Arts and Culture Trust of the President.

1998 Publication of *The House Gun*. Appointed as UN Goodwill Ambassador in the campaign to eradicate poverty.

Notes on Contributors

Lionel Abrahams is a poet, fiction writer, critic, editor and publisher who lives in Johannesburg. His volumes of poetry include *The Whiteman's Blues*; *Thresholds of Tolerance*; *Journal of a New Man*; *A Writer in Sand* and *Live Birds in a Dead Tree*. *The Celibacy of Felix Greenspan* is a work of fiction. He has edited *Purple Renoster*, *Quarry* and *Sesame* and the fiction of Herman Charles Bosman. He is the recipient of many awards, including a Medallion from the English Academy of Southern Africa.

Tatamkhulu Afrika is the pen-name of Ismael Joubert, a poet and fiction writer born in Egypt who now lives in Cape Town. His six collections of poetry include *Nine Lives, Dark Rider* and *Maqabane*. He has also published two novels, *Broken Earth* and *The Innocents* as well as a collection of novellas. His awards include the CNA début award and the Olive Schreiner Award.

Joan Baker is a short story writer who lives in Cape Town. Her work has been published in journals and anthologies. 'Wild Flowers for Poppie' is the title story of a forthcoming collection of short fiction.

Ken Barris is a writer of fiction and a poet who lectures in architecture in Cape Town. His publications include *An Advertisement for Air*; *Small Change and Other Stories* and *The Jailer's Dairy*. He has received the Ingrid Jonker Award for Poetry and the M-Net Fiction Prize.

Elleke Boehmer is a writer of fiction and a literary scholar. She was born in Durban but now lives and works in Britain where she teaches in Post-colonial Studies at the University of Leeds. Her novels include *Screens Against the Sky* and *An Immaculate Figure*. She has published widely on Post-colonialism.

André Brink is a writer of fiction, playwright, translator and literary theorist based in the Department of English at the University of Cape Town. He is the author of thirteen novels, including *Looking on Darkness, Rumours of Rain, A Dry White Season, A Chain of Voices, States of Emergency, An Act of Terror, To the Contrary, Sandcastles* and *Devil's Valley*. His awards include three CNA Awards, the Martin Luther King Prize, and the Prix Médicis Etranger. He has also published several scholarly volumes on literature.

Dennis Brutus is a poet and scholar who was born in Salisbury, Rhodesia, of South African parents. Banned from all gatherings in 1961, he later served a term of eighteen months on Robben Island. He left South Africa in 1966 and now teaches literature at the University of Pittsburgh in the USA. His poetry collections include *Sirens, Knuckles, Boots; Letters to Martha and Other Poems from a South African Prison; A Simple Lust,* and *Stubborn Hope*.

Guy Butler is a poet, autobiographer, playwright, historian, anthologiser and literary scholar. Born in Cradock, he served in Italy and North Africa with the allied forces during the Second World War and until his retirement held the Chair of English at Rhodes University. His poetry includes *Selected Poems* and *Songs and Ballads*. His autobiographies include *Karoo Morning* (1977), *Bursting World* and *A Local Habitation*. He is the recipient of a Medallion from the English Academy of Southern Africa.

Stephen Clingman is a literary scholar and biographer who was born in South Africa and now lives in the USA where he chairs the Department of English at the University of Massachusetts. His publications include *The Novels of Nadine Gordimer: History from the Inside* and *Bram Fischer: An Afrikaner Communist*.

Ampie Coetzee is literary scholar, translator, anthologiser and critic based in the Department of Afrikaans at the University of Western

Cape. He was a co-founder of the publishing house Taurus and editor of the *Southern African Review of Books*. His publications include *Poësie en Politiek*; *Marxisme en die Afrikaanse Letterkunde* and *Letterkunde en Krisis*. He has also compiled several selected volumes of the poetry of Breyten Breytenbach including *And Death as White Words* and *Die Hand Vol Vere*.

J M Coetzee is a novelist, translator, linguist and literary theorist based in the Department of English at the University of Cape Town. His novels include *Dusklands*, *In the Heart of the Country*, *Waiting for the Barbarians*, *Life and Times of Michael K*, *Foe*, *Age of Iron* and *Master of Petersburg*. *Boyhood* is an autobiographical narrative. His essays have appeared in *White Writing*, *Doubling the Point*, and *Giving Offence*. His awards include two CNA Awards, the Geoffrey Faber Memorial Prize, The James Tait Black Memorial Prize, the Booker Prize, the Sunday Express Book of the Year Award and the Jerusalem Prize.

Lisa Combrinck is a poet who lectures at Vista University in Pretoria. A selection of her poems 'The Shadow of Desire' appeared in the anthology *Essential Things*. She is the convener of the Literary Panel of the National Arts Council of South Africa.

Jeremy Cronin is a poet, critic and Deputy Secretary General of the South African Communist Party. He was jailed for seven years under the apartheid Terrorism Act. His poetry collections include *Inside,* for which he received the Olive Schreiner Award, and *Even the Dead.*

Achmat Dangor is a poet, novelist, short story writer and playwright. A director of the Urban Foundation, his fiction includes *Waiting for Leila*; *Z Town Trilogy*; and *Kafka's Curse*. His poetry includes *Bulldozer* and *Private Voices*. He is the recipient of the Mofolo/Plomer Prize and the Herman Charles Bosman Award for fiction.

Leon de Kock is a poet, fiction writer and critic. He has published *Bloodsong*, a volume of poetry. *Civilising Barbarians* is a critical study on early South African literature. The recipient of the Thomas

Pringle prize for poetry, he is editor of *scrutiny2*, the journal of the Department of English at the University of South Africa.

Ingrid de Kok is a poet and director of the Department of Adult Education and Extramural Studies at the University of Cape Town. Her poetry includes *Familiar Ground* and *Transfer*. She was advisory editor of the *World Literature Today* issue on South African literature and co-editor of *Spring is Rebellious: Arguments about Cultural Freedom*.

Shaun de Waal is a short story writer and Books Editor of the *Mail & Guardian*. He has published a volume of short stories, *These Things Happen*, and is a recipient of the Thomas Pringle Award for Literary Reviews.

Charles Jonathan (Jonty) Driver is a poet, novelist and educationist. Born in Cape Town, he was the President of the National Union of South African Students in 1963 and 1964. After ninety days in detention he left South African for England. While at Trinity College, Oxford, the South African authorities refused to renew his passport. He is now a British citizen. His four novels include *Elegy for a Revolutionary*. His poetry includes *Occasional Light* and *In the Water-Margins*.

Dorothy Driver is a literary scholar and critic based at the University of Cape Town in the Department of English. She is the editor of *Pauline Smith* and co-editor of *Nadine Gordimer: A Bibliography*. She is regional correspondent for the *Journal of Commonwealth Literature* and editor of *Southern African Review of Books*. She is a recipient of the Thomas Pringle Award for Literary Criticism.

Francis Faller is a poet and Vice-Principal of the Johannesburg College of Education. His poetry appears in *Weather Words* and *Verse-Over*. He is a winner of the Sanlam Literary Award.

Gus Ferguson is a poet, cartoonist and publisher. His poetry includes *Snail Morning* and *Carpe Diem*. He is the proprietor of Snail Press and Firfield Press and editor of *Slugnews* and *Carapace*.

Jane Fox is a poet and fiction writer working in publishing in Johannesburg. She has published *The Dancer,* a volume of poems and stories in journals.

David Goldblatt is a photographer who lives in Johannesburg. His publications include *On the Mines* and *Lifetimes: Under Apartheid*, for which Nadine Gordimer wrote the introductory texts, and *The Structure of Things*.

Jeremy Gordin is a poet and journalist. He is managing editor of the *Sunday Independent*. His poetry includes *With My Tongue in My Hand* and *Hard On*. He co-wrote *The Infernal Tower* and ghost wrote *A Long Night's Damage: Working for the Apartheid State*. He is a recipient of the Vita/Nortje Memorial Award for Poetry.

Günter Grass is one of Germany's foremost writers. His publications include several novels, including *The Tin Drum*; *Dog Years*; *The Rat* and *The Call of the Toad*, and his plays *The Plebeians Rehearse the Uprising* and *Max: A Play*. His drawings and poems appeared in *Drawings and Poems*; *Etchings and Words* and *Show Your Tongue*. His other publications include *In the Egg and Other Poems*; *On Writing and Politics* and *Two States One Nation?*

Geoffrey Haresnape is a poet, short story writer, novelist and literary scholar based in the English Department at the University of Cape Town. A former editor of *Contrast* and editor-at-large for *New Contrast*, his publications include poetry, *New-Born Images* and a novel.

Seamus Heaney is a poet, essayist, literary scholar and Director of the Field Day Theatre Company in Dublin, Ireland, where he lives. His poetry includes *Death of a Naturalist*; *Door into the Dark*; *Wintering Out*; *North*; *Field Work*; *Station Island*; *The Haw Lantern*; *Sweeney's Flight*; *Seeing Things* and *Spirit Level*. His essays appear in *Preoccupations: Selected Prose 1968-78*; *Government of the Tongue* and *The Redress of Poetry: Oxford Lectures*. His many distinctions include the Nobel Prize for Literature.

Jenny Hobbs is a novelist, short story writer and book publicist who lives in Johannesburg. She has published three novels, including *Thoughts in A Makeshift Mortuary* and *The Telling of Angus Quain*. She has also published novels for young readers.

Peter Horn is a poet, critic and literary scholar. He is based in the Department of German Literature at the University of Cape Town. His poetry includes *Silence in Jail*; *An Axe in the Ice*; *The Rivers that Run Through Us* and *Poems 1964-1989*. His essays include *Writing my Reading*. He is a recipient of the Alex la Guma/Bessie Head Fiction Award.

Chenjerai Hove is a Zimbabwean novelist, poet and editor. His publications include the novel *Bones* which won the Noma Award for Publishing in Africa. His poetry includes *And Now the Poets Speak*, *Up in Arms* and *Red Hills of Home*.

Maureen Isaacson is a short story writer and Books Editor for the *Sunday Independent*. She worked as a researcher and copywriter on the *Fifties People of South Africa* and *The Finest Photos from the Old Drum*. Her fiction appeared in *Holding Back Midnight and Other Stories*. She is a recipient of the Book Journalist of the Year Award.

Antjie Krog is a poet, fiction writer and journalist. A former editor of the *Suid-Afrikaan*, her poetry includes *Jeruslemgangers*; *Lady Anne Barnard* and *Gedigte 1990-1995*. *An Account of a Murder* is a novel translated from the Afrikaans, *Relaas van 'n Moord*. Her coverage of the Truth and Reconciliation Commission is published as *Country of My Skull*. She is a recipient of the Eugène Marais Prize, the Dutch Flemish Reina Prisen Geerling Prize, the Rapport Prize, the Hertzog Prize, The Pringle Award for Excellence in Journalism and the Foreign Correspondent's Award for outstanding journalism.

Karen Ruth Lazar is a literary scholar based in the Department of English at the University of the Witwatersrand. She has published widely on South African literature and on the fiction of Nadine Gordimer.

Hugh Lewin is a journalist who has worked for newspapers in South Africa, England and Zimbabwe. He is the founder of Baobab Books in Zimbabwe. His publications include *Bandiet: Seven Years in a South African Prison*. His children's fiction includes *Jafta: The Wedding* for which he received the Parents' Choice Award. After years of exile, he now lives in Johannesburg where he is a director of the Institute for the Advancement of Journalism.

Don Maclennan is a poet and literary scholar who lives in Grahamstown. He has published plays, short stories and scholarly works as well as six collections of poetry, including *Collecting Darkness*; *Letters*; *The Poetry Lesson,* and *Solstice* for which he received the Sanlam Literary Award and the Olive Schreiner Award.

Johnny Masilela is a fiction writer and journalist. His stories have appeared in local journals and anthologies including *Crossroads*. His autobiographical writings are published in *Deliver Us From Evil: Scenes from a Transvaal Upbringing*.

Joel Matlou is a short story writer and artist who lives in Mabopane. He works as a clerk in Pretoria. His fiction is published in *Life at Home and other Stories*.

James Matthews is a poet, novelist and short story writer. A former journalist and publisher, his work includes *The Park and Other Stories*; *Cry Rage*; *Pass me a Meatball, Jones*; *No Time for Dreams* and the novel *The Party*.

Zakes Mda is the pen-name of Zanemvula Kizito Gatyeni Mda, poet, playwright, novelist, painter, film-maker and literary scholar. He lives in Johannesburg. His publications include *Bits of Debris*; *When People Play People: Development Communication Through Theatre*; *Four Plays*; *She Plays with Fire* and *Ways of Dying*. His awards include the Amstel Playwright of the Year Award, the M-Net Award for Fiction and the Olive Schreiner Award.

David Medalie is a writer of fiction, anthologiser and literary scholar based at the University of the Witwatersrand. His publications include *Shooting of the Christmas Cows and Other*

Stories and *Encounters and Other Stories*.

Mbulelo Vizikhungu Mzamane is a literary scholar, novelist, short story writer and poet. He is Vice-Chancellor of the University of Fort Hare. He is the author of several books of fiction, including *Mzala*; *Children of Soweto* and *Children of the Diaspora*.

Njabulo Ndebele is a fiction writer, poet, literary scholar and former Vice-Chancellor of the University of the North. His publications include *Fools and Other Stories*; *Bonono and the Magic Tree*, and *Rediscovery of the Ordinary: Essays on South African Literature and Culture*. He is a recipient of the Noma Award for Publishing in Africa.

Mike Nicol is a novelist and poet who lives in Cape Town. He has worked as a journalist. His novels include *The Powers that Be*; *This Day and Age* and *The Ibis Tapestry*. His non-fiction includes *A Good Looking Corpse: The World of Drum* and *The Invisible Line: The Life and Photography of Ken Oosterbroek*. He has published two volumes of poetry, *Among the Souvenirs* and *This Sad Place*.

Lewis Nkosi is a novelist, playwright and literary scholar who was born in Durban. He has lived in other parts of Africa, Europe and the United States since the 1960s when he was exiled from South Africa. His novels include *Mating Birds* and a Dutch translation of *Underground People* still not published in English. His essays include *Home and Exile*; *The Transplanted Heart: Essays on South Africa* and *Tasks and Masks: Themes and Styles of African Literature*. He is a recipient of the Pen International Writer's Award. He is Professor of English at the University of Wyoming.

Essop Patel is a poet and lawyer who lives in Johannesburg. He has published several volumes of poetry, including *They Came at Dawn* and *The Bullet and the Bronze Lady*. He is co-editor of *The Return of the Amasi Bird*.

Lesego Rampolokeng is a poet and performer who lives in Johannesburg. His publications include *Horns for Hondo* and *Talking Rain*.

507

Ronald Suresh Roberts is writing a biography of Nadine Gordimer. A graduate of Balliol College, Oxford, and Harvard University, he is the author of *Clarence Thomas and the Tough Love Crowd: Counterfeit Heroes and Unhappy Truths* and is co-author of *Reconciliation Through Truths: A Reckoning of Apartheid's Criminal Governance*.

Albie Sachs is a writer and critic with a background in law. He serves as a judge in the Constitutional Court of South Africa. His publications include *The Prison Diary of Albie Sachs* and *The Soft Vengeance of a Freedom Fighter*. He has also published widely on constitutional law and human rights.

Anthony Sampson is a journalist and former editor of *Drum*, who now lives in the UK. He is currently working on an authorised biography of Nelson Mandela. His publications include *'Drum': A Venture into the New Africa* and *The Treason Cage: Opposition on Trial in South Africa*.

Morakabe Raks Seakhoa is a poet and former General Secretary of the Congress of South African Writers. Now working for the Southern African Writers Organisation, his poems have appeared in *Essential Things*.

Sipho Sepamla is a poet and novelist who was born in Krugersdorp. He worked as a teacher and edited the journals *New Classic* and *S'ketsh* as well as serving as director of the Federated Union of Black Artists, a Johannesburg arts centre. His poetry includes *Hurry Up to It*; *The Blues in You is Me*; *The Soweto I Love*; *Children of the Earth*; *Selected Poems*; *The Root is One* and *Goree*. He has published several novels, including *A Ride on the Whirlwind*.

Mongane Wally Serote is a poet, novelist and elected African Nationalist representative in the National Assembly. He was born in Alexandra. His poetry includes *Yakhal 'inkomo*; *Tsetlo*; *No Baby Must Weep*; *Behold Mama, Flowers*; *Selected Poems*; *The Night Keeps Winking*; *A Tough Tale*; *Third World Express* and *Come and Hope With Me*. His fiction includes a novel *To Every Birth Its Blood* and his essays are collected in *On the Horizon*. He has won the Ingrid Jonker and the Ad Donker Poetry Prizes.

Ari Sitas is a poet, dramatist and sociologist at the University of Natal. He is a founder of the Junction Avenue Company and the workers' theatre movement. His poetry includes *Tropical Scars and Songs, Shoeshine and Piano. William Zungu: A Xmas Story* is a novella and *Dead Fish and Dreams of Love Again* is the libretto of an opera.

Colin Smuts is a short story writer and director of the Open School. He has compiled several publications of children's writing and art, including *Two Dogs and Freedom* and *In this Land*. His fiction appears in *Scenes from Another Day*.

Gladys Thomas is a fiction writer and dramatist. Her poetry appeared in *Cry Rage,* which she co-edited with James Matthews. Her play *Avlon Court* received the Bertrams VO Award for African Writing. Her stories have appeared in numerous anthologies and magazines.

Mike van Graan is a playwright and arts consultant who lives in Cape Town. His Trilogy of one-act plays, *Dinner Talk*, from which 'Thabo for Thabo' is taken, was performed in Johannesburg, Cape Town, Durban and Free State during 1998.

Marlene van Niekerk is a poet, short story writer, novelist and literary scholar based in the Department of Afrikaans at the University of the Witwatersrand. Her poetry includes *Sprokkelster en Groenstaar*. Her stories appear in *Die Vrou Wat Haar Verkyker Vergeet Het*. Her novel *Triomf* won the Noma Award for Publishing in Africa and the M-Net Prize for Fiction.

Chris van Wyk is a poet, short story writer and novelist. He is a former editor of *Wietie* and *Staffrider*. His publications include *It's Time to go Home* and *Year of the Tape Worm*. He has also published several books for children. He is a winner of the Olive Schreiner Award for Poetry and the Sanlam Award for Fiction.

Ivan Vladislavić is a novelist, short story writer and editor who lives in Johannesburg. His publications include *Missing Persons*, *The Folly* and *Propaganda by Monuments*. He has won the Olive Schreiner Award and the M-Net Prize for Fiction.

Per Wästberg is a Swedish journalist, novelist, poet and anthologiser. He is editor of *Dagens Nyheter* and President of the Swedish PEN. He has published several novels, including a trilogy dealing with love and sexual roles in contemporary Sweden. He is also known for his documentaries on Southern Africa. He is a member of the Nobel Academy of Sweden.

Stephen Watson is a poet, critic and literary scholar in the Department of English at the University of Cape Town. He has published several volumes of poetry, including *Poems 1977-83*; *In this City*; *Cape Town Days* and *The Return of the Moon*. His prose appeared in *Selected Essays* and *A Writer's Diary*.

Peter Wilhelm is a novelist, short story writer and poet who lives in Cape Town where he works as an editor. His publications include several novels, among them *Dark Wood*; *Summer's End*; *The Healing Process* and *The Mask*. His shorts stories are collected in *LM and Other Stories*; *The End of A War* and *Some Place in Africa*. His poetry appears in *Falling into the Sun*.